Charles Waterton

Charles Waterton
Creator of the First Nature Reserve

by Barbara Phipps.

YouCaxton Publications
Oxford & Shrewsbury

ISBN 978-1-912419-67-8
Printed and bound in Great Britain.
Published by YouCaxton Publications 2019
YCBN: 01

YouCaxton Publications
enquiries@youcaxton.co.uk

Front cover from an original water colour of Walton Hall by Harry Bunney

CONTENTS

FOREWORD

by Bill Oddie.

Charles Waterton (1782-1865) has been called the "Sir David Attenborough of his day," though I have my doubts that Sir David would regard that as entirely a compliment. Personally, I would suggest Waterton was more like John James Audubon. Naturalist adventurers both. I recall first seeing Audubon's "Birds of America" and not only being intrigued by the birds, but even more captivated by the adventures, discoveries and dangers he encountered as he tracked down the avifauna of the USA with a shotgun over his shoulder, and a paintbrush in his hand. Back then the only way to identify an unfamiliar species, was to shoot it. Whilst at the same time, avoiding being shot by the local Red Indians!

I admit that when I first saw that copy of Audubon's book, I was disappointed that it wasn't fully illustrated with his unique art work. But believe me, the words told a vivid and alarming story. Birdwatching in those days was a bit riskier that just plonking yourself in a hide with a digital camera and a couple of thousand pounds worth of optical equipment. I was about to say that you would never catch Sir David doing that, but actually that is exactly what he does, except that he is accompanied by a team of cameramen, researchers, and autograph hunters. The script is subject to scrutiny by "health and safety" and a "risk assessment." Danger and discomfort are to be avoided if at all possible, whereas the 19th century naturalist/explorers were, I suspect, lured by the search for the unknown, no matter what risks were involved.

So, WAS Waterton the Sir David of his day? Well, in so far as he travelled in South America, surviving on the food of the forest, as it were. A typical evening meal was of grilled monkey, ant-eater and roast wasp grubs! If only he had known a few TV executives he could've founded "I'm a Celebrity, Get Me Out of Here!"

Certainly, Waterton had a show business gene in him, especially in the art of taxidermy. Waterton literally made up some of his specimens. One can only assume he did it mainly as a joke. His fame was quite widespread, especially when he exhibited a specimen he called a Nondescript. "The only one of its kind in captivity, or out." The creature was distinctly humanoid, perhaps it was a prototype yeti? Apparently droves of people rolled up to marvel at the Nondescript. I admit I really can't see Sir David perpetrating a ruse like that, unless it was Red Nose Day.

However, Waterton had another project with a much more serious intent. He was a practical conservationist who was aware that owning and managing the landscape may be the only way to protect our rapidly diminishing wildlife. The demise had begun in the nineteenth century and frankly, continues today. Waterton himself owned considerable grounds on his own property. He built a stone wall around it, high enough to deter poachers and foxes, and protect the flora and fauna. Waterton can justifiably be given credit for creating the first nature reserve. It is a concept that has spread not just around Britain, but also right across the world. Mind you, I am not sure about the RSPB selling stuffed water voles.

BILL ODDIE
5th March 2019.

INTRODUCTION.

When I first thought of writing about Charles Waterton, my intention was to focus upon the law suit, as described in chapter twenty-eight. After a fair bit of research, I realised there was much more to be told, and it dawned upon me that to convey the true character of the man, I would have to write from his point of view alone, that is to say, in the first person. The format had interested me for some time, but I had feared its limitations. I soon discovered that in the case of Charles Waterton, it felt like a release.

Perhaps I should point out that this is not a biography. There are several of those on the shelves and all have their value, but I wanted to write something that brought Charles (I felt I was on first name terms with him by now) to life in a way that gave the reader a true idea of his character, his logic, and his love of life. In short, I wanted to show what made him tick.

This book is fiction based in fact, but is mostly fact. There was no need to make up an exciting adventure or a fascinating character, Waterton's life was packed with death defying escapades. The fiction is the glue that holds it all together as a story. Some passages are taken directly from his own writing.

In his own words, at the age of fifty-five.

I was born on the 3rd of June, in the year 1782, at Walton Hall, near Wakefield, in the County of York. This tells me that I am no chicken. In fact, I feel as though I am not more than thirty years of age, am quite free of all rheumatic pains, and am so supple in the joints, that I can still climb a tree with the utmost faculty. I stand six feet high, all but half an inch. On looking at myself in the glass, I can see at once that my face is anything but comely. A continual exposure to the sun, and to the rains of the tropics, has furrowed it in places, and given it a tint. My hair, which I wear very short, was once a shade between brown and black. It has now the appearance that it has passed the night exposed to a November hoarfrost. I cannot boast of any great strength of arm, but my legs, probably by much walking, and by regularly ascending trees, have acquired vast muscular power, so that, on taking a view of me from top to toe, you would say that the upper part of Tithonus has been placed upon the lower part of Ajax.

PROLOGUE

A curious thing occurred today, washing over me like a flood tide. I was at the grotto, sitting in my favourite spot in the upper temple, with my sister-in-law, Little Helen Edmonstone. Without warning, my stomach knotted and tears filled my eyes to overflowing. I cried as I had as a child whenever I found a chick fallen from its nest, but that was some eighty years ago, and I do not recollect ever having felt so overwhelmed as I did today. Being the kind person she is, Little Helen enquired of the reason for my distress.

"I was thinking of the future," was all I could say. Taking a kerchief from my pocket, I blew my nose. We then sat together in silence. I think she was as puzzled as I. "I usually find this place so comforting to body and soul, but today I find myself in fear of that which will happen after my death, which cannot be so far away."

"Surely, Edmund will take care of the estate?" A wry smile crossed my lips. Little Helen knows as well as I that Edmund has no interest in my work. I let the question go and leaned back, resting my head in the cradle of my hands. The warm September sun worked its balm and my mind turned to the present, where it is always occupied with interesting matters. Little Helen's mind, it transpired, was still engaged with the reason for my melancholy. I should not have been surprised that she required more detail of the thoughts that had precipitated my tears. "You will leave a rich heritage, Charles. Your literary works are respected and appreciated for their accuracy and foresight." She referred, of course, to my little book, 'Wanderings in South America.' Over the years my little book has been translated into French, German, and Spanish. It sold well in the United States, but I never took out a copyright, so consequently I have no idea how many copies have been printed or sold. Its popularity brought with it a certain notoriety. My observations have not always been appreciated as I challenged established belief, and have endured mockery at the hands of closet naturalists. But Little Helen had missed the point. I sat up straight.

"That which has been written will remain, it is true, but it is all this for which I fear." I pointed a forefinger and swept my arm in the widest curve. "I have tended these acres since I was a child, encouraging the birds, and discouraging the poachers, the foxes and the rats. There is no question as to who will win the battle, after my days are done." At this, she bowed her head in what I assumed to be silent agreement. The heavens concurred, as heavy clouds filled the sky, casting their gloomy shadow.

Later that evening, as Little Helen, Eliza and I dined on an excellent pea fowl, it became apparent that Eliza had been told by her sister of my earlier distress. A sombre air hung around the room as a maid cleared the table. When she left the room, Eliza suddenly brightened like a night sky illuminated by a comet.

"There is something which you must do, Charles." She paused, perhaps she expected me to say something, but I waited for her to continue. "So many people have read your books, and benefitted from your observations, but they do not have the privilege, as we do, of knowing you."

I almost choked. "Whatever are you talking about? Are you suggesting I go out and shake everyone by the hand? Or that I should find some path of science that would enable the whole world to see my parkland. You are talking nonsense." I thought this would make her laugh, but her countenance became more serious.

"Write your memoirs, Charles. The emotion you felt today, if put into words, would demonstrate your reasoning, your determination to find the truth and your dismissal of assumption when it masquerades as fact. Write from the heart, Charles. Write it all down. You have a long and faultless memory. I have always been fascinated by the way you can recall the details of a conversation, even those of your childhood. The world in two hundred years' time will still be talking about Squire Waterton, as you are so affectionately known. I am sure of it."

I could not help but laugh at this burst of enthusiasm. The title of 'Squire' has been bestowed upon me by the villagers of Walton. The title 'Lord Waterton' was taken from us by the Protestant Queen Bess, due to my ancestors remaining true to the Catholic Faith. As the twenty-seventh generation of Watertons, there is certainly a great deal of history behind my incumbency of the estate, not least the seven saints in my family tree. I would have been the twenty-seventh Lord Waterton had it not been for the lust of Henry VIII.

It had never crossed my mind that anyone would be interested in my person.

"A curious notion, Eliza my dear. Have I not written enough already? Surely you cannot believe that anyone would be interested? Certainly, my birth-right has influenced my life's path, but is that not true of every man? I have sought the truth, ridding my mind of accepted theory, and used observation and logic at every turn. At times, this has been at odds with the beliefs of the so-called men of science, and I have been ridiculed, but you know it has never troubled me. Time will prove me to be right, and indeed has already done so in many instances."

"Give it some thought, Charles, I implore you. No-one can predict the future, and many a man of vision has been ridiculed in his own time."

That night, as I awaited a visit from the barn owl on my bedroom windowsill, it occurred to me that perhaps, if I were to scribble some thoughts, I could bequeath something of the logical thinking, which has guided me in all things, to the scientists of the future. I could show how a childish fascination became my life's work. It will be a tale without an ending.

I have never done anything without good reason. It is my hope, therefore, that by committing my reasoning to paper, I may dispel my reputation for eccentricity, which I particularly dislike. However, if by defying convention I am eccentric, then so be it. In my defence, I will say this is unfair, with the exception of my opinion of the Hanoverian rat, which I concede is as much God's creature as any other. My actions are otherwise all perfectly sound, and I ask, is it eccentric to bring a smile to the lips of one's fellow man? Can humour be wrong? Shame, shame I say. No man ever considers himself to be eccentric. It is the view of others. An eccentric is an illogical fellow, and that is something which my greatest critics cannot level at me.

To this effect, the end must return to the beginning, and my earliest recollections. To assist the reader, should there ever be one, I have drawn my family tree, and that of the Edmonstones.

The Watertons

Charles Waterton m. Mary Cressacre-More

|

Christopher–Anne(m. Michael Daly)–Thomas(m. Anne Bedingfield)–
brothers, John–Martin–Edward

|

Charles–Thomas–Christopher–Helen–Isabella–William–Edward

The Edmonstones

Princess Minda m. William Reid

|

dau. Helen m. Charles Edmonstone

|

Charles–Robert–Eliza–Helen–Anne–Bethia

PART ONE

CHAPTER ONE

A Childhood Home.

I view my childhood years as being relatively carefree. I recall being occupied with the business of outwitting those who would have me conform to the baffling rules of society. My world was small, confined to the parkland surrounding my home, and from my childish perspective, I was the axis around which it turned.

The most remarkable feature of the whole estate is taken for granted by those who know it well, but visitors are always astounded by the fact that Walton Hall stands upon an island.

'Ea sub oculis posita negligimus; proximorum uncuriosi longinqua sectamur.'

'Those things which are placed under our eyes we overlook; indifferent as to what is near us, we long for that which is different.'

Built by my father in 1767, in the then fashionable Palladian style, his design replaced the fortified mansion which had served the family for three centuries. I wish I had seen it, but not a trace remains other than the water-gate. Not even a sketch of the old place. The Lombardy poplar tree planted by my father in 1756 had witnessed its demolition. Hitherto the lake had been no more than a moat. The oak panelling in the entrance hall came from the old place. My father told me it had been in a ninety-foot-long dining hall. The swivel bridge has been replaced by a single span iron footbridge.

The rooms atop of the house have no ceilings. Father had not considered it necessary, preferring to spend his money on fireplaces and window glass and renewing the pipes which bring spring water underground to the island. According to Father, the old mansion was on the point of collapse, the walls buckling and sinking, damp rising from the ground and rain pouring in from above. To put it concisely, it was falling down. Nevertheless, I wish he had not had the underground passageways blocked off. I accept that fortifications and escape routes were no longer needed in the late eighteenth century, but the tunnels would have made my childhood forays into the woods at night less hazardous. As it was, I was forced to climb out of my bedroom window, across the kitchen roof, down a short drainpipe and away across the footbridge. To my everlasting amazement, I was never detected.

The family crest of an otter with a pike in its mouth is carved in stone above the front door. The motto, *'Better kinde frembd than frembd kyen'* can be seen above the porch. The ancient Saxon translates as *'better a stranger becomes a friend, than a friend becomes a stranger.'*

Coal for the fires and other household necessities are taken across the water by boat. Charon's ferry is a little flat-bottomed barge. I shall relate the circumstances which led to her naming in a later chapter.

The parkland occupies about two hundred and sixty-eight acres, eighteen of which are taken up by the lake. Away from the island, in a hollow on the north-west side, the farmyard and stables are situated along with a flower garden, kitchen garden, glass house, orchard and nuttery. A little way behind this, Father built a high retaining wall and planted a fernery and gardens. I have further developed the area by having my masons construct three shelters. One is a single room cottage. The other two are known as the upper and lower temples, being sited on the upper and lower levels, each with a conical roof supported by six stone columns. The whole area is the aforementioned grotto, which can be seen from the south and west facing bedrooms. I will tell more of the grotto, but for now I will say simply that it is enjoyed by many.

At the end of the avenue, just inside the park gates, stand two gatehouses side by side with a central path, common to both. These are occupied by the gate-man, Kaye, who does a good job. The previous occupant has left my employ to open a little store in the village, so he is now my tenant. He and his wife had so many children, they outgrew the gatehouses.

With the benefit of hindsight, I appreciate that Mrs Bennett had my best interests at heart, but the housekeeper failed to understand the mind of a boy who loved the outdoors. Tree climbing, bird nesting and sailing on the lake, were all I desired. She was forever shouting at me, 'I save your life twenty times a day, Charles Bernard.' She always addressed me with both my Christian names. Our game of cat and mouse began the moment I could escape the nursery, and continued until I was sent away to school.

Only the unusual is embedded in my memory in detail, along with every feature of the house and parkland as it was then. Much of the fabric remains unaltered. The variety of the landscape, with woodland, open pasture and arable fields, marshland and lake has always enticed a wide variety of birds and animals.

Of my brothers, Christopher and Edward were the ones who showed interest in outdoor life, particularly Edward. Thomas and William preferred to study.

I was scolded, at one time or another, by all the adults in the household. Not all at the same time of course, and always over my lack of concern for my safety. My longevity has proved their fears to be unfounded.

On one occasion I was on the old stable roof, drawn there by a starling's nest. Mrs Bennett saw me and remonstrated that I should come down immediately, before I fell to certain death.

"I am perfectly safe, Mrs Bennett." I said, standing upright on the apex to prove there to be no danger, upon which she ran back over the bridge, returning quickly, armed with some pieces of Cook's gingerbread.

"Come down, Charles Bernard, or I shall feed this to the hens." She knew I would find the gingerbread irresistible. Her bribery worked, and I scrambled down the drainpipe in a flash, knowing I could return to the nest as soon as the housekeeper's feathers had lost their ruffle. The very writing of this tale brings a smile to my lips and the taste of gingerbread to my mouth. It is still a great favourite of mine.

During summer-time my sister, Helen, was my most frequent companion. I remember her pleading with the nursery nurse to allow her to join me. She was not so agile in the trees as I, and fear prevented her from climbing more than twelve feet above the ground. The fact that I am double jointed means I can twist my fingers alternately around the smaller branches, making things much easier for me. Once, when we were at the highest point of Stubbs Wood, and I was at the top of the tallest elm, I told her I could see all the way to Wakefield, but still she dared not to join me.

On another occasion, Helen and I came across a lark's nest beneath the Lombardy poplar, close to where the medieval bridge had once made landfall. I knew there was a nest in the area, for I had observed the species many times but not found their home. I was surprised to find it so close to the carriageway. They build their home on the ground but are wise enough to land some distance away and run amongst the high grasses. To land straight to their nest would be to announce the location of their home to the crows. As we gazed down upon the eggs, I wondered what it would be like to eat one, shell and all. On impulse, I took one and swallowed it. My sister was certain I would die, and ran back to the house to tell Mother. I thought my physical appearance of perfect health would allay all such fear, but was mistaken. Mother forced me to swallow a powerful mustard emetic, which incapacitated me, retching like a victim of the black death for the remainder of the day. Whether she did so to teach me a lesson, or as penance, or because she feared for my health, I shall never know. I now know that to swallow the egg was not dangerous. The episode did, however, have a long-term effect insomuch as it resulted in my everlasting hatred of the taste and smell of mustard.

The significance of our Catholicism must be mentioned at this early point of my scribblings, although I know not of what interest it may be to a reader. In order that we might worship in the True Faith, Father and Mother engaged Monsieur Raquedal, a French priest ousted from his homeland by the revolution. His room was next to mine, on the uppermost floor. Next to Monsieur Raquedal's room was the chapel, dedicated to St Catherine of Alexandria. I remember teasing him that he could never be late for work. He had looked shocked, spluttering something about sanctity.

The other rooms were gradually filled by my siblings but never as cramped as it sounds, because I was sent away to school before Edward was born. Three bedrooms were later vacated when Thomas, Christopher and I left for Stonyhurst, that most wonderful of schools. William and Edward went to Stonyhurst as soon as they were old enough.

The schoolroom at Walton Hall was on the floor below our bedrooms, and here Monsieur Raquedal, and Mr Bartram, who lived in the village, instructed my brothers and me during our early years. Naturally, it was the privilege of the priest to instil the truth and importance of our faith. Mr Bartram encouraged a neat hand with the quill, with limited success in my case. Both instructed us in the classics.

We were occasionally visited by Father Albert Underhill. This bravest of men celebrated Mass in a little chapel in Lady Lane, Leeds, when it was still against the law to do so. Mother particularly admired him for this, and after he had made one of his visits, she would be aglow with the love of God for days. Monsieur Raquedal was less easily impressed. My sister, Helen, once told me she had overheard him asking God to show him how to keep Father Underhill away.

"He's jealous, Charles. He thinks our chapel is his, or perhaps it is because Mother finds Father Underhill so engaging."

Nowadays, much has changed, and much remains the same. Eliza and Little Helen have their own sitting room on the first floor. We employ a cook, a housekeeper, two housemaids, a personal maid for my sisters-in-law, a manservant and a butler. The housekeeper and butler are accommodated on the ground floor of the house, within earshot of the bells. Other household staff are accommodated on the eastern side of the top floor. Eliza and Little Helen tell me they are happy with the domestic arrangements, and who am I to argue?

I have three game keepers, two grooms, two gardeners, a smith, a woodman and a gate-keeper as well as those employed at the home farm. We have no need for a footman, nor a resident priest or schoolmaster, so the household is smaller than it was in my parents' time, but perfectly well run thanks to Eliza's organising skills.

The grooms live in the rooms above the stables, as do the farm and estate workers, unless they are tenanted elsewhere on the estate or in the village.

My most important members of staff are the gamekeepers. Jack Ogden was a mason when he first came into my employ, but latterly took on the role of head keeper also. He lived in a cottage at the stables until his death a few months ago, and I find myself needing two men to replace one. Chickens, domestic geese and pea fowl are accommodated below the hayloft, where they roost. The kennels are separate, a few yards from the main building. There have always been two or three pointers about. My father kept them for hunting, and quite possibly his father also. I am particularly fond of the breed, and they work well with the keepers. The fashion to dock their tails does not appeal to me. The thinking is that a long tail will be bitten by a fox, although I never heard of this happening, and it has certainly never happened to any dog of mine. Cats abound, and earn their food in the rodent department. For this reason, cats are allowed in the house, and are thoroughly spoilt. Contrary to popular opinion, this does not detract from their usefulness. A cat is either a hunter, or he is not. They are outdoors at night, but can warm themselves at the saddle room fireside anytime they choose to do so. A window is left ajar to facilitate this.

But now I must return to my childhood, and a new chapter in my life.

CHAPTER TWO

My First Journey.

At the age of ten I was sent to a school in County Durham. Catholic schools were a rarity, and even though private worship had been made legal by this time, schools had not, so maybe my parents felt they had few options, and that my staying at home was not one of them. I was there for four years. Had it not been for the friendship of Edwin Jones and Joe Bowren, my time there would have been unbearable.

The journey took two days, with an overnight stop in York. This can now be achieved within hours upon the railway, but there was no such thing in those days.

The Reverend Arthur Storey, a profound Latin scholar, was the Master, but it was Father Robert Blacoe, a slim and pious looking man, who met me in Bishop Auckland. There was no conversation along this last seven miles of my journey. He spoke only to confirm I was the expected new pupil and then pointed to a horse and cart. I wondered if he had taken a vow of silence at some time and never fully regained the ability to converse. Only when he died two weeks later did I realise he had been in poor health, and quite possibly, a great deal of pain.

Master Storey was quite the opposite, not having the appearance of a priest in either his dress or posture. Topped off with a wig, his short, rotund figure made him look more like a reject from society than a priest. He wore a cravat and a horribly food stained waistcoat beneath a frock coat, the latter being too small for him. Stockings were stretched to their limit over his fat, lumpy legs as if intended to give support. He limped from one leg to the other, constantly sighing as he muttered about his undeserved gout. A knowledgeable man and a lover of the classics, he expected all boys to have his enthusiasm for Latin and Greek. With hindsight, I do not think he enjoyed being a schoolmaster. When we boys had pleased him, he would send for two musicians. One played the Northumberland bagpipes, and the other the flageolet. After the concert we would have fruit, cakes and tea. If a boy had not pleased him, however, the birch was in his hand as quick as a flash of lightning.

Twenty beds lined the dormitory, ten to each side in regimented order, with a single blanket neatly folded where a pillow might have lain. A vaulted ceiling rose above the beams, and at first sight I considered the possibility of climbing up there. A thick layer of cobwebs covered the only window. As I brushed them aside and wiped the sticky threads to my breeches, my thoughts turned to my bedroom window at home, my preferred nocturnal escape route, and the climbing of trees all night long. The night before my transportation, I had made a descent more rapid than intended. I rarely miss my footing, and my pride was hurt more than my arm, although the bruising was quite impressive. Knowing I would not have the opportunity to spend the night on my favourite perch in the great oak tree for some time, I considered it had been worth it. How I loved to observe the owls and bats. Indeed, it is still one of my greatest pleasures, never ceasing to marvel at their grace, envying their freedom. To my mind, those who would have their mantra as *Carpe Diem*[1] do not seize enough. *Carpe Nox*[2] is its equal.

My first impressions of Tudhoe were not conducive to similar activity. From the dormitory window, the stone wall fell at least fifty feet to a downward sloping meadow. As I pushed open the rotting casement, slivers of sodden wood cascaded to the ground, and legions of woodlice fell to the dormitory floor, teeming in heaps. Those which landed on their feet scuttled away beneath the skirting board. I scooped up and dropped a handful of the armoured creatures which had been unfortunate enough to land on their backs, giving them a second chance. Leaning out of the window, I looked first to the left and then to the right, where I saw my salvation in the form of a fall pipe running within a yard of the window. I determined to inspect its strength from below at the first opportunity.

"H-hello. W-w-what's your name? I'm Jones. Edwin Jones"

---

1   seize the day

2   seize the night

The interruption startled me, and I bumped my head on the window frame causing a further shower of woodlice. "Waterton, Charles." I replied.

"W-w-what are you d-doing?" A little shorter than myself, a mass of blonde hair made Edwin appear younger than his frightened look indicated.

"I'm knocking these creatures out my hair." I remember wondering how anyone could be frightened of woodlice. "They're quite harmless, unless you are a piece of rotting wood of course. Fascinating creatures." Edwin stared at me, open mouthed. "It's why my parents sent me here."

"Th-they sent you h-here to knock woodlice out of your h-hair?"

I stared back. "No. I think they sent me here to curb my fascination with nature, and to learn how to be a gentleman, although I am not sure how the latter is to be taught by priests."

"I-I'm here to c-cure m-my s-s-stammer." He forced the words out in a staggered rush as if they were escaping an invisible demon. I crouched down and pointed at the insects, turning one over with the tip of my forefinger.

"Look. They can't right themselves." My new friend knelt beside me. "I have studied woodlice in the past and noted two interesting things about them." Edwin overcame his fear and picked one up, narrowing his eyes to focus on it. "As I have said, they cannot right themselves, and the other thing I have noted is that they are always to be found in damp conditions."

"Why?" Edwin asked.

"I am uncertain, but I don't think they have lungs I think they breathe through their skin. I hope they have a decent microscope here, I would like to confirm this."

"I-I think you're right on both counts. The ones that landed the right way up are making off." His stammer lessened as his interest in the woodlice increased.

"I think we should unpack, although there does not appear to be any provision by the way of furniture. I suppose we just leave our clothes in our trunks. If you don't mind, I'll take this bed near the window."

"I-I prefer to keep away from draughts." We returned our attention to the woodlice for a while, and then Edwin continued, "I-I have some butter biscuits in my trunk. W-would you like to share them with me?"

"What a strange question, Edwin" I replied, "I shall, of course, be delighted to help you with your biscuits." He opened his trunk, carefully setting aside a sketch book, a small, white towel and some breeches, to reveal a package in waxed paper. The fresh biscuits were mostly broken. Edwin's jaw sagged with disappointment.

"C-cook's biscuits are always so c-crumbly." I took a medium sized piece and popped it in my mouth.

"I declare this to be the tastiest butter biscuit in the world." Edwin gave a quick, sharp laugh, which seemed to take him by surprise. Sitting side by side on the edge of his bed, we admired our feast. Before we had completely devoured it the sound of boys' voices took us to our feet. The remaining biscuits were quickly replaced in the trunk, with the towel and breeches atop. Before the door opened, we had wiped our mouths and shaken our clothes of every last trace of a crumb.

The routine of the day began early. Matins was said and forgiveness prayed for, long before sunrise. This was usually followed by a break-fast[3] of bread and sausages. Latin verbs were supposed to commence immediately afterwards, but it was the habit of the masters to fall asleep for half an hour or so. This being the case on my first morning of exile, I took the opportunity to explore my new surroundings. I concluded that Tudhoe School for Catholic Boys was not really a school at all, but a farm. It certainly was not what I had expected. What had once been the dairy now shared its purpose with a laundry copper. The henhouses were still occupied, and proud clucking from within told of a freshly laid egg. I found no evidence of arable farming, and no great horses, just the rough haired pony who shared a stable with the cart which had transported me from Bishop Auckland. My first impression of the kitchen garden was one of promise, not for its neatness, but rather the opposite. Its unkempt

---

3   Waterton always hyphenated the word 'break-fast'

state provided a haven for birds in the forms of camouflage and food, necessities for the survival of all creatures. Sheep grazed in a meadow adjacent to what appeared to be a sports field, but I found the most interesting beast to be the pig. I recall climbing over the gate and into the sty, where I scratched the back of a large sow. Mud and muck squelched through my boots with the consistency of thick black treacle, but with a less pleasant odour."I'd jump out o' that sty right quick if I were yous, young sir." My preoccupation with the sow had rendered me oblivious to the approach of a giant, just as the woodlice had been my preoccupation when Jones startled me. A tower of dishevelment leaned on the wall, his clothes hanging about him like a bell tent. His head appeared as the boss of a very hairy pyramid. A matted beard and wire wool hair which stuck out in all directions. Arms hung from his elbows like hams, diverted from the perpendicular by his bulk. "She's due to farrow, and like most ladies in such a condition, she's likely in a bad mood." I gave the sow one more scratching behind her ear and slowly moved away, climbing back over the gate. She seemed gentle enough to me, but I was prepared to take the advice of one who knew her better than I.

"Charles Waterton, sir." I proffered my hand.

"No cause to call me 'sir.' I'm Joe. Joe Bowren." He tipped his head towards the school. "Cook, butcher, brewer of ale an' all other jobs they chooses to give me. I'm guessin' you are a new boy, Master Charles Waterton."

"I am—and I'm pleased to make your acquaintance, Mr Joe Bowren."

"And I *said* yous can calls me *Joe.*"

"Can you tell me where the nearest trees are, Joe?"

"Trees? What yous want to know that for?"

"Because I like to climb trees to see the birds' nests." Joe gave such a mighty growl, I feared he might turn into a bear. He shook his head and wiped away a tear with a grimy hand. "What is so funny, Joe?"

"I'll tells yous what's funny, young Master Waterton. There is trees all right. They be in Croxdale Wood, about a mile yonder." Joe waved an arm to the south, to what looked to be little more than a copse compared to the acres of ancient woodland in the parkland of Walton Hall. "But if yous takes Joe's advice here, you won't be a goin' there."

"But"

"Pardon my interruptin', but if yous is caught, the only bit of a tree yous is goin' to be near is the birch rod, an' yous will be nearer than yous might likes to be."

I considered the implications of this, having no cause to dispute his advice, but thought it a risk worth taking, and when I said as much, he laughed a bear roar laugh, linking sausage-like fingers together beneath his belly as if he were holding himself together. I could not help but laugh with him, not quite knowing why, but unable to take my eyes from the shaking mass. Our laughter subsided, and I suddenly felt sobered.

"I think I shall not like it here too well, and must make the best of it."

Joe frowned and scratched his head as if to aid his comprehension. "Well I don't understand why yous wouldn't like it 'ere. I mean most boys is just 'appy to 'ave some food in their belly, and I sees to it that you don't go 'ungry, unless you are bein' punished by way of a bit o' starvin'. Yous have a roof over yous 'ead, an' clothes on yous back." His little speech turned the tables, and it was I who was puzzled. While no-one at Tudhoe was in danger of starving to death, Joe's girth and that of Master Storey indicated an uneven share.

"You are right, Joe. I am fortunate in many ways, but I am two days' journey from my home, and have been told that if I do any of the things I truly enjoy, I will be severely punished. I have no idea why my parents thought I should be educated by people who think deprivation and beating is a good idea." Joe heaved up his shoulders until his neck disappeared, and then dropped them down with a sigh so deep I felt its rush upon my face.

"Come with me, Master Charles," he said, "an' we will collect eggs from the 'en 'ouse."

Master Storey often gave us some Latin nouns to learn before returning to his study. A few of us would have our heads in our books, while the rest larked about. Edwin's desk was beside mine, and we usually chose to study.

The first time I saw the priest who replaced Father Blacoe was one morning when I looked up from my nouns and saw him in the doorway. Unfortunately for me, I was the nearest to him.

"I am Father Joseph Shepherd, and you will obey me to the letter or suffer the consequences," he wheezed. He stood over six feet tall, his thin outline silhouetted in the arched frame of the schoolroom door, standing there as if he did not want to come further into the room. We all stood up and stared at him. I disliked him immediately and intensely. Instinct told me that the consequences this man had in mind would be far worse than the sharpness of Mrs Bennett's tongue. An uncomfortable silence filled the room. No-one spoke. I felt obliged to fill the void.

"Are you to give us religious instruction as Father Blacoe did, sir?"

"I did not give you permission to speak." His words came out in a jet of stinking breath. "What is your name?"

"Waterton."

"You mean, 'Waterton, Father.'"

"Are we your flock, Father Shepherd?" I replied, unable to see anything fatherly in the man. His appearance was the antithesis of that of Master Storey.

"Silence! I shall not pander to your spoiled and privileged past." Father Shepherd scuffed his feet across the floorboards as he entered the room. We all stood stock still, not knowing what to expect as he walked around us as if inspecting pigs in the market place. I felt the corners of my mouth twitch, and my shoulders shook with the urge to giggle. I bowed my head to disguise my amusement. "I see you quake in fear, Waterton." I dared a low glance at Edwin, expecting to see a smile but his face was as pale as the whites of his eyes. He looked terrified. "Good. That is good, Waterton. You learn quickly." He turned on his heel as he left the room, hissing, "Back to your work."

"What an awful man." I could barely speak, having been overcome by a fit of the giggles. "I can see he will be difficult."

"H-how can you f-find it f-funny? I was r-really f-frightened."

"Oh come, Edwin. The fool thought I was quaking in fear when I was bursting to laugh at him. How can I take him seriously?" I think my levity cheered my new friend. "Can you box?" I put up my fists and jumped around, boxer style.

"I-I can, b-but not now. I'm not the m-mood. Perhaps later. I'll study the nouns."

I had been at Tudhoe for some weeks, making nightly forays to Croxdale Woods via the downpipe, before I was caught. There was no doubt in my mind as to who was guilty of this act of treason. I had been snitched on by George Frobisher, a somewhat spherical boy who had taken a dislike to me. A sentiment, I must say, which travelled to the mutual with great speed. Father Shepherd had been standing at the bottom of the drainpipe as I made my descent and dragged me away without a word. His strength defied his skinny frame, especially, as I grew to learn, when fuelled by anger. He threw me into a cellar and locked the door. "I shall deal with you in the morning, after I have spoken with Master Storey."

Thinking the Masters would accept the harmlessness of my sin and consider my sentence served, I expected to be released for break-fast. Alas, whatever transpired between them did nothing to dispel the anger of the shepherd who so despised his flock. He paced up and down the otherwise empty schoolroom. I pictured Frobisher at the dining table, feeding his face in order to maintain his shape. Father Shepherd held the birch rod in his right hand, tapping it on the palm of his left in rhythm to his pacing the stone floor.

"If you are ever again seen outside the school boundary, Waterton, Master Storey will have to write to your father. And what do you think he will say?" I drew breath to inform him that my father would not be surprised, but he ranted on, not giving opportunity for reply. "I'll tell you what your father would say, Waterton. He would say I should beat you." I jammed my lips tightly shut, keeping a twitch from playing corners of my mouth. Did they really think a beating or two would contain me within a treeless boundary? "Let me tell you, Waterton, it is my belief that you have absconded on several occasions. Nay, it is a fact. I know this because while you have been incarcerated in the cellar, I have searched your chest." My heart sank. "Your collection of birds' eggs has been destroyed. Now, hold out your hand." His reference to my eggs took everything else from my mind. I pictured their shattered shells, crunched to dust, no doubt, under the foot of a man who purported to be a man of God. The thwack of the rod on my hand creased my brow in concentration, its sting as nothing compared to my sense of loss. With the second blow, I recalled with satisfaction that Jones and I had devoured all the gingerbread found in my trunk. Mrs Bennett must have put it there and we had tucked in heartily. The third contact with the birch brought to my mind the darning needle I used to blow the eggs. Stuck in the lapel of my jacket, it was safely hidden from Father Shepherd. The solution was simple.

Ego committur in principeo iterum.

I would have to start all over again.

To every perceived problem, there is a solution. This maxim, more than the soreness of my palm, kept me awake that night, turning from side to side on my straw filled mattress. If I were to resume my nocturnal forays, I had to find a way to silence Frobisher, and any other pupil who might think to ingratiate himself by means of betrayal. Joe and Edwin were the only ones I could trust. My stomach growled, a reminder that other than the crust Joe had sneaked to me in the cellar, I had not eaten all day. At best, Joe's culinary skills kept us alive, but lacked the hand of Cook at Walton Hall. His swede, carrot and potato, mashed with butter, had tasted quite well, but always looked as if it had been eaten before and rejected by the stomach of its recipient. I would rather have eaten the vegetables raw but did not say so. Adversity, however, always concentrates the mind, and Joe's larder was never empty. It struck me that if I were to somehow procure some extra sustenance, this could be exchanged for the silence of those who sought to betray me. I decided to discuss the matter with Joe, and choose my words carefully, not wishing to insult the man who took his duties so very seriously. With the embryo of a plan, even the straw mattress gave some comfort as I dreamt of cold meats and bird nesting.

With Father Shepherd keeping a close watch on my movements, I feared it might take a while to set up my plan. There was no point trying to bribe Frobisher and the others until I had Joe's co-operation, but as luck would have it, the moment arose the very next morning. I had devoured my sausages and bread with relish, and was passing Master Storey's room on my way to the schoolroom. The door flew open with such force that I thought a hurricane or a tornado must have been coursing through the building. Then I saw Joe's frame in the doorway. I cowered behind a high-backed chair. Joe looked as if he were about to blow up, his cheeks puffed out so much his eyes had all but disappeared in a face the colour of a turkey's crop. Taking two steps to Joe's every stride, I following in the wake of his flapping coat as he stormed through the school and down to his pantry. I thought he was not aware of my presence as he took a cleaver in one hand and lifted a whole pig carcass in the other. Mighty blows fell in rhythmic fury as he dismembered the beast.

"Are you pretending that pig is Master Storey, Joe?" I ventured. He turned to me, his fat fingers turned white with his grip of the cleaver. I feared I had annoyed him even further, and then his beard twitched as a hint of a smile played on his lips, just visible through the forest of hair. Resting the meat and cleaver on the chopping block, he leaned back, hands on hips, and began to growl. Rolling back and forth with each breath, Joe's rocking, growling laugh eventually subsided and he wiped his tears with the back of his hand.

"Young Master Waterton, yous be a caution. That yous do."

"What did he say to make you so angry?" Joe's face fell to seriousness.

"Well, it's like this, see. I knows I'm not the best cook, but I do like to see yous boys with full bellies. That Master Storey says I should pay more attention to the quality of food on their plates. *Their* plates mind. I tells 'im I don't 'ave time for fancy stuff, so 'e says I 'as to give yous boys less food. That way I won't 'ave so much work and can feed *them* better. Theys is 'avin' visitors. Four young priest fellows, and I is to feed 'em all, but no extra food. 'Ow is I supposed to do that then?"

"I think this is not so bad, Joe."

"Not bad? It's terrible. 'Ow can I 'old my 'ead up and see 'ungry boys? Tell me that and I'll says it's not so bad."

I explained my dilemma. Joe listened, a furrowed brow narrowing his eyes in concentration. "I still don't sees 'ow—"¬

"Do as they say, Joe, and in a few days' time my fellow pupils will be feeling hungry, especially Frobisher. I will volunteer to steal food from your pantry in exchange for his silence regarding my nocturnal adventures and"

"Now look 'ere, young sir. I don't likes stealing, not at all, an' especially not from my pantry."

"Please hear me out, Joe. You will have left some food out for me to take back to the dormitory for us to share. It won't be stealing because you will know about it. I won't take anything you have not left for me."

"And what if one of them Masters catches yous wandering about in the night? What if yous gets a beating?" I thought his concern for my welfare quite touching, but had misunderstood his reasoning. "You will snitch on your friend Joe," he continued, "and I will be out of 'ere with no 'ome an' no job quicker'n yous can say 'pigswill', that's what."

"No! No, Joe! I would never betray you." I remonstrated. "I care not that I must endure a few strikes of the rod in exchange for my freedom. It is no great thing. I will be sent to the madhouse if I am incarcerated within the boundaries of this school. I *need* to climb the trees, to observe the birds—do you not understand? I need to acquire Frobisher's silence."

Without a word, Joe turned his back to me, picked up the cleaver and returned his attention to the pig.

My father was a good man. He paid for the education of two poor boys in the village of Walton. After his death, I sought to continue the practice. Why do I mention this now? Let me explain. A few years ago, when renewing the lease on the school house, I came across my letters from Tudhoe. They were wrapped in paper marked 'County Durham' in Father's handwriting, and tied with a ribbon. Mother must have tied them up because the bow was very neat. At some point, they had been placed with the papers regarding the school on Shay Lane. But that is of no matter. I thought to throw them away, to destroy any vestment of memory of that place, but the reminder of Tiger Duff, and his influence upon me, made me keep them and I am glad of it, for here is one of them, verbatim.

The Catholic School,
Tudhoe,
The County of Durham.
Maundy Thursday, 1793.

Mi Pater et Mater,
I trust you are in good health and that the warmer days of spring are to your liking. Being some distance further north, there is little sign of leaves on the trees of County Durham.
I have a good friend in Edwin Jones. He is an excellent artist and paints the landscape with skill. I find it curious that his parents have sent him here to cure his stammer. Furthermore, I find it curious that Father Shepherd thinks the cure is to beat him. He thinks the birch rod is the answer to everything, so perhaps I should not wonder at it. In my opinion it makes matters worse for the poor fellow. Master Storey and Father Shepherd take their duties seriously, and do not always understand my character, or my love of the trees and birds. Father Shepherd has his perceived solutions to my interest in nature, as alluded to above, but Master Storey seems pleased with my aptitude for Latin, which I continue to find the most enchanting of languages. Prayers and supplications feature highly in the strictly observed daily timetable, which starts at 5.00.a.m.
Last week the school was visited by a man named Tiger Duff. He is the tallest man I have ever seen, a giant. He told all the boys here of his travels, and of a particular adventure in India. He has inspired me to travel when I am old enough. Tiger is not his real name, but rather one he has acquired due to the scar on his face. I think to be attacked by a Bengal tiger and survive is a most unusual thing. I felt

quite jealous. The scar is very deep and runs from his temple to his jawline. He let me touch it which was very thrilling for me.

Master Storey has dyed some hen's eggs to a shade of purple for Easter, and we are to play games with them, although I would rather see one on my plate. The food is enough to keep one alive, but not to engender any love of culinary matters. The cook is a good fellow.

Yours affectionate son,
Charles Waterton.

It is a curiously formal letter but was written from the heart. I had folded the paper carefully and applied sealing wax. It is still there for the most part, with my fingerprint pressed into it. I had licked my forefinger before pressing it into the hot wax. Joe posted it for me, as he did all my letters. Had I given it to Master Storey or Father Shepherd, it would have been opened, and my description of life at Tudhoe would not have reached Walton Hall.

Father was not alone in keeping correspondence.

Walton Hall
16th May 1794

Dear Charles,
I trust all is well with your schooling and that Master Storey and Father Shepherd will, in due course, be writing to me with a good report of your studies.
It pleases me to inform you that your mother is safely delivered of a son. Your new brother is named Edward.

Your affectionate father.
Thomas Waterton.

I sat on the edge of my bed and refolded the letter along its precisely creased lines. The sealing wax, embossed with the otter and pike, had been broken before it was given to me. The seal is mine now, along with everything else I inherited at Walton. I keep it in the bureau exactly where Father kept it. Since his death, all my correspondence bears its mark. The broken seal came as no surprise that day.

It never crossed my mind that Mother would do anything other than produce a healthy child. She was a robust woman, some would say formidable. Quite the opposite to my own dear Anne. The two most important women in my life shared a Christian name, but nothing else. My wife was a gentle, delicate creature, with the blonde hair of an angel. But I digress, and will write of her when the time comes.

With the arrival of Edward, I now had four brothers and two sisters, and they all enjoyed excellent health. I put the letter in my trunk, beneath my spare britches and shirt, wishing Father had written more interesting news. How I longed to know of the trees and birds of the parkland. Had the owlets fledged successfully from the oak tree? How many pairs of ducks had nested on the island? Were the buzzards circling the skies in any great numbers? On reflection, and imparted by its absence, the only other information was that the Masters had not sent any report of my conduct.

CHAPTER THREE

A Matter of Survival.

As I pondered whether this was a good or bad thing, Frobisher entered the dormitory and kicked at my trunk, falling upon my bed with a groan.

"There you are, Waterton. I shall die of starvation in this place." In dramatic gesture, Frobisher swept his forefinger across his neck. "My stomach thinks my throat has been cut."

"I think you are better placed than the rest of us."

"Don't be ridiculous, Waterton. I have a greater appetite, and therefore am suffering at the hands of that devil of a cook more than anyone."

"Conversely, Frobisher," I replied, "it could be said that should starvation approach, you are better placed for survival than most, having your fat to live off."

"Well not for much longer. I have written to my parents. They will be contacting Master Storey, and when they do, Joe Bowren will be told to leave." I stifled a giggle.

"What's so funny, Waterton?"

"You are."

"Why?"

"To whom did you entrust your letter?"

"To Father Shepherd."

"I thought as much. You see, Frobisher, you put your trust in wholly the wrong person and are entirely mistaken regarding the blame for your growling guts. Joe cut our rations on the order of the Masters, and your letter will never be read by your parents because the Masters Storey and Shepherd will have read it and confiscated it." Frobisher blanched and I knew I had my enemy within my grasp as his little piggy eyes glistened and his jaw dropped. "There is a solution however, should you care to hear it." The bedstead creaked as he rolled onto his side and his belly flopped like leavened dough. He rested his head on the palm of his hand, an elbow sinking into the mattress.

"Continue."

"I am prepared to venture into the pantries at night to support your greed, in exchange for your silence regarding my preferred nocturnal activities."

"You will be caught—and punished."

"*If* I am caught, I shall be punished, that is true, but equally true is that it is none of your business. I need to know we have an understanding in the matter."

"What about the other boys?"

"They will have their share of whatever I am able to procure." A silence fell. Frobisher smacked his lips as his belly rumbled.

"Then we shall give it a try. Although I have to say I believe you are quite mad, Waterton, but if your madness provides sustenance as you say it will, I am willing to indulge your folly."

My plan worked better than I could have hoped. The four young priests had good appetites, and we boys enjoyed their company. When they mentioned the lack of food, I was confident enough of our friendship to tell of my arrangements, and they were happy to be a part of my scheme.

The months trickled by. The onset of a particularly harsh winter increased our appetites and the arrangement between Joe and myself worked to everyone's benefit. Frobisher was less hungry than he would otherwise have been, Joe was content that we had sufficient food, and I enjoyed my freedom. Occasionally, I persuaded Edwin to accompany me, when I would instruct him in the skill of tree climbing.

I have given little thought, over the years, to my time in Tudhoe. The continual game of cat and mouse (which I had first honed to avoid Mrs Bennet), the beatings, the expeditions to Croxdale Woods, either alone or accompanied by Edwin, all merge into one memory. More importantly, my collection of eggs increased each springtime. All were stored carefully and discretely on the top shelf of Joe's pantry. My greatest joy was to add a new specimen, to observe and compare it to others of similar colour and size.

Over those four years, visits to Walton Hall were infrequent. On such occasions, I would take my eggs home. Grainger, the head groom, showed me how to make wooden trays to set them out. I catalogued and labelled them in my neatest handwriting. On one occasion, he presented me with a chest. He had attached runners inside so the trays became drawers. I still have it and have made many more since.

The humdrum of childhood is easily forgotten, but I will tell of the sequence of events which preceded my release from Tudhoe, for I recall this most distinctly.

Master Storey had a cat. Lucy was a pretty little tortoiseshell thing, and the Master showed great tenderness towards her. As previously stated, he was also the owner of a wig. In fact, he had two wigs. One was a flaxen thing with one row of curls, worn only when in school. The other was of better quality and regularly powdered, being reserved for the days when he went to Durham, some four miles away. When he appeared in the schoolroom wearing his powdered wig, I knew I there would be one less pair of eyes upon me that day. On one such occasion I took myself off to the village. The sun was making its lazy way towards the horizon, or to be correct, the horizon was making its way towards the sun. No matter, it was late afternoon and I was enjoying a freshly baked bread bun, the kind that is baked on the oven bottom, giving it that delightful, hidden crust. Tudhoe had a very fine bakery, and the aroma from that establishment was a magnet to any boy with a penny in his pocket. Sitting on the edge of the village pond, I spotted a large dough tub, the type used in a bakery for rising. I can only assume that this one was no longer fit for its original purpose and had been discarded. How or why it came to be at the edge of the pond, I never knew. Beside it lay a rotting fence post. It too, no longer fit for its original purpose. In my eyes, the two objects took on the shape of a boat and oar. The tub was quite stuck in the mud and it took some heaving and pushing to launch my vessel. The pond was quite shallow, and the post made more of a punting pole than an oar. I soon learned that a dough tub is not designed for boating, and it made for a very unstable vessel. Balancing with care, I knelt down, and was making some headway to the middle of the pond when I was suddenly distracted.

23

"Waterton!" I looked up. The sun gave silhouette to the figures of two men. One I did not know, but the other was the unmistakable shape of Master Storey. Without a thought, I stood up. Capsize was inevitable, and my boat sank to the muddy bottom.

At the time, I was unaware of my Father's friendship with Sir John Salvin of Croxdale Hall. Years later, when he visited Walton Hall, I heard his laughter, and knew in an instant that this was the man who had been my saviour. His amusement at my shipwreck doubled him up. He took a silk kerchief from his cuff, dabbing his eyes as I waded towards them, dripping with stinking water. Master Storey, equally speechless, had turned a dangerous shade of purple. Knowing my gratiating quality to be my knowledge of Latin, I sought to calm the storm. I have always had a fondness for the classical languages and had thought Master Storey quite liked me for it—or at least didn't dislike me quite so much as Father Shepherd did.

"Terribili squalor Charon."

"What did he say?" Sir John chuckled.

"He says, 'Charon is a terrible ferryman.'" The priest's unblinking eyes never left my face. "He refers to the ferryman of Greek mythology who takes the dead to the underworld."

"I implore you, Master Storey, do not punish the boy. A youngster should not be punished for such enterprise." He turned and walked away, still laughing. Master Storey hobbled after him as quickly as his gout would permit.

It is as a consequence of this incident that our little coal barge at Walton Hall is known as 'Charon's Ferry,' as alluded to in my prologue, for unless she is carefully loaded, the little boat is somewhat unstable.

A few days later, and to continue with the sequence of events, I observed a pair of starlings nesting under a roof tile, and as Master Storey had been wearing his powdered wig at break-fast time, I once again assumed him to be going to Durham. When I saw Father Shepherd disappear into his room, I climbed onto the roof to take a closer look. I am fond of starlings, with their bright, shiny livery and admire the way they live as a community. They always seem to be in such a hurry. Seven perfect little blue eggs lay amongst the straw and I thought of how busy the parents would be when their children hatched, and their every moment devoted to the wellbeing of helpless chicks. This made me wonder what it would be like to be a bird-parent. I concluded the only way to find out would be to take an egg and incubate it, and so I took off my jacket and tucked an egg in my left armpit. As I was putting my jacket back on, a kestrel flew overhead, causing me to lose my balance and fall. The landing was not too bad, as I fell into some mud. Unfortunately, it splashed the stockings of none other than Master Storey.

"Waterton!" He screamed as I scrambled to my feet.

'Twas the starlings, sir. They have nested beneath a roof tile. A kestrel distracted me."

"Follow me, Waterton." I did as I was asked, knowing my fate would be particularly harsh. Master Storey had given his word to Sir John Salvin that he would not punish me for the incident with the dough tub, and this was his opportunity to redress the balance.

"I have slept little since Sir John's visit, Waterton."

"I'm sorry to hear..." He flexed his fingers as he hobbled goutily to his study. "Shall I close the door, Master Storey?"

I think, on reflection, that my lack of fear annoyed him further. He did not reply, but I noted that same shade of purple rising from his collar, so I closed the door anyway. I stood up straight and would have looked him in the eye, but my attention was taken by the flaxen wig on the shelf directly behind him. It was moving. The unmistakable markings of Lucy the cat provided the reason for his wearing the powdered wig. Lucy had chosen the flaxen wig as her nest, and the mewing from within told of a number of kittens. Her choice had been the cause of my supposition of being safe from the birch, and my observations and presumptions regarding his wig wearing habits had let me down once again.

"Drop your britches and grip your ankles." I accepted my fate with a sigh of resignation. As I bent over, I felt the rumble of flatulence within. Rather than hold it, I forced the stink from my backside. We had had boiled cabbage the night before, and so my gas was particularly potent. He repeatedly struck my protruding bones with great force and temper.

On previous occasions, his application of the birch had been measured and precise, but this time he grunted, puffed and panted with fury. As he raised his arm for the sixth time, I moved swiftly, twisting down and to the side. My teeth sank right through his muddy stockings, causing him to shriek in agony as he fell to the floor. The rod skittered away.

"I shall not forget this, Waterton!" He grasped a chair leg to haul himself upright, blood spurting from his leg.

"No, Master, I don't suppose you shall, and for my part I shall remember your stupidity in thinking you can achieve obedience by the use of violence. I do not think that when our Lord said, 'suffer little children to come unto me,' he had in mind a birch rod. You should be aware of Christ's teachings more literally and look after your flock with kindness." Feeling rather satisfied with my impromptu speech and its calm delivery, I left the room, passing Father Shepherd in the passageway.

"Is that Father Storey I hear, Waterton?"

I nodded. "It is. He is in a little discomfort—*tortorem cruciator*. The torturer is tortured."

To my relief and delight, the starling egg was intact, secure and warm in my armpit. God had joined forces with fate to land me on my right side. Confident that Master Storey and Father Shepherd would be otherwise occupied for an hour or two, I took the opportunity to take another walk to the village bakery. With my last tuppence, I bought a hot meat pie and set off along the familiar lanes, heading for a tree where I could wedge myself within its branches, and suspend my sore buttocks, as I had on other post birch rod occasions. I climbed carefully lest I drop the pie, or worse still, break the egg. I had been at that wretched school for almost four years and sometimes wondered if the world continued to exist beyond the horizon. My thoughts led me to wonder why people shouted when they were angry. Was there some long-ago belief that alleged wrongdoers were deaf? At over five feet, I was almost as tall as Master Storey. I smiled at the thought that one day I would look down upon him both literally *and* metaphorically. I could not have known, at that time, that my days at Tudhoe were now numbered in single figures. I had long since given up hope of the Masters realising their beatings simply compounded my resolve to do as I wished. If they were correct in their teachings of penance, then I was a model pupil. I never missed any lessons, and could recite most of the synoptic gospels, and that of St John. Surely my interest in all things made by God was not a sin?

Replete with pie, I reached inside my shirt and carefully transferred the egg from left armpit to right. I wriggled into the most comfortable position possible and my eyelids became weighted with lead. The cheerful song of a robin faded from consciousness as I drifted off to sleep.

The tuneless efforts of a woman's singing voice pervaded my dreams of climbing the highest cliffs in the world. Just as an eagle's egg came within my grasp, consciousness overcame sub-consciousness, and I opened my eyes.

"As I was going to Scarborough Fair
Singing, singing, buttercups and daisies..."

I lowered myself from my vantage point to stand squarely before the tattered figure of a beggar woman so stooped that she could not see me until we were no more than five yards apart. That she was poor was obvious. Her bedraggled skirt trailed in the mud, darkening the hemline. One shawl covered her head, while two more were fastened tightly around her shoulders and tucked into her belt.

"Good day to you, madam. I hear you are in good cheer." Her head twisted to one side showing clear blue eyes narrowed against the sun.

"Could be better, could be worse. Winter is past and the frosts done with."

"I have not seen you before. Do you live in Tudhoe?" I asked.

"Tudhoe? Is that the name of this place?"

I crouched to look at her face. "Near Tudhoe, yes. It is the nearest village."

"Ah, that's better. I can see you now. If what you say is true, I am living in Tudhoe today. Sit beside me and I will tell your fortune, young sir." She lowered herself to a tussock of grass.

"I'd rather crouch if you don't mind. I have a sore backside." I suppose I was staring at her, which was rude of me, but I was trying to decide to what degree her dark pallor was due to the elements, and what part to the dirt and dust of the road. A strap hung around her neck bearing a bag that dangled before her. I itched to know its contents.

"I can see without looking at your palm that you are misunderstood by those who believe themselves to be your betters." My jaw dropped. I felt my eyes widen and for once I was speechless. "I dare say if I were to see your hand, it would bear the scars of cruelty." I held my palm towards her. Her misshapen fingers grabbed it quickly as if she feared I may change my mind. "How long have you been in these parts?"

"Three years, eleven months and six days." Her grip tightened, belying their twisted shapes, and with eyes closed, she shook my hand from side to side.

"Then you will be pleased to hear your time here is almost done. You are to travel." She ran the fingertips of her free hand over the lines of my palm. Her nails were long and cracked, and ingrained with dirt.

"Will I be able to go wherever I want?" My mind filled with thoughts of a life on the road, and of climbing trees whenever I wished.

"No, never. You will never be as free as I am, young sir. What is your name?"

"Charles. Charles Waterton. I am the eldest of the twenty-seventh generation of Watertons." She let go my hand, laughing and coughing in equal measure. From within her bag she produced a clay pipe with the longest stem I had ever seen, and a small silver box.

"I see you are surprised that a beggar woman should have silver box." She appeared to await a reply, but for the second time, I had none. Opening it a little on delicate hinges, she blew gently upon hidden contents. A wisp of smoke emerged, and she lit her pipe. "I can tell you this, Charles Waterton—you will carve your own path." She took my hand again, staring intently at my palm before staring at me intently. "It is a long path, with many high mountains to climb and many deep valleys to suffer." I withdrew my hand.

"I have no money for you."

"And I have asked for none."

"I think..."

"What do you think?"

"I think you are very clever, and that you have chosen the life of the road. I think you do not have the gift of a soothsayer but are a very observant person who has deduced my position by means of my appearance and conversation." She laughed and coughed so much that her face turned from ruddy brown to the scarlet of a cardinal's robes. I feared she would die there and then at the roadside and wondered what I would do if that were to occur. My discomfort forgotten, I leapt to my feet and patted her gently on the back until the coughing stopped.

"I do believe, we have more in common than any might guess, do you not?" She asked.

"Perhaps." I took the darning needle from the lapel of my jacket and held it out to her. "I would like to give you this."

"Do you have no use for it?"

"Yes. I do. I use it to pierce the birds' eggs before blowing their contents, but I think you have greater need, to mend your clothes, perhaps."

"Then I will take it, and thank-you, for a gift of sacrifice is a gift well given." I walked over to the hedgerow and found a small branch that had fallen from the oak tree. I snapped one end and removed the leaves.

"Here, take this." I said, "Its shape and length lends itself to help you. Rest your thumb on the fork and you will find it a greater help than some fancy gold topped cane." The woman leaned heavily on the stick as she heaved herself to her feet. She nodded in approval before walking away down the lane, resuming her singing. As I watched the diminishing figure, I wondered whether or not I regretted giving her the needle. Her need was undoubtedly greater than mine, but that was not the same as my not needing it at all. The egg in my armpit would distract my mind for the immediate future, and I hoped maybe Joe would have a needle I could use when I was in a position to resume bird nesting. Meanwhile I would feign injury to my arm, wear a sling, and await the arrival of my firstborn starling.

CHAPTER FOUR

The Challenge.

Edwin sat on the edge of his bed, his jaw slackened in shock as I told of my encounters with Master Storey, and with the beggar woman.

"You actually bit him? Drew blood?"

"I did, and would do it again if the prize were the same."

"What prize, other than a sore backside?" I reached inside my shirt and held out my egg.

"See the beauty, Edwin. Worth every stroke."

"Will you blow it?"

"No. I cannot. If you remember I gave my needle to the beggar woman. No, Edwin. I have a better idea. I am going to hatch this little blue beauty in my armpit. I will pretend I hurt my shoulder when I fell from the roof and wear a sling. In twelve days' time, I shall be a mother."

"Is it a robin's egg?"

"Starling. They are similar, very similar. Such a blue. Curiously the egg of a robin is slightly larger than that of the starling."

"Why do you love the birds so, Charles?"

"Love? I don't know about that, but I do envy them. I envy their flight you see. Can you imagine what it must be like to soar in the sky? The views—the freedom."

The sound of Frobisher's footsteps on the stairs took my forefinger to my lips. I knew Edwin would not betray the secret of the egg.

"There you are, Waterton. I have a challenge for you." I despised the way Frobisher always said, 'there you are' when starting a conversation. Stating the obvious being just one of his irksome habits. "What is it? Are you hiding something?"

"No," I said, "I am not, other than an injured arm. I fell from the roof when"

"You were birdnesting, I assume."

I nodded. "Quite so, I was about to visit Joe Bowren when you came in. I need a sling, but let me assure you, Frobisher. I shall take your challenge as soon as I am able."

Edwin tugged at my coat. "You don't even know what his challenge is," he whispered, but none too quietly.

"Which just goes to show how stupid you are, Waterton." Frobisher laughed, his chins wobbling like jelly as they flowed over the top of his collar. Wiping the sweat from his hands with a kerchief, he walked to the window and pointed at a herd of cows in the meadow. "Because I dare you to mount the tallest cow in that herd and stay on her back for one minute."

"I accept!" There could have been no other reply. "As soon as I am fully recovered, I shall take up your challenge with pleasure."

"I knew you would, Waterton, because you are a fool who thinks himself a jester. Either way, you will provide amusement."

His jibe did not trouble me, and I know there are many who think me a fool. During my lifetime, I have set myself greater challenges than riding a cow, and on many occasions, I have been the victor. I refer to accepted theories of science, which I have disproved on many an occasion. But more of that later.

I could not know when the starling would hatch. I knew incubation to be about two weeks, but I did not know how long it had been incubated when I took possession. The sling did its job admirably, and my enforced calmness no doubt convinced Father Shepherd that his rod had, at last, tamed my character. As I was walking down the stairs from the dormitory, holding the iron rail with my free hand, my mind was taken up with the duties of a mother. Finding and chopping worms, whilst keeping my baby warm would be the order of the day, and I was devising ways to fulfil my duty within the routine of the school day. Distracted by such thoughts, I failed to hear the approach of fellow pupils. Just as the first came alongside, another rushed past him to be first in the dormitory. I was pushed to the wall and felt rather than heard the crack of the egg, followed by a damp warmth in my armpit. I reached inside my shirt. The egg was crushed. My enforced conformity had been a waste of time and the anticipation of parenthood dashed in a split second. The skin and bone of the chick with its soft yellow beak made a pathetic sight. The two dark bulges that would have become the bright eyes of my baby, would remain forever blind. A lump formed in my throat as grief shuddered though me with the coldest of draughts. I consoled myself with the thought that the likelihood of successfully rearing the chick had always been doubtful. Wrapping the corpse in the now redundant sling, I walked to the meadow and left my baby atop a gatepost. Stepping back, I did not have long to wait before a crow found an easy meal for her own chicks.

I returned the sling to Joe. Edwin was with me. We were on our way to see the latest litter of piglets. Heavy rain bounced up from the cobbles.

"I see you have recovered from your injury," Frobisher shouted from the opposite end of the yard, "no sling?"

"How very observant, Frobisher." I shouted back.

"Then you will be ready for your challenge."

I had forgotten all about the cow but was glad of the reminder. It took my mind from the death of my chick. "Indeed, I am. It will be an interesting experience."

"No time like the present, eh? I'll watch from the dormitory window."

I turned to Edwin, "Do *not* follow me. Count the seconds I stay on her back." I left him crouching in the hedge bottom, peering through the hawthorn, and just within the school boundary. The jape was not worth the risk of Edwin being punished for complicity, and I reckoned counting was not a punishable offence, even by the standards of the Masters. The cows raised their heads lazily as I approached. Several of them had calved in the past week, others remained wide of girth. Rain steamed from their backs as the sodden ground sucked at cloven feet. I had walked across the meadow many times on my way to Croxdale Woods, using the thirty-strong herd as cover. Confident of their trust, I talked to them as I always did, running my hands over their flanks as I walked amongst them. The tallest beast was on the far side, I could see her clearly, a calf suckling at her udder. She turned her head towards me, curled horns bowed across her face in magnificent display, with tips almost touching at her nose. Great strings of saliva swung to the ground as she shook her head. Her calf watched me, innocence shining from eyes which seemed too big and too black for his face. Great clouds of moisture steamed from the mother's nostrils. She shuffled sideways as I approached, leaning into me and pushing me away from her baby. As she turned her head, I took my chance, grabbed a horn and swung onto her back. The violence of her reaction took me by surprise. By lowering her head to the ground, she prised the horn from my grip leaving me only her neck to hang onto. I pressed my knees into her sides. With a great heaving of her body she let out such a bellow as to wake the dead, bucking and twisting as the herd scattered in wild panic. I hung on as she arched her back to unseat me. When this failed, she charged towards the hawthorn hedge and I feared she intended to take me straight through. As a matter of honour, I could not jump off and lose the challenge, and so I leaned forward, taking hold of her horns once again, being entirely helpless to prepare in any other way for the consequences. When no more than an arm's length from the prickly hedge, she stopped dead. With front legs splayed and hooves sinking into ground, she bucked like a stallion, ridding herself of her unwelcome load. I flew over the hedge, landing with a thud next to a pale faced Edwin.

"How did I do? Did I last a minute?"

"I-I have no i-idea. I forgot to count, but I doubt it. The racket those cows are making will bring the Masters. Y-you shouldn't have done it. Not when they have calves."

"I expect you are right." I stood up, and attempted to remove the mud from my clothes, but succeeded only in spreading it further and muddying my hands into the bargain. "It could have been worse. I cleared the hedge, and no bones broken. My first flight! Not too bad, although I need to practise my landing."

"Master Waterton! Master Waterton!" Joe Bowren hurried towards us as fast as the mud would allow.

"I fear this is bad news, Edwin."

"How do you know?"

"Did you ever see Joe move so quickly?"

Edwin shook his head. "No."

"Neither have I—and in my limited experience, good news is patient, whereas bad news has an urgency." Joe stopped a little way before them, bending forward, his hands on his knees.

"What is it, Joe?" Edwin asked.

A full minute passed before Joe found breath to speak. "'Tis a message I was asked to give to Master Waterton."

I don't know why, but I was filled with foreboding. I froze. Chilled to the bone in a way no frost could penetrate. "Is it news from my family?"

"It may be, young sir, or may not. Master Storey 'ad a letter this morning but I can't say 'oo from."

"Why not?"

"Because I don't knows!" he shouted. "The Master Storey says yous are to go to his room straight away, where he and Father Shepherd is a waitin' for yous."

"Hide me, Joe."

"What?"

"W-why do you want Joe to hide you?" Edwin squeaked.

"Because, Edwin, until I know why I am wanted I will not give myself up. I want you to find out what's going on."

"And h-how –c-c-can I do that?" Edwin's stammer returned in force at the mere thought of an encounter with the Masters. "I-I can't j-just say, 'why do you want Charles?'"

"All you have to do is listen outside their door. They are bound to be talking about whatever it is."

Joe lifted the lid of the laundry copper. He had emptied it earlier and no more than a few embers glowed in the fire beneath.

"Get you in, Master Waterton." I scrambled in, and Joe replaced the lid. Before long, the warmth of my hiding place began to dry my clothing and warm my backside. Vapour rose around me like a stinking shroud. Stifling a cough, I raised a corner of the lid with one finger to let some steam escape. Peeping from my cosy refuge, I saw no-one. The usual sounds of the yard told me that there was no great search party after me, not yet. The hens clucked, the ducks quacked and the geese squabbled. The pigs were squealing frantically, which meant Joe was about to feed them. I let go the lid and settled down to contemplate the possible reason for my required attendance. Using logic, I decided it fell into two options. If it were a result of the letter from Walton, it had to be news of a death. Any other news would wait. The second option was far more likely and had nothing to do with a letter. Either Master Storey or Father Shepherd had seen me ride the cow and I was in for another dose of the usual. Maybe that wretched Frobisher had snitched on me. If, on the other hand, it had simply been the terrible noise that had drawn their attention, then I knew I had only myself to blame for not having anticipated the reaction of the entire herd. After a while, I dozed.

"Ch-Charles! Ch-Charles!" I lifted the lid at the sound of my friend's urgent voice and wafted away the steam. I must have looked like a ghost emerging from miasma. Edwin blanched.

"I thought you were a rat."

"Well I'm not. I was asleep if you must know. The warmest, most comfortable sleep I have had in all my miserable years at Tudhoe." I then heard the words I had dreamt of and longed for.

"Come on, Charles. You are to go home—for good."

"What! Are you sure?"

"Yes. Father Shepherd is with Master Storey in his room. Your father has written asking for you to be sent home. I heard them discussing what they called *implications*.

I climbed out of the copper. "What did they say?"

"Master Storey seemed annoyed, he spoke of losing the income, but Father Shepherd said the school would be a better place without you."

"Did they say anything about the cow?"

"Not a word. I don't think they know anything about it."

The interview was brief. Master Storey sat behind his desk with Father Shepherd standing to his right. A letter lay before the Master. I recognised father's handwriting.

"Your father has written to me, Waterton. He says you are to go home. Pack your trunk, and Bowren will take you to Bishop Auckland in the morning."

Of all my misdemeanours, the incident with the cow had to be one of the worst, but I was not birched. I can only assume they were unaware of my rodeo show until after my departure, thus depriving one or the other of the Masters of their parting blow. Naturally, I was delighted to be going home.

The rhythmic gait of Nellie's hooves accompanied creaking cartwheels as Joe and I travelled along the lanes. Dawn crept in a thin, yellow line, sending a family of rabbits to their burrow as the bitter wind turned heavy mist to rain, stinging my face with a thousand thorns. I pulled a piece of sackcloth around my shoulders.

"Can't she go any faster, Joe? I don't want to miss the post-coach. We must have been travelling for over an hour and are still nowhere near Bishop Auckland."

"Yous won't miss it, Master Waterton. Old Nellie has to pull me all the way back so I don't wants to tire 'er. The wet makes 'ard work for the ol' girl."

"You won't be back in time to cook the Masters' break-fast."

Joe chuckled. "Well then, one of thems should 'ave brought yous. That way only one of thems would be put out." We laughed together, unable and unwilling to disguise our amusement.

"I expect neither of them wanted to bear my company for a second longer than they had to—I shall miss Edwin though."

"Speakin' of young Master Jones—I told 'im to give the boys some bread to keep the grumbles from their bellies."

"What will you do about the night-time arrangements?"

"I dunno, but I expects your friend Frobisher will find a way."

"No friend of mine."

"I knows—I knows more'n folks thinks."

"I think you are a very clever fellow, Joe. I have been pleased to call you my friend."

"Is that so, Master Waterton. Well I 'as been pleased to be of acquaintance." Joe held the reins in his left hand as he pointed to the right. "See them turrets—them's Bishop Auckland Castle."

Twenty minutes later, Joe passed my trunk up to the driver, lifting it above his head as if it were no weight at all. I proffered my hand and winced at the grip of a giant.

"I shall miss your company, Joe. I hope we meet again one day." If I was not mistaken, Joe's eyes glistened as a smile twitched at the corners of his mouth.

"Might yous be comin' back?"

"That is highly unlikely, but until I am old enough to be the master of my own destiny, I cannot be sure."

"Yous is a queer cut, Master Waterton, and Joe 'ere wishes 'e well. Now gets yous in that post-coach."

There were no other passengers, but I was happy enough in my own company. The first stop was a coaching house in Darlington, where I was provided with a welcome bowl of broth. Despite the biting wind, I preferred to take my refreshments outside, away from the stench of stale beer and pipe smoke. Although hot and filling enough, there was nothing else to recommend it, and the bread was so stale it grazed my gums. The bustle of the yard diverted me, for some part, from the poor standard of the rations. Horses were changed and post-bags deposited and collected. I thought it best to keep watch on my trunk lest it be unloaded in error, or stolen. I had little in the way of clothing, but seventeen blown eggs were in there, all ready for cataloguing.

Before long I was on my way to York, sharing the coach with an elderly man. If the coach had been fully occupied, and all the passengers the size of my fellow traveller, it would have been rather cramped. With one hand on a gold-topped cane, the gentleman leaned into the worn upholstery and closed his eyes. While the rumbling wheels on the turnpike disguised any noise, the stench of my companion's flatulence could not be mistaken. I rolled up the blind and stuck my head out into the fresh air, proving beyond doubt that the stink came from within.

"Shut that down! There's a draught fit to cut a man in two." Eyes bulged from a reddening face.

"I'd rather be cut in two than be gassed, sir,"

"What are you talking about, young whippersnapper?"

"I am talking about the foul smell that is coming from your rear and filling this coach." The man drew breath as if to speak, and then let it go with a harrumphing wheeze. He began to laugh, his amusement quickly turning into a fit of coughing. With his face the colour of a turkey's crop, he took a kerchief from his breast pocket and dabbed his eyes.

"Pies."

"I beg your pardon, sir."

"Pies. Do it to me every time. My wife says I shouldn't eat 'em but the fresh pastry tempts me, and I am weak."

"Weak willed, maybe, sir," I said, "but there is nothing weak about your leak." He started to laugh again, beating his fist upon his chest.

"So, may I leave the blind up for a while? I do believe the wind has abated. I mean the weather wind, not yours." Amongst the coughing and laughing, and the beating of his chest, I discerned a nod.

The landscape softened as we passed the entrance to Castle Howard, its great dome just visible between the rolling hills. With the North Yorkshire Moors in the east gradually giving way to the broad flatness of the Vale of York, the towers of the minster could be seen in the distance.

Once within the walls, narrow twisting streets that formed the labyrinth of the ancient city presented tantalising glimpses of the minster. I craned my neck as we rattled along Deangate. Sliding along the seat, I rolled up the other blind as we passed the south door.

Clattering hooves competed with the clamour of the yard as the driver reined in the horses. The Olde Starre Inn stood a little way back from the narrow street of Stonegate. Oil lamps struggled in vain to light the front of the inn as mist swirled around the yard. My fellow-traveller and I alighted. He shook me by the hand, raised his hat, and with a mocking smile, bowed, and walked away. My trunk was passed down from the roof and taken inside. Rather than enter the inn, I followed the stablemen as they led the horses to an inner yard. The stablemen wasted no time in unhitching the team from the harnesses of leather and chains. The strong bays were admirable creatures, obedient to the touch and words of men. Grainger once told me that Yorkshire coach horses were bred for their strength and biddable nature, and anyone who has witnessed them closely would not argue with that. They were rubbed down, stabled and fed, and taken for a night's rest. A shiver took me indoors. It had been a long day.

The sparsely furnished room, with its single bed and washstand, was clean enough in comparison to the dormitory at Tudhoe. I did not dwell upon it my thoughts were for the future. I licked my lips in anticipation of climbing out of the window at night, across the kitchen roof and down the wall to the footbridge, the woods and the owls. No more Frobisher. No more birch rod. There was a price to be paid of course—no more Joe and no more Edwin. On balance, I decided I was pleased to be going home.

Sounds of the ale drinkers drifted up to my room. Feeling more tired than I had ever done after a night of birdwatching, sleep quickly overtook me.

The following morning, with my trunk once again strapped atop, and a bowl of hot porridge filling my belly, I stepped to one side to allow two ladies to board. They, and their gowns, all but filled the coach.

"Would you care to sit up front?" The driver growled with the voice of a smoker. He spat a glob of blood and phlegm to the ground. In a flash, I climbed up to sit beside him before he had time to change his mind. Gloved hands pulled the lead horse rein and we set off, the harnesses linking the bays into one unit. With his many layers of coats, and his weather-beaten skin, I found it impossible to guess his age.

The buildings closest to the banks of the Ouse were flooded. After crossing a bridge, we passed under Micklegate Bar, hooves echoing beneath the medieval arch. A flick of the whip took us to a brisk trot as the morning sun glinted on the brasses, its thin warmth compensating a little for the breeze. Even if it snowed, I would have preferred to be atop rather than squashed, or gassed, in the warmer confines below.

"What's your name then, lad?"

"Charles. Charles Waterton."

"Well, Master Waterton, we have twenty-five miles between us and Leeds."

"How long will it take?"

"Well now, that depends." He turned away to cough, growl and spit down wind. "We should be there for one o'clock, but there's been rain these past weeks. It could be heavy going after Tadcaster, if Mistress Wharfe isn't behaving herself." The deep throated laugh sounded like the gurgling of a drain and displayed the most discoloured teeth I had ever seen. That is to say, those which he still had, for most were missing. I stared at him with the guileless innocence of a much younger child.

"Do you mean the *River* Wharfe?"

"I do that, Master Waterton. You see, rivers are like women. Just when everything is nice and cosy, they jump out o' bed, and start running all over the place. A man don't know what to expect."

"There is a bridge, though."

"Oh, yes. A very fine bridge. That isn't the tricky bit. It's when she gets out o' bed and goes a runnin' in the fields, that's when she gives me a whole load o' trouble. There's one bit of road that's 'specially low. We could be lucky and have no more than a patch o' mud. That's what I hope, and hope dies hard. That's what I say."

I remained in my lofty position while the driver refreshed his palate with a pint of ale in Tadcaster. With the post bags deposited and collected, we set off again. With a flick of the driver's wrist, his whip touched the ear of the lead horse and we set a brisk pace. He twisted the reins into one hand and pulled a pipe from his pocket. I believe I was staring at him again as he wedged it in a convenient gap in his teeth. With a dexterity that can only have come from many years' practice, he produced a tinder box from his jacket, and one-handedly lit his pipe. The smell of burning tobacco drifted to my nostrils. The sight of his teeth and the sound of his cough made me decide there and then that I would not take up smoking.

"And what is Master Waterton to do in Leeds on a fine day like this?"

"Nothing, I hope. Someone will meet me there. I expect it will be Grainger."

"I'm pleased to hear it. A city isn't right for a young lad." I didn't understand what he was talking about, and didn't particularly want to encourage further conversation, lest he started again about rivers and women.

As it transpired, the mud of the low ground merely covered the rims of the wheels, or as the driver put it, 'she only wet my ankles.'

To my surprise, Father was waiting for me, mounted on a grey hunter. A bay stood patiently to his right on a lead rein. Grainger was to his left, with a pony and cart. Father dismounted and shook my hand. This was not the reception I had expected. In truth, I had not known what to expect, or even thought about it. Some sort of admonishment would have been less puzzling. What could precipitate such a welcome? Grainger gave a wink of recognition as he carried my trunk to the cart.

"Good to see you, Master Charles."

"Good to see you, Grainger, I have more eggs to—"

"Come Charles." Father pulled at my jacket as he shouted above the clamour of the yard. "Your mother is anxious. She wants you home as quickly as possible. Grainger will follow."

"Thank-you, Father." I led the mare to a mounting block and swung into the saddle. "I have not ridden for some time. There was no opportunity for such things at Tudhoe."

"Your mother is anxious, not annoyed." Father nodded, and we set off. I thought it a curious choice of words but did not dwell upon Mother's mood. All would become clear in due course, and for now I was content to enjoy the final part of my journey, happy to breathe the air of freedom.

Leaving Leeds behind, the bustling streets gave way to the turnpike and open fields. We cantered away, slowing to a trot through the villages and the town of Wakefield. Father never spoke another word, but the silence was a comfortable one. I tipped my chin to a pale spring sun. Nothing could dampen my spirits. My skinny legs squeezed the horse's sides, urging her to keep pace with the larger hunter. *Vivat temporis.* Live the moment.

A crow cawed its hoarse greeting from the top of a beech tree as we trotted down the avenue to Walton Hall. We dismounted at the stable block, and a groom led the horses away. Hens and turkeys followed him in their noisy expectations. I resolved to visit the stables in order to inspect the martins' nests in the beams above the stalls, but first, I had to go through the formalities of greeting Mother and my siblings.

Trying to match Father's stride, I crossed the footbridge in his wake. Six faces looked down from the second floor. Helen held the baby Edward. Thomas, Christopher, William and Isabella all waved, and I waved back. As we approached the portico, the double doors opened as if by magic. I knew it would be Dawson. The butler had a sixth sense of perception which alerted him to any approach. Mrs Bennett, who so often caught me out in my adventuring, shared this uncanny power. If my years at Tudhoe had taught me nothing else of use, I had learned how to be as wily as a fox, but doubted I could walk the stone path in daylight without detection. As Dawson took our coats and hats, the thunder of feet and trills of laughter tumbled down the broad, shallow staircase. Brothers and sisters rushed to greet me. Old More, the clock which has been in our family for centuries, struck five, easily heard from its position on the first landing of the staircase. The landing is wide, and known as the organ gallery, although it has never housed an organ. This magnificent timepiece was named after its original owner, Sir Thomas More, chancellor to the Old Goat, Henry VIII, and an ancestor on my mother's side. I have no reason to doubt that it once belonged to him. Mrs Bennett always called it Chancellor More. The clock does not have a second hand, dating from the times when we did not rush to catch a train, and life was a more leisurely business.

These days, many of my specimens are displayed in the hall and on the staircase. As my museum expanded it ascended the stairs and now fills every space, including the landings, but on the day I now describe, there was none of that. Just Old More and the family portraits, the most interesting being the Holbein of Sir Thomas More.

Mother was in her usual chair, by the window. I kissed her on the cheek, stepping back to give a short bow. I was not, and am not, in the habit of kissing, nor bowing and so I don't know why I felt compelled to do so. I think she was as shocked as I. She shook her head and handed me a letter.

"Read this, Charles," she said, "and then tell me why it was written." An involuntary shudder ran from my head to my toes as I recognised the handwriting of Master Storey.

The School House
Tudhoe
The County of Durham.
April 2nd, 1796.

My Lord Waterton,
It is with a heavy heart that I take pen to paper. Our God knows that Father Shepherd and I have used every discipline at our disposal to encourage your son towards a fulfilling and worthwhile life, but despite our efforts and methods (which have proved successful with every other pupil) he refuses to appreciate the value of a Catholic education. I say 'refuses' because without a doubt, Charles is the most intelligent of boys. His studies pose no challenge to him. He understands perfectly that which is expected but is strong willed to the point of wilful and persistent disobedience. His frequent absences from the school boundaries in order to pursue his obsession for climbing trees, and generally having no regard for our rules, have led us to the conclusion that Tudhoe School for Catholic Boys is no longer able to accommodate your son.
Please understand that our concern is, first and foremost, for the education of all our pupils.
It is, therefore, with utmost regret, and, after much deliberation and debate, we ask you to find an alternative educational establishment for your son.

Yours Sincerely,
Reverend Arthur Storey.

I refolded the letter and handed it back to Mother.

"Your father and I would like to know why Master Storey and Father Shepherd have asked us to remove you."

"Yes, Mother. I expect it is due to my having bitten Master Storey's leg." Father was standing behind her. He had one hand on her shoulder. I saw his grip tighten. Mother gasped as if her breath had been sucked from her body.

"You bit him?" Father shouted.

"Yes, Father. I expect he will remember the sharpness of my teeth."

"Why, Charles?" Mother asked. "Why did you bite him?"

"I don't know."

"But you must know." Father sounded incredulous. "You surely didn't just walk up to him and bite him."

"Oh, no. Of course not. No, Father, he was beating me you see. He did not beat me often, that was more usually Father Shepherd's work but he only beat my hands. Master Storey was very angry because I had splashed his stockings with mud when I fell off the roof. He had made me drop my britches, and when I was bending over—"

"Charles—" Father began.

"Show me your hands." Mother interrupted him. I stepped forward and stretched out my arms, palms towards the floor. "Turn them over." As I did so, my fingertips began to shake. Mother gripped my wrists as her eyes fell upon flesh made frail by scars, old and new, sucking her breath away for the second time in as many minutes.

"Forgive my shaking, Mother. I think it must be in subconscious anticipation of the Shepherd's crook." She let go, and I hid my hands behind my back. "He did not understand my need to visit the woods."

"No, I don't suppose they did. Go to your room, Charles," she said, "your father and I need to discuss your future."

"May I not go to the lake, Mother. I need to see the waterfowl."

"No, Charles. I think it best that for today, you observe from your room."

Before I was able to object, Father's decisive tone sealed my fate. "Your mother and I have much to discuss. In the morning, you will ride with me. You need to know the estate. The waterfowl can wait."

"What do you mean? I know every tree in the woods, every path, every stream. What can you show me?"

"Your father has spoken, Charles. That is the end of the matter. Supper will be served at seven o'clock. You will join us in the dining room."

"What about my brothers and sisters?"

Mother sighed. "Thomas will join us, as will Monsieur Raquedal. The others are not yet old enough."

"But I would prefer—"

"Go to your room, Charles."

"Yes, Mother."

I bowed again, first to Mother and then to Father, still not understanding why.

My bedroom had a crucifix on the wall, alongside a picture of a hunting scene, a small mirror, a wardrobe, a washstand, a towel rail, a chair, a desk, a small rug and a single bed.

I listened carefully to my every step from my bed to the west facing window, noting with satisfaction that the floorboards creaked in exactly the same places as they had before. My room is on a corner of the house, so has the advantage of two windows, one facing to the west, the other to the north. I kicked off my boots, and lay on my back. With hands clasped behind my head, I studied the construction of the rafters, and how they made excellent perches for any bird that might choose to fly in through an open window. I determined to leave my windows open at night in the hope that one might fly in to keep me company. It came to me that I could sit up there and wait, rather than go out if the weather were too bad. The peaceful comfort weighed upon my eyelids. Only when Mrs Bennett blustered through the door, did I realise I had been asleep.

"Did you not hear the bell, Charles Bernard?"

I swung my feet to the floor, wriggling my toes appreciatively in the little rug. "No. I didn't. Sorry, Mrs Bennett. I would not vex you for the world."

"It is not me who is vexed. Hurry along. Your mother and father await you in the dining room."

"What about Thomas?"

"Yes, he is there too." The housekeeper shook her head as I rushed past her, leaping down the stairs, two and three at a time. Grabbing the newel post, checking my speed as I opened the dining room door. Mother and Father were seated at opposite ends of the long table. Thomas to Father's right, and Monsieur Raquedal to his left, next to my own, empty seat.

"I apologise unreservedly. I"

"Please be seated, Charles." Father nodded towards the empty chair. As I grabbed my spoon, everyone lowered their heads. Monsieur Raquedal's voice dominated.

"Gratias agimus sumus misterator Dominus panem ad manducandum." His words of thanks to the Lord were more brief than those of the Tudhoe Masters, and for much better food.

Father ordered me back to my room as soon as supper was finished and I cannot say I was sorry. Exhaustion quickly won, and I fell to a deep sleep. The wide-open window may have admitted a visitor, but I found no evidence. Not so much as a feather.

CHAPTER FIVE

The Estate.

With a wistful glance towards the woodland, I mounted the steps and swung into the saddle. The trees would have to wait a little longer. Father kicked his horse to a trot and my bay followed with no need of encouragement. To my delight, she was as fresh from her night's rest as I, giving a little buck as we rode up the tree lined avenue. I gripped her girth with my knees and patted her neck.

"Here, Charles." Father waved me forward to ride alongside him. "We will firstly take the route of the navigation. Construction has commenced at Barnsley, and I need to show you how I have protected our parkland."

As we passed the gate-keeper's cottages, parallel lines of posts stretched as far as I could see.

"Is this it, Father? Is this the proposed route? I didn't notice it yesterday."

"It *is* the route, Charles. No longer merely proposed, I am pleased to say." He guided his horse through a narrow gap, and I followed. My eyes were drawn to the treetops as if by magnets as we rode between the lines of fencing.

"But what will happen to these trees, Father?"

"They will be felled."

My heart sank to my boots. "Is there no other way? Can the navigation not be routed through some tenanted pasture? There is plenty of grazing land."

Father reined his horse, turning in the saddle to face me. "Charles. Listen to me. I have attended countless meetings regarding this and believe me, this is the best route. If my fellow committee members had had their way, the navigation would have gone straight through our parkland and Stubbs Wood. It would have involved the destruction of many more trees, including some ancient oaks, before wending its way to the River Calder. I consider myself to be a naturalist, but there has to be compromise with progress."

The bay danced beneath me, and I concentrated on keeping my seat as she stepped impatiently from side to side. I slackened the rein a little and she took her opportunity. With flaring nostrils, she twisted her body, and bolted up the incline.

"Pull her head around, Charles! Pull her head." Father shouted as the thundering hooves of his hunter came alongside. "She will not bolt if she can't see where she is going!" I pulled on the left rein, but not so hard as to distract her from her bid for freedom. I stood in the stirrups, shifting my weight so she could gallop even faster. "Pull her in, Charles! Stop her, I say!" Father leaned out of his saddle and tried to catch hold of the rein. Seeing his intention, I tugged the opposite way, taking the rein from his reach, and then I let my steed have her head. A mile or so later, she slowed. Father grabbed the rein, controlling both horses and bringing them to a standstill at the perimeter of the parkland. I sat back in the saddle.

"Are you all right?"

"Of course I am, Father. Was that not the most marvellous gallop?"

Father shook his head. "Charles, I despair."

"Despair? Of what?"

"The purpose of our ride is to show you the estate, not to chase around like lunatics."

"But Father—"

"No, Charles. Let me cut you off there." He held up his palm. "You may know every tree worthy of climbing, and every bird in the wood, but there is more to running an estate than schoolboy pleasure. Now, follow me. We will walk the horses back along the navigation route. I will point out where there are to be bridges, where the land needs to be blasted and quarried, and where the locks will be built. I will explain why this route is the best possible for the estate. If you listen carefully, you will learn—"

"If it were my decision, the wretched navigation would not enter our land at all, not even across the farmland, and no trees would—"

"Do not interrupt. Listen, watch, and learn, Charles. I will introduce you to some of our tenants." Father kicked his horse to a canter, and we headed towards Rose Farm.

Some three hours later we returned to the stables. We had ridden along the navigation route and surveyed the pastures to the west of the estate. Grainger appeared and we handed over the horses. Father and I walked side by side towards the footbridge.

"So, Charles," he said, "do you now understand why your mother and I are so concerned?"

"Concerned?" I saw Father grind his teeth in a sideways motion. "No, I don't understand, and I don't understand why you look so angry. What have I done now? What is it, Father? We have had a perfectly amicable ride, and I have learned a lot. Surely you are not still angry about the bolting—it was nothing much. I would say there had been more cause for concern when you placed me in the care of the Masters of Tudhoe. I am perfectly safe here." Father stopped and turned to face me.

"We shall resume your education in practical matters tomorrow."

I watched him cross the footbridge before wandering off along the lakeside. The blackthorn and hawthorn trees were heavy with blossom, their bright green buds bursting with enthusiasm for the summer ahead. Bluebells still carpeted the woodland, feasting on the light before the deciduous foliage forced them back underground. Fierce brambles, impenetrable to humans, clung to the rotting leaves of the previous summer, their fruits long since devoured. Fox and badger paths tunnelled through thickets. Songbirds filled the air with both joy and dispute as they chose their partners for the coming season. From the tiniest wren to the magnificence of the kite, every bird was busy. Beakfuls of nesting material, twigs, moss and leaves were carried to the marital home. Surrounded by the optimism of spring, I felt my own heart soar with the birds. To my delight, a pair of common swans were surveying the small island, their ungainly walk so much at odds with their ease of swimming and of flight. The first I knew of the presence of Canada geese, camouflaged as they were by reeds and bushes on the far bank, was the beating of the cob's wings on the water as he ran across the surface of the lake in defence of his territory, neck outstretched, the claws of his webbed feet breaking the surface of the water. The threat of a battle was enough. Wingspan is everything in the politics of the birds, and the geese knew they could not win against a swan. They flew off for less contentious ground. At the lakeside, grass had been trimmed close to the ground by vegetarian fowl, and made slippery by their deposits, making for a treacherous walk. Moorhen and coot, wild duck and shoveler duck, all intent on their business of building and eating, ignored the distant 'crek-crek' of the corncrake and the all-seeing eyes of the grey heron, whose young would already have hatched. Fascinated by the diving birds, I counted the seconds of their underwater adventures, scanning the lake as I awaited their jack-in-the-box reappearance. At the edge of the woodland, where the going was less muddy, I lay back with entwined fingers creating a pillow as I stretched my arms behind my head. Sunlight forced my pale blue eyes to slits. Silhouetted branches bowed under the weight of argumentative rooks. Then, suddenly, silence, followed by the high pitched 'chip-chip-chip' of the osprey. The magnificent fellow hovered some fifty feet above, circling and then hovering again, before turning to a headlong dive, switching at the very last moment to a feet-first plunge. The pike he lifted from the water was as big as a man's arm. I scraped my heels back towards my body, raising my knees to sit upright, better to see the trophy carried away. I tried to imagine the feast, talons and beak ripping through the fish, giving sustenance to the osprey and his mate whilst at the same time saving the lives of countless waterfowl chicks which would otherwise have been prey to both osprey *and* pike.

My own midday meal would have been cleared from the table by now, and unlike that of the osprey, my stomach would have to wait until teatime. Mealtimes were set precisely within the walls of Walton Hall. I considered returning to the house to try my luck in the kitchen, but my chances of slipping past Mrs Bennet were too slim to warrant the time it would take. Instead, I carried on to the far end of the lake where a slab of stone bridged the brook. I climbed one of a pair of broad leaf oak trees nearby, curling up in a twisted branch, its curve matching that of my back. Before long the hypnotic effect of birdsong lulled me to sleep.

Father and I rode out every morning for a week. He introduced me to our tenant farmers and showed me the boundaries of the estate. He owned several properties in the village, from small cottages to larger houses. I regret to say, I argued with Father quite a lot on these expeditions. When a tenant invited me into his cottage, Father would have none of it, saying,

"Hold your tongue, and don't make a fool of yourself." He told me that no tenant had ever invited him inside. I think he was jealous. When, within earshot of the farmer, I pointed out the dreadful state of the roof at Rose Farm, he agreed that repairs were necessary. As we left, he said,

"You should not have said anything in front of the tenant."

"Why not?"

"Because there is a cost involved, and now it will be all around the village that I am making repairs. Other tenants will be asking for goodness knows what."

"But if—"

"Enough, Charles."

We rode towards the village. "See here, Father." I pointed out a triangle of land bordered by the field boundary, the navigation route, and Shay Lane. "What is to happen here?"

"That piece has become the property of the navigation company." A bridge is to be built, and a retaining wall is to support the slope, thereby defining the line of the waterway where the land naturally falls away." Father pointed across the lane. "See how the land continues to slope. If the route were to follow the boundary, it would adversely affect the construction of the bridge and the locks."

"You mean make it more expensive?"

"Once again, we are talking about compromise. Just before the navigation passes under the lane there will be workshops and stabling for the towing horses. Because the land you pointed out amounts to no more than four roods of rough pasture, it is better left for them to do with as they see fit."

"Look at the birds, Father. It is their home." I pointed out chaffinches, blue-tits, great-tits, pied wagtails, thrushes and blackbirds. "See how hawthorn, blackthorn, yew and holly provides cover for them."

Father sighed with boredom. "Progress has to be embraced, Charles. Transport is the key to everything, and the birds will stay or go, as they see fit."

The days melded into one, the flow of the season lengthening the days and shortening the nights. By mid-June I had a list of thirty species of waterfowl, nine birds of prey, five species of tit, and seven songbirds, all of which had nested in either Stubbs Wood or Haw Park Wood. Six pairs of herons had fledged their chicks.

Mr Bartram and Monsieur Raquedal made no complaint. With their unspoken consent, I completed my studies as quickly as possible, leaving my brothers slaving away over their books while I began the business of the day. Mrs Bennett berated me each evening regarding the state of my clothes, but with muddy streams, brambles and high trees all in abundance, I was not to blame if my clothes suffered.

"You will fall to your death one day, Charles Bernard, and then where will we all be?" I would give her my most cheerful smile.

"I expect everyone would still be here without me, and you would not have to worry, or ask a maid to mend my britches." Then she would strut away to her room, huffing and puffing like a steam pump.

One afternoon, when the weather was particularly humid, Mr Bartram released Thomas and Christopher from the stifling school room. I was about to set sail across the lake. There were several nests on the little island, with wild duck and pochard breeding alongside one another.

"Can we come with you?" Christopher asked. Delighted at the opportunity to show my brothers the wonders of the lake, I held the line as they boarded my sailboat, *Percy*.

"Sit beside each other and take an oar each. When we get to the island you must sit still and not upset the birds."

"Shall we go ashore, Captain?" Thomas saluted. "We could be shipwrecked mariners."

"No, you cannot. The island belongs to the birds. If you don't do as I say I shall tip you out."

"Better do as the captain says." Christopher laughed. "We don't want to be lashed by Mrs Bennett's tongue." I stepped onto the boat and placed the mooring line at Christopher's side. Thomas pushed us away from the wooden landing, and I raised the sail.

"There isn't much wind," I said, "but when we are away from the house, we might pick up a breeze. Meanwhile, my crew, you must row."

"I shall be glad of the breeze," Christopher wiped his brow with his shirtsleeve. He had been rowing for no more than a minute. "It's too hot for this." We progressed slowly, our course meandering as my crew struggled to synchronise their efforts. Just as I predicted, the breeze caught the sail as we left the lee of the house. The oars were stowed, and I navigated towards the little island. The sun shone relentlessly. I pointed out the nests to my brothers. Not one of us noticed the clouds until first spots of rain broke the glass-like surface of the lake with rippling circles. Thunder rumbled as black clouds raced to steal the sun.

"We must turn back," Thomas said, but just at that moment the wind billowed in the sail and the little boat took off at speed across the surface. I clung to the tiller. Day turned to night as the rain pelted down, boiling the water with its heavy splashes and filling the boat. Great forks of lightning illuminated the parkland.

"I think you will have your wish, Thomas," I shouted above the storm, "lower the sail, or we shall be shipwrecked mariners. Take off your shoes, Christopher, and use them to bale out the water. We are sinking." Despite the poor visibility, I knew we would land near the little creek on the southern shore. The adventure lasted no more than a few minutes, and I recall feeling a little disappointed as we disembarked, dragging *Percy* further up the bank. I took one look at my brothers and laughed.

"What's so funny?" Thomas asked.

"You are. You look so miserable."

"Well I *am* miserable" Christopher said, "I am wet through and cold. What is amusing about that?"

"This is an adventure, Christopher. If Helen were with us, she would agree with me."

"Which is the quickest way back to the house?"

"By boat, of course. We can gather fallen branches to build a shelter and wait for the storm to pass. I have done it before."

"Charles," Thomas shook his head, "I think I speak for Christopher when I say we do not want to go in the boat, we do not want to build a shelter, and we do not want to wait here for the storm to pass. We are not afraid of the weather and intend to walk home."

"I agree with Thomas," Christopher spoke through chattering teeth. "Never again will I go in a boat, but that does not mean I am a coward."

"'Never' is a big word, brother, and in time you may rethink your decision. I never said you were a coward, but as Captain Waterton, I must stay with my vessel. The bridge over the creek is that way. Cross it, and the path will take you alongside the lake for a while and then through the woodland to the avenue. I expect even you two can find your way home from there."

They set off, and I started to gather fallen branches, leaning them against the trunk of an ash tree, but within minutes I abandoned the plan. The dark clouds were sweeping away like the velvet curtains of a theatre, opening to a stage of brilliant sunshine as the next act began. Birdsong filled the air, and steam rose from the woodland. I returned my attention to *Percy,* baling out until I deemed my vessel to be seaworthy. Once out in open water, I spotted my crew squelching through the mud at the lakeside. I would have waved to them, but their heads were fixed downward in misery. I tacked along at a fair pace. Knowing I would be home before them, I resolved to ask Mrs Bennett to arrange for jugs of hot water to be put in their rooms, and have a maid lay out some dry clothes.

Far from thanking me for this, the entire household railed against me as if I had had a master plan to drown my brothers, or at the very least, be the cause of their deaths by pneumonia. I attempted to explain to Mrs Bennett that if Thomas and Christopher spent more time outdoors, their bodies would be impervious to chills. I told Dawson that if my crew had obeyed their captain they would have been home more quickly, and less likely to succumb, but the butler tutted and disappeared into the pantries. For the following two weeks, my brothers were confined to their bedroom, with a roaring fire in the hearth and the windows shut. Thomas was not permitted to come to the dining room, lest the cooler air were to instigate a fit of coughing. Thus, mealtimes were like a vigil for the dead, rather than the usual social gathering, with Mother and Father glaring as I ate every morsel set before me. Cutlery clattered, soup slurped, my very breathing seemed to echo around the room. Mercifully, Monsieur Raquedal and Mr Bartram kept any opinion they might have had to themselves. Only when the usually pessimistic Doctor Goode announced that Thomas and Christopher would survive with no ill effects, did conversation return to the dining table.

About a week after this return to normality, a conversation took place over dinner, of which I was the subject, but from which I was excluded. Monsieur Raquedal began the exchange.

"May I ask, sir, if you have any plans for Charles' future education?" Eyes around the table darted between my father and the priest. Dawson stood silently in a corner, rocking back and forth, heel to toe, heel to toe. A maid moved silently around the table. I never could like Monsieur Raquedal. The priest's fawning manner had the mark of faked humility. I suppose Father, and especially Mother, for she was the more devout, considered themselves lucky to have him as part of the household, performing with great efficiency the roles of priest and tutor. This, however, did not blind me to the fact that Monsieur Raquedal, with his limp and crooked spine, had quite an easy time of it at Walton Hall. The priest rarely left the grounds. He had an irritating habit of starting a conversation with 'may I ask,' instead of just coming straight out with a question.

Father sighed deeply. "Thanks to yourself, Mr Bartram here, and his schooling at Tudhoe, Charles is not uneducated. The difficulty I face is that he has no understanding of his position, no social skills, and no sign of maturity whatsoever. At almost fourteen years of age, his manner is, shall we say, disappointing." My brother wiped the corners of his mouth with his napkin, casting me a look which told me my intervention would not be welcome. "Do you have any suggestions, Monsieur? My wife and I would be grateful for your guidance."

"I do." He paused, as if wresting with his mind as to whether he should continue. "You may recall, I mentioned some time ago the priests and scholars of the Jesuit School you attended in Liège had been forced to flee the French revolutionaries."

Mother dropped her spoon. Soup spattered the tablecloth. "Why didn't we think of it, Thomas? They established their school in Lancashire some two years since." To my horror, Mother was as excited as a child with a picnic basket.

"Ah—yes. You are right, of course I remember." Father smiled. "I have been intending to visit. I believe a former pupil owns it."

My heart sank. Another school, another exile. More vindictive priests, embittered, no doubt by having to leave the continent and settle in Lancashire.

"Yes, indeed." Mother pressed her palms together. She sounded as pleased at the prospect as I felt miserable. "Charles must go there. Thank-you for reminding us, Monsieur Raquedal. Stonyhurst. That is the name of the estate, is it not?"

The priest nodded. "You are quite right, m'lady."

"Why do you think the priests at Stonyhurst could succeed where Master Storey and Father Shepherd failed?" Father asked.

Mother's shoulders slumped. "Maybe they can't. I..." A short silence ensued.

"I correspond with one of the Fathers there." Mr Bartram said. "They have known suffering and persecution, it gives a person a certain perspective. In my opinion, they are more worldly than most." He stared at Monsieur Raquedal as he spoke, but the veiled criticism of the priest went unnoticed by my parents and Thomas.

"Thank-you, Mr Bartram." A smile of satisfaction lit Mother's face. "May I say, no-one knows Charles better than yourself, and Monsieur Raquedal," she waved her arm towards the priest, "so if you think it a good idea, I'm sure it is."

"Let us not be overwhelmed by an apparent solution, my dear. We must not be guilty of grasping at straws. Before any decision is made, I must go to Stonyhurst and speak with the priests, there is no point in paying priests to birch him. That much we have learned. Monsieur Raquedal and Mr Bartram could come with me, but as a former pupil of the Jesuits, I am sure I shall have their ear. I suggest we say no more on the subject until we know they are willing to take him."

"Why would they not take him? He is an intelligent Catholic boy." Mother asked. With the meal finished, Father waited until the servants had left the room, before turning to me.

"This is your opportunity to give your opinion, Charles. What do you have to say about this?"

"I say I was beginning to wonder if I were invisible."

"That is not what I meant. You know we have your best interests at heart."

"Then I will say this. If they beat me, I will bite them, as I bit Father Shepherd." Mr Bartram and Monsieur Raquedal gasped, and by doing so, revealed they had not been privy to the reason for my return. Thomas tried, somewhat unsuccessfully, to stifle a laugh. "When you visit," I continued, "you might like to inform them of that."

"I was not thinking specifically of what was undoubtedly a pivotal occurrence," Father said, "I was hoping for something more positive from you."

"If you deem it to be in my best interests, as you put it, Father, then I will do my best to please you, I can say no more."

"Then that," Father said, "is the end of the matter, until such time as I can visit Stonyhurst. Mr Bartram, I would be obliged if you would write to your friend and inform him of my intention."

Thomas and I left the room and went upstairs. He stopped at his door and turned, beckoning me to join him in his room. I thought he looked paler than usual.

"Charles." He whispered. "Here, come here." He closed the door behind me. "Come over to the window. No-one will be able to hear us from here."

"What is it? Are you ill?"

"Sshh. Keep your voice low. No, no silly. Of course I'm not ill. Do you see mother fussing about me?"

"No, but—"

"Then you know I am in perfect health."

I stepped towards him, taking his cue, and whispering. "What is it then?"

"Hush, and listen. If our roles were reversed, I would expect you to tell me."

"Thomas, you speak in riddles. Whatever your secret is, it is safe with me. You know that."

"I have no secret." He shook his head. "Simply that I'm afraid that they will send *me* away to school too."

"Really? I thought it would be just me. It's all this business of being the eldest. But why are we whispering?"

"Because I don't want to put the idea into anyone's head if it isn't there already. Monsieur Raquedal is always prowling about." He pouted. "I don't like him."

"Is that why you think he will be listening?" I had ceased to whisper.

"Not especially." A floorboard creaked on the landing. Thomas put his forefinger to his lips and pointed. I rushed to the door and flung it open.

"Monsieur Raquedal! Such a pleasure to see you." The stoop of the man did not entirely excuse his pose. He had been listening at the keyhole. "Have you been here for a while? My brother and I were discussing the benefits of travel." Thomas feigned a cough, turning to face the window. The priest righted himself as best he could.

"I-I dropped a coin, Master Charles."

"A coin? Was it a sovereign? I think it must have been for you to stoop so low. Does your back trouble you, Monsieur?"

"No. No more than usual, but I thank-you for your concern." He spoke with steely bitterness. "It was but a penny."

"A penny, sir, is a great deal of money if you are penniless and owe."

"I am not penniless."

"I'm sure you are not, my father sees to that, but let me help you search."

"If you find it, you can have it." He waved his arms dismissively. "Give it to the poor." He limped away. Thomas buried his head in a pillow, muffling his giggles and instigating a fit of coughing. I took the pillow from him.

"He has gone, brother dear. No need to smother yourself." If I go to this Stonyhurst, I shall write to you, and you will write to me. It cannot be worse than County Durham. Nowhere could be worse than that and I shall have your letters to sustain me, although I expect I shall be beaten at some point. I can only hope that before I am once again cast to the wind, I see the summer out and the young birds fledged."

CHAPTER SIX

A Summer Respite.

Afternoon sun beamed through the glass of the drawing room. I shifted my weight from one foot to the other, wishing I had taken off my coat. I noticed grey hairs at Mother's temples. I wished either she or Father would say something, but they just stared at me until I felt bound to say something.

"Did you have a good journey, Father?"

"I did, thank-you, Charles, and I am happy to say, I have secured a place for you at the Jesuit school in Lancashire. What do you have to say about that?" My feet were riveted to the ground, my lips sealed with the finality of it. I suppose I had hoped he would return to say the place was not to his liking. "There are boys much younger than yourself who have been working down a coal mine for six or more years. You are a very fortunate young man and—"

"Yes, Father. I know."

"Please do not interrupt. You are to remain here for the summer." My eyes drifted to the lake, where the cob swan was chasing a grebe. The smaller bird had swum too close to his wife and family, and was being told as much by the flapping of wings.

"What do you have to say to that?"

"Thank-you. This means I shall be able to observe the breeding season."

"Charles!" He shouted, "please do me the honour of looking at me when I speak to you." I dragged my eyes from the window. There was a sadness in Mother's eyes.

"What is it, Mother?" I asked. Father gripped her shoulder, just as he had when I told them about Father Shepherd.

"Your mother wishes to know how you feel about going away again." His voice softened. "That was my purpose in asking what you have to say. I was not referring to your summer months at home."

"Oh. I thought—sorry—I misunderstood. I was thinking of the birds, you see. Will there be birds near the school? Is it in a town or in the countryside?"

"Go to your room, Charles," Father said, "and stay there until you are called."

Lying on my back, I stared at the rafters. I wondered if the separation from family was the fate only of the eldest, or if Thomas was right, and that I might be joined by him. To deny my male siblings an education beyond the scope of Messrs Bartram and Raquedal, would be to assume I would not predecease my Father. I therefore concluded that if education was paramount to the inheritance of an estate, then my younger brothers were also destined for Stonyhurst.

Monsieur Raquedal's footsteps crossed the landing, and a door latch clicked into place. I jumped from my bed, Father's instruction forgotten, and knocked on the priest's door.

"Come in, Master Charles." He held the door wide. "Has your father secured a place for you?" I couldn't recall ever having been in the priest's room before. To my astonishment, there was no bed, the only furniture being a narrow table with a neatly folded blanket before it. The fine linen and lace cloth gave the impression of a tiny altar with a candle, a crucifix and a Bible, each equidistant from the others.

"Where is your bed?"

"I sleep on the floor." I stared at him, and then at the bare floor, wondering what it must be like to have no mattress. "I am sure you did not knock on my door to enquire of my sleeping arrangements, Master Charles. Is there something I can help you with?"

"Yes, there is. Is Stonyhurst in a town or in the countryside?"

"I believe it is very much in the countryside. Quite a remote spot."

"Good. Thank-you. That is all I need to know." I turned to leave, my mind darting between the prospect of observing the wildlife of rural Lancashire, and the way the meagre furnishings of Monsieur Raquedal's room contrasted with his appetite.

"Please, be seated." Monsieur Raquedal swept his arm in an arc. I sat on the floor with my legs crossed at the ankles. I leaned back, palms to the floorboards, wondering what gems of information I was about to hear.

"In a few days, Charles, you will pass through the gates of Stonyhurst. I feel it is my duty to tell you of the history of the school, for this knowledge will enable you to appreciate your education in this fine, and unique, place."

"But Stonyhurst, as I understand it, has only been a school for a few years. There can't be much history."

"Stonyhurst is just a building, it is not the school any more than the Vatican is the Catholic Church. The establishment you are about to attend was established in 1593, in St Omer." My heart sank as I realised I was unlikely to escape for some time. "The Society of Jesus has educated the young English Catholic boys on the Continent for the past two hundred years, surviving war, plague, betrayal and poverty. You are about to become a part of that heritage, and to benefit fully from that privilege you need to understand why it is more than just a school."

I sat upright, pulling my legs towards my body, my arms wrapped around them. "Do you have a cushion, Monsieur Raquedal? Mr Bartram told me the priests came from the continent in an old boat."

"Mr Bartram told you correctly, and no, I do not have a cushion," he sighed. "As I said, the school was first established at St Omer, the priests removed to Bruges for a while, and then to Liège. Your Father attended at Liège. Escalating persecution in the revolution forced the priests and their pupils to leave the continent altogether. Their journey was a hazardous one to say the very least. But perhaps it is best if I leave this aspect of your education to the Fathers at Stonyhurst. I see you have no appetite for it today." I jumped to my feet and rubbed my backside with both hands. "Perhaps, in my desire to educate you in this matter, I break the tenth Commandment."

"How so, Monsieur?"

"I envy you, Charles. For the first time in my life, I am jealous."

I finished my dinner and put down my knife and fork.

"Your mother and I would still like to hear what you think of the prospect of going to another school, Charles. Have you thought about it at all?"

"Oh, yes." I grinned. "I think it will be a wonderful place. Monsieur Raquedal and Mr Bartram here have told me a great deal about it." I turned to the priest, who nodded in consent."

Father frowned. "I did not know you had been there?"

"I have not, but I have been able to tell Charles of the history of the school."

"You will recall," Mr Bartram said, "that I correspond with Father Clifford. Monsieur Raquedal and I often discuss theology, as well as the geographical journeys of the Jesuits."

"But you are not a Catholic, Mr Bartram." Father said. My eyes darted from one adult to another.

"Indeed, I am not, but I am a Christian, and I have no prejudice against a faith which teaches the ways of Christ."

"Why not?" I asked. All eyes turned to me, as if I had intruded on a private conversation. "I mean, why don't you become a Catholic, Mr Bartram? It is the True Faith."

"Charles!" My mother's tone surprised me. She sounded shocked at what I had thought to be a polite invitation. The schoolmaster raised his palm towards her. Please, Mrs Waterton, do not distress yourself. It is a reasonable question from a young man, and one which I shall attempt to answer." Mr Bartram turned to me. "There are many religions in this world, Charles. In this country, we share our faith in Christ, and should not allow differences created by politicians to meddle with a mutual respect. To comprehend the present, we must look to the past. I am of the Church of England. This family, directly descended from the Catholic Lord Chancellor of England, has greater reason than most to regret the religious legacy of the Tudors. In those days, the church had much greater power. It could be argued that the church was the power. Some centuries earlier the Jesuit knights, known as the soldiers of Christ, had set out to convert the Muslim world to Christianity. Their methods were military, that was the way things were in the days of the Knights Templar, but they were doomed to fail. Because of these noble tactics, and despite their peaceful doctrine of today, the Jesuit priests are still held to be a greater threat to the Church of England than is the Church of Rome."

I shuffled in my chair. "I still don't understand why a person cannot choose to be a Catholic."

"You are right to question such things, Charles." Mr Bartram smiled. "Religion and politics, while inextricably entwined, make poor bedfellows."

"But—"

"Consider this. You are a great one for studying the birds and their habits. They fly in the same sky, they swim on the same lake, but the sparrow does not mate with the lark."

"But—"

"Now Charles," Father said, "you must not question Mr Bartram further. You tire us all with your endless questions." I thought this unfair and was about to say so when Mr Bartram continued.

"I do not mind, sir. When I was a child, I used to question my father upon all manner of things, and he only ever replied, 'the sky has no ceiling.' After his death I began to understand the wisdom of his words. We should not restrict our thinking to that which is known. Charles has an enquiring mind, and that is a good thing, provided he channels his thoughts to the future."

"I am sure we are grateful for your words of wisdom, Mr Bartram." Father frowned. I sat on my hands, shifting my weight from one bony buttock to the other, unconvinced of Father's gratitude. "You may leave the dining table, Charles." I pushed my chair back and left the room. The day was fine and bright, and there were nests to visit. I pondered Mr Bartram's words as I walked. The conversation had posed more questions than it had answered, but had somehow shown understanding, rather than the usual despairing criticism. The thought lightened my step.

The days passed in routine. Monsieur Raquedal celebrated Mass for Mother every morning in the chapel. The sanctuary was no more than a bedroom furnished as a place of worship. It could never be consecrated, but Mother said it brought her as close to God as was possible without the inconvenience of travelling to Leeds.

Break-fast was served at eight o'clock, and afterwards Mr Bartram or Monsieur Raquedal would commence their teachings. Upon my release, Mrs Bennett always contrived to be near the schoolroom door to remind me of dinner being served at half past one o'clock. She would point to Old More. "When Chancellor More says it is one o'clock, you must be here, Charles Bernard, to change your clothes."

"I shall, I shall, Mrs Bennett." But I rarely was. Something would take my interest, and all thoughts of clocks, routine and dinner would evaporate. Only hunger would remind me, and by then the sun would be far in the west and I knew I would be too late for dinner. Mrs Bennett would have her usual rant, and I would point out that I was perfectly fit and healthy, unlike those who ate too much and exercised too little. In between tea at five o'clock, and supper at seven, the whole family attended the chapel for prayers.

Moonlit nights were a bonus, giving me opportunity to study the nocturnal creatures. There was one occasion, however, when I concede that Monsieur Raquedal may have saved my life.

"Charles! What are you about?" I had had one leg out of a landing window, and the other about to follow. In my dream I was on my way to a crow's nest in Haw Park Wood. Monsieur Raquedal had me by the shoulders.

Next morning, at break-fast, he alarmed Mother quite unnecessarily by telling her how he had heard me shuffling around, gone to investigate, and found me on the windowsill, fast asleep.

To return to my nocturnal observations, tawny owls are the kings of the sky. During the hours of darkness their silent flight is key to hunting success, as mice, voles, young rabbits and leverets fall victim to the hunger of their fluffy broods. I knew their nesting places and which trees to climb for the best view. As darkness falls, they leave their home and perch on a favourite branch. From these childhood observations, I always knew where to find them.

Hedgehogs are by far my favourite ground dwelling creature, and the brown rat my most hated. While I recognised the cunning of the rat, I have not been able to admire this characteristic since the day Father told me of their arrival in England, upon the ship that bore the Protestant George.

"With their devious and conniving Act of Succession," Father told me, "the politicians have contrived to ensure no trace of Catholic blood will ever flow in the veins of a British monarch. They would rather put a monkey on the throne than a Catholic, but have settled for George Hanover. With his arrival upon our shores, the Hanoverian rat overran the towns and cities, forcing the black rats (we Catholics) to live in isolated pockets of the countryside." I have always thought it a powerful analogy.

During daylight hours, buzzards took over from the owls, gliding lazily as they searched the meadows for food. Ravens preferred to let others do the killing, then with their hop and skip gait would eat and defend their food at the same time.

Having observed the habitat and habits of the birds and other creatures, be it during the moonlit hours or the daylight, I put pen to paper each evening, recording the appearance of each species, their nesting and feeding habits and skills. My collection of eggs already exceeded the capacity of my trays, and Grainger obligingly helped me to make more, and another case.

The summer passed all too quickly. If I were not climbing trees or rowing on the lake, my next favourite occupation was to visit the tenant farmers to discuss the weather, the crops, the livestock, and congratulate them on the safe arrival of yet another child, or commiserate upon a death. Father advised me not to mix with the peasants, as he called them, and I knew better than to mention my visits when at the dining table—or anywhere else for that matter. I liked to talk with the villagers, and they often invited me inside their homes. When Father visited the tenants, he never dismounted, giving him greater opportunity to look down upon the poor. I didn't dislike Father for this, and none of the tenants complained. That was the way of things, and still is, for the most part.

The day before I was due to leave for Stonyhurst, Thomas. Christopher, and I were summoned to the drawing room. We stood side by side in front of Mother and Father. Father cleared his throat.

"I am pleased to be able to tell you that all three of you are going to travel with me to Lancashire." We brothers turned to look at each other, eyes wide. Thomas and Christopher grinned at me.

"We are going to see where you will be, Charles." Thomas said.

"I think you misunderstand me, Thomas." Father said. "You will be staying there as pupils. All of you." It took a few moments for us to realise what was being said. Far from being banished alone, I was to have the company of two of my brothers. Thomas was eleven years of age, and Christopher just nine. Lucky, lucky brothers were to escape the strictures of Tudhoe. "Thomas and Christopher, you may leave the room. I wish to speak with Charles alone." My brothers glanced at me as if to ask, 'what have you done now?' before leaving me to my fate.

Mother must have seen our silent exchange, for as the door closed, she said, "You are not to be chastised, Charles. Your father has a gift for you." My eyes flew wide in astonishment as Father put his hand in his pocket and produced a small cannonball.

"This," he said, "is to remind you of your heritage." He put it in my hand and I inspected it closely. It had no remarkable features.

"How so, Father?"

"Never allow it to go out of the family keeping. This cannon ball, although insignificant in itself, was used against Oliver Cromwell when his forces attacked here. Be seated, Charles and I will tell you the tale which has been passed from father to son throughout the generations since that time." This was the first and only time I sat with my parents in the drawing room. Father continued thus,

"At that time, the fortified mansion stood upon this island. The old water-gateway was three stories high. The day I speak of was in 1644, shortly after the Battle of Marston Moor where Thomas Waterton, your great-great-great-great grandfather, was killed. Parliamentary soldiers returning from the battle set up on the hill opposite the bridge and began to fire at the walls. The bridge had been swung away when the soldiers were first seen. Thomas's widow, Alice Waterton, ordered an iron swivel gun be carried to the top of the water-gate. It carried balls the size of that which you now hold in your hand. One soldier was seen going up the footpath through the wood. He carried a keg upon his shoulder, and the assumption was that he was going to the village for ale, and that he would return by the same route. Under this supposition, the swivel gun was pointed to bear on the path. When the returning soldier came into view, the gun was discharged, fracturing his leg."

"Did he survive? How is it we have the ball, Father, I—"

"Please, Charles. Let me finish, and you will then know as much as I do. When I was about your age, your grandfather told me the story of the cannon ball and the swivel gun and pointed out where the soldier was thought to have fallen. Curiosity caused me to dig for the ball at the spot, and there I found it, nine inches below the sod."

"That was deep, was it not, Father?"

"Almost a hundred and fifty years has passed, Charles. Leaves had fallen, grass died back and so forth. The depth was not so surprising as the fact that I found it."

"Thank-you, Father, for entrusting me." Father nodded, indicating I could leave. I put the cannon ball in my pocket. As I reached the door, Father said, "It is not a matter of trust, Charles. You are my eldest son. It is your duty to pass this on to *your* heir."

I closed the door behind me and leaned upon it, sighing deeply.

CHAPTER SEVEN

To Stonyhurst.

We travelled from Walton to Leeds in the carriage, driven by Grainger, staying one night at an inn before travelling on by post-coach to Skipton. After a comfortable night at the Old Swan, we enjoyed a hearty break-fast of porridge and kippers. Thus replete, Father hired two horses and two ponies to take us to our Lancashire destination. I began to wonder if we were on the right road, having trotted and cantered for over two hours, when two dilapidated gate-houses marked the entrance of Stonyhurst Park, and the long, straight carriageway. We reined in, that we might observe the magnificence of the house. I hadn't given another thought to Monsieur Raquedal's words until that moment. His envy was directed at my spiritual education, but the house itself could not fail to impress the dullest of visitors. Far in the distance, the imposing west facing frontage, framed by massive trees, nested into the landscape of the fells. Weeds grew high down the centre of the carriageway. It took a full ten minutes to trot to the ornamental lakes, the house looming larger with every pace. Low in water and flanking the last few hundred yards, the oblong lakes gave sanctuary to many waterfowl. I had to squint my eyes against the dancing reflection of sunlight, sparkling with diamonds wherever the reeds, rushes, and bog grasses had failed to conquer. The plethora of waterfowl cheered me, balancing my mood with the daunting prospect of an unknown future. Father would be back at the Old Swan before nightfall, enjoying a hot meal, while my brothers and I would be at the mercy of the priests.

"Stonyhurst Estate belongs to the Weld family." Father said. "Like our own, they have long been educated by the Jesuits."

"Do they live here?" I asked. "It is very generous do you not think? If I owned such a fine house, I doubt I would allow—"

"No, Charles, they do not live here." Father sounded irritated. "They have no use for the house. They live at Lulworth Castle, in Dorset."

"So do you mean that they are not being generous?"

"I mean nothing of the sort, but it will have been no sacrifice." We rode on for a while. My mind returned to the beggar woman in County Durham, wondering if she still had my needle.

"A gift of sacrifice is a gift well given."

"What did you say, Charles?"

"Oh, nothing. Just something someone once said to me. What I meant to say was that if a man were to make himself homeless for the benefit of others, that would be a great sacrifice."

"Indeed, it would, but it is difficult to foresee the circumstances that would lead to such a gift, especially in the case of the Welds." We reached the gates, and Father reined his horse to the left. "This way, Charles. The stables are around here. I expect someone will have seen us approach."

"We are expected though, are we not? The priests know we are coming?" Before Father could reply, a man, short in stature and wide of smile, stood before us, with another, older man a few paces behind. The first wore gaiters, and had a great cloak wrapped around his body, its hood almost hiding his face. The second man was dressed as a worker, with sackcloth to his shoulders, and a very dilapidated hat pulled down around his ears. I detected his clothes to be of good quality, but they were old and tattered with patches at the knees and elbows.

"Mr Waterton! Greetings and a warm welcome to Stonyhurst," the cloaked man said. How has your journey been? Are you hungry? Of course you are. Mr Sparrow here will take the horses. We have refreshments ready and waiting. Will you be staying overnight? You know you are welcome."

"No, thank-you. I—"

"Very well, very well, as you wish. Your sons will be happy here, I'm sure. Follow me. Follow me." He took a couple of paces towards an arched doorway, and then stopped. "But I forget myself. How rude. How rude. I am Father Clifford, and you must be Charles. I nodded. "I have been speaking as though you were invisible."

My brothers grinned, they seemed as excited as I was dubious.

"I am Thomas."

"I am Christopher."

"I am very pleased to meet you all. Follow me." We walked behind him, Father first, then me, then Thomas, and then Christopher, through another archway, and across a small pasture, towards the house. A dozen or so sheep raised their heads to stare at us before returning to the more interesting pastime of eating. The smell and sound of pigs introduced the occupants of a small enclosure. Chickens, ducks and geese all made their presence known as they pursued our little procession. I found I could now match my father's stride, each making for two of the priest's. Once inside I had expected to see or hear some other boys, but the walls echoed with nothing more than neglect, our footsteps a disturbance to the peace. I would like to have explored some of the rooms, but hunger, and the distinct possibility I might lose my way in the labyrinth, kept me in line. Father Clifford pulled open an oak door, its creaking hinges releasing a shower of rust, adding to the pile on the floor.

"Here we are." He stepped back. We proceeded through a small porch, and into a cobbled quadrangle. Its walls reached for the sky in a mismatch of styles, telling of piecemeal construction. So high were the walls, and so small the quadrangle, they seemed to lean inwards like frowning giants. I committed to memory some useful looking hand and footholds for climbing. An ancient portcullis hung over a high arch. By the position of the sun, I guessed this led to the long carriageway. A small rectangular building occupied one quarter. Father Clifford indicated we should go in. "When we first arrived, we ate and slept in this little room. We call it Sparrow's Hall after our good and hard-working Mr Sparrow. He was here to greet us after our long journey, just as he was here to take your horses today."

"Do you say, Father Clifford, that Mr Sparrow lived here alone?" I asked.

"Yes. Yes, that's right. He is still in the employ of the Weld family. I don't know what we would do without him. No, I don't. It's a fact, so it is. We are to employ an assistant for him. Yes, he needs an assistant. That's right."

"Does Mr Sparrow know his way around the whole house? How many rooms do you use?"

"Quiet, Charles," Father said, "you ask too many questions."

"Oh, no. No, Mr Waterton. A boy cannot ask too many questions. It is the sign of an enquiring mind. Yes. An enquiring mind. But we must eat this delicious mutton stew that Hareng has prepared for us. There is all the time in the world for your questions, Charles, but my growling stomach says they must wait." He bowed his head and clasped his hands together. Father and I did likewise.

"Deo gratis, quia cibus noster et."

"When I was at Liège," Father said, "we observed silence at mealtimes."

Father Clifford shook his head. "We rather fell out with that practise on our journey, and never fell back in with it. I do not think our Lord minds too much. We believe there are times for silence, but no longer consider meal times to be one such. The boys may converse quietly, and none are permitted to leave the table until all are finished. We believe this equips them for adulthood in the wider world."

For my part, I was happy to concentrate on the stew.

"Tell me, Father Clifford, how do you discipline the boys?" Now here was a question of interest to me. My spoon passed between bowl and mouth without pause, but my ears were sharply tuned. Thomas and Christopher stared, wide eyed.

"If your question really asks as to whether or not we beat the boys, I can say it is only as a last resort. Yes. Very much a last resort. In fact, now I come to think of it, we have had no occasion to use violence for some time. You see, we have developed a system of penance in accordance with our beliefs." He stroked his chin as if trying to recollect something, before taking up his spoon and returning his attention to the mutton. "It is our philosophy, Mr Waterton, that a happy boy will learn more than a miserable one. We do our best to educate the individual. Father Wright first thought of it, and I think he is right. Fear is a poor incentive." His words were like the song of a mistle thrush to me, and Hareng's stew better than anything Joe Bowren had ever produced, but still no match for Cook at Walton Hall. I devoured my ration in no time at all. "We have rules, of course, and your sons will be instructed accordingly."

An hour later my brothers and I stood with our backs to the great house, watching Father ride away, our steeds trotting behind him on lead reins. How I longed to be with him, to return to the parkland, the trees and the creature inhabitants. The night before we had started our journey, a barn owl had come to my windowsill for the first time. I wondered if he would return tonight. Mrs Bennet would have shut the window, so he would not be able to enter, even if he wanted to.

Our feet were rooted in the ground until Father disappeared from view. Flanked by my brothers, I placed an arm around each of them as we walked in silence, back towards the building that was to be our home, each in our own thoughts.

Shouts of encouragement told of a game being played behind the great door, which I now knew to hide the quadrangle. The happy voices of my fellow pupils told of finished studies, and recreation. We ran to join them. As we entered, their game stopped abruptly, as if they had seen a ghostly apparition. Then they crowded around us, a sea of smiling young faces. Every boy wore a blue swallowtail coat with brass buttons, a checked waistcoat, and linen breeches. "The Masters Waterton, I assume, for we are expecting no-one else. I am Father Wright." A tall, gaunt looking man stretched his hand over the boys' heads. "Boys! Do not crush our new pupils, they have had a long journey."

"I am Charles, and I am pleased to make your acquaintance, Father."

He clapped his hands twice. "Off you go." The boys scampered away, and we followed the priest through a small doorway to the right of the portcullis, and up a spiral staircase, its wooden steps creaking with every footfall. Another door took us into a small room, the warmth of a roaring fire battled with the draughts as a gale whistled around a broken pane, forcing thick smoke down the chimney. Rain suddenly lashed the window and I thought of Father, hoping he would soon be safely back in Skipton.

"Let me look at you, for it is my task to find each of you a uniform. You are very thin, are you not, Master Charles?" he opened a large wicker basket and started rummaging about amongst its contents.

"Why do we have to have a uniform, Father Wright?" Thomas asked.

There was only one chair in the room, and he sat upon it. "Well now, it is a long story, but I will keep it as brief as possible." We sat on the floor, next to the fire.

"When we journeyed from the continent two years ago, running for our lives from the revolutionaries, we were in such a bedraggled state that the good people of Selby mistook us for Frenchmen and pelted us with stones." I felt my jaw drop. "It seems unbelievable, I know, and had I not been there myself, I would doubt the tale."

"Explain to us, please, Father." I said.

"Ignorance fuels fear. Few English people have met a Frenchman, but they nonetheless fear them as the enemy. Not without reason, we may say, considering the French persecution of all things hierarchical forced us first from St Omer, and then from Bruges and Liège. They have put their royal family, and hundreds more associated with them, to the guillotine. In the eyes of the uneducated, a Frenchman is any person they do not recognise. We sailed a tedious fifty-five miles up the winding river to Selby, where we were surrounded by a jeering crowd. I recall one man shouting, 'they deserve all they get for killing their king.' As you can imagine, we had no desire to tarry, and acquired a canal boat as quickly as we could to take us to Leeds, where we endured a similar scene before continuing to Skipton. Father Ellerker and Father Semmes were beyond endurance and took a chaise for the last fifteen miles of our journey while Father Kemper and the rest of us walked. Our company consisted of twelve pupils, three Fathers and four ecclesiastical students, myself being one of them. We had completed our education but were still studying to become priests. One servant also came along. Hareng cooks for us." Father Wright gazed upwards, his lips moving as he counted. Let me see—twenty of us in total. We were exhausted. We seldom see any of the local people, but nonetheless our pupils wear their blue jackets to identify them as belonging to our school, and not mistaken for a marauding Frenchman. We chose blue for its lack of military connotations."

"I assume, then, that there is little contact with the world beyond the estate." I said.

"You assume correctly. This part of Lancashire is more isolated than other parts. The local people, all Protestant of course, are a suspicious lot. One might argue that this is not without reason. Eighty years is not a long time in the history of Christianity, and it is less than this period that so-called witches were hung not far from here. The witches of Pendle will never be forgotten, of that I am sure." To say his words alarmed me did not fully convey my terror as my childish imagination pictured my limp body hanging from a tree.

"How far are we permitted to explore the countryside around the estate?"

"For your own safety, you must stay within plain sight of the house, and not venture into the woods. If you do, our prefects will detect you, and bring you back." He handed a swallowtail coat to me and I put it on. The shoulder seams fell down my arms, the sleeves covering my hands completely. I turned back the cuffs. If wearing ill-fitting clothes was to save my neck, I decided I would do so, and willingly.

"That's right, Master Charles. I think we must address each of you by your Christian names. We cannot call for Master Waterton and have all three of you responding. That would not do at all." Father Clifford held the fronts of the coat, placing one over the other." I think we will ask Hareng to move the buttons. I'm afraid the only others I have would be far too short in the body, and you haven't finished growing yet, I'm sure."

"The breeches will fit well, Father, if I fasten my belt around them, and I can wrap the waistcoat to double the breast."

"Quite so. Quite so."

"How many pupils do you have now, Father?"

"Yesterday we had fifty-two boys in our care, you and your brothers make fifty-five and as you have seen for yourself, they are a happy crowd. Including myself, there are seven priests. Our isolation means we trouble no-one and no-one troubles us. But now you must go and see Hareng. She will be in the kitchen. Ask her if she would be so kind as to adjust the fit of your coat."

"May I ask directions to the kitchen, Father?"

"Go back down the stairs, turn right, and follow your nose," he beamed. That's right, follow your nose. When I have found uniforms for Master Thomas and Master Christopher, they will follow you. Tell Hareng they will be there shortly if any alterations are needed."

The sun shone directly upon my face, and I determined not to open my eyes until I knew my whereabouts. Seconds passed. I knew I could not be in my bed at Walton Hall. The stink of flatulence reminded me of Tudhoe, but the smooth sheets, told me this was no such nightmare. Despite the bright warmth upon my eyelids, the memory shuddered through me, and I opened my eyes. The other seven beds were empty. Finding my uniform neatly folded at the foot of my bed, I dressed quickly. Hareng had done her best to make it fit. The sound of voices took me to the quadrangle. Two boys of about the same age as myself left the game of quoits and approached me. The taller of the two held out his hand."Hello. I'm Stephen and this is Tom." I shook their hands in turn. "Father Clifford said that when you woke, we were to tell you to go to the kitchen for some bread."

"Am I very late? Have I missed break-fast? Where are my brothers?" The boys laughed. It struck me that I had heard more laughter since arriving at Stonyhurst than in all my years at Tudhoe. I determined not to think of my former school. This was a new start.

"Break-fast?" Tom smiled. "You have missed Mass, first morning studies, break-fast and second studies."

I blinked. "What time is it?"

"Ten o'clock. We rise at five. You have just missed your brothers, they are in the kitchen." I was speechless. Not because I had slept for over twelve hours, but because I had been permitted to do so.

The smell of fresh bread acted like a magnet, but as soon as I entered the kitchen, all thoughts of food evaporated from my mind. Thomas and Christopher were seated at a long table. Hareng leaned over a cooking pot, stirring its steaming contents. Mr Sparrow faced me, but my eyes were transfixed on the back of the man who stood between us. There was no mistaking the figure of Joe Bowren. I was lost for words. Hareng turned from her pot.

"What is it, young sir? Are you hungry?"

I was speechless. Joe turned around, and in a flash, I found myself lifted from the floor by my old friend.

"Master Waterton! 'ow is you 'ere? Oh, but am I glad to see yous. So glad am I yous is 'ere."

"Put me down, Joe," I gasped, "you are squeezing the breath out of me." He dropped me to the ground. "I do believe yous is growed almost as tall as I is."

Mr Sparrow coughed. "I assume you two are acquainted."

"Beg pardon, Mr Sparrow," Joe snatched his hat from his head, and made a short bow. "But young Master Waterton 'ere was a pupil at my previous employ."

"In that case perhaps we should ask him about your skills and abilities."

All eyes turned to me. "Joe would never see us hungry, sir, not if he had his way. I don't know if he can bake bread. Supplies were obtained from the local bakery in Tudhoe." I paused, not wanting to say anything that might jeopardise Joe's position. "He can butcher a pig and make a meal from vegetables. He brews weak ale."

"Anything else?"

"He is very kind."

"Well then," he turned to Joe, "I think Master Charles' testimony is most encouraging. I will show you to your quarters, Mr Bowren." Joe winked at me as they left the room.

"Do you have some bread, Hareng? I missed break-fast."

"I do, and if what you say about zat big man is true, it is good zat I can bake it. There is no bakery around 'ere." She put a plate on the table and pointed to a stool. "I'll find somet'ing in ze pantry."

I called after her. "You speak very good English, Hareng."

"Zank-you. I learn it from ze boys, and Meester Sparrow." She returned with half a loaf, some cheese and a knife.

"Are you happy here, Hareng? Is it a good place? I think it is, because my fellow pupils laugh a lot, despite the smoking chimneys and the damp sheets." I looked into her eyes, they were like muddy pools, glistening with distant focus. "Are you thinking about your home? I didn't mean to cause you pain."

"You are a chatterbox, yes?"

I chewed on some bread. "I don't mind if you prefer to not answer my question."

"I will say zis. I am 'appy 'ere. Ze fazers, zey are good and kind. I work for zem in Liège before we come 'ere. Lancashire is a very cold place in ze winter, but I do not mind zat in exchange for a peaceful life. Now, you take your bread and cheese, and go from ze kitchen. You too, Master T'omas and Master Chreestopher."

Stonyhurst,
Lancashire.
October 17th 1796

Dear Mater et Pater,
I trust this letter finds you in good health.
The sheets here are always damp, and the fires smoke terribly, but this does not matter to me. I am most content, and think I would like to stay forever.
Our day starts with the celebration of Mass. Next, all pupils have one hour's study, after which, break-fast is very welcome, but must be finished by seven thirty, when we recommence lessons which last until ten o'clock. We then have one hour's correction of themes before one hour of Latin.
Our studies are varied, including such subjects as English, French, German, Latin, Greek, Hebrew, sacred and profane history, geography, arithmetic, algebra, geometry, astronomy, experimental physics, and mathematics, but I find that even the most tedious of subjects are not without merit in this place.
I have friends, Tom Lorrimer, James Alexander, and Stephen Clothier. When our studies are satisfactorily finished for the day, we are permitted to play games, but I prefer to observe the birds. In the distance, towards Longridge Fell, I have seen peregrine falcons

and merlins, kites and buzzards. The upland moors provide ideal circumstances for these noble birds.

All this, I am happy to report, fits well with the Jesuit motto, with which Father will be familiar. Ad Maiorum Deo Gloriam. To Greater Glory.

There are boundaries, of course, beyond which we are not permitted to wander. The prefects patrol with diligence.

I am,

Your Obedient Son,
Charles Waterton.

It was not long before I decided to explore the wider countryside of Lancashire. Joe's role had developed into one which kept him outdoors most of the time. He liked it that way. Unlike men of smaller frame, he rarely felt the cold, and when he did, he simply put another layer of sacking over his shoulders and around his legs, turning him into a shuffling mountain of rags. He and Hareng had come to an agreement, an understanding that the kitchen was her domain, and the supply of meat and vegetables was his responsibility. Root vegetables were stored in one of the barns to last us through the winter.

Early in the November of my first term at Stonyhurst, as I returned to the official boundary of the school, I was spotted by a prefect.

"Come back here." The prefect shouted. Those fellows took their responsibilities all too seriously for my liking. I was only just beyond the boundary and ran into a copse of yew and laurel. He gave chase and we played cat and mouse for almost half an hour. Many species of birds liked to hide in there, and from earlier birding expeditions I knew the place like the back of my hand. I made a break for it and ran away down a hedgerow, then doubled back to the farm buildings. Luckily for me, Joe Bowren was there, bringing in straw for the pig sty. Light was fading but I knew I could rely on my old friend.

"Save me, Joe. Cover me up with litter." He dug a hollow in a dung heap, and I climbed in. He piled fresh straw on top followed by several forkfuls of horse muck just as the prefect bounded in.

"Have you seen Charles Waterton?" He was quite out of breath.

"Sir, I have not spoken a word to Charles Waterton these three days, to the best of my knowledge."

The prefect went away. Joe had not lied. Tired from my afternoon of freedom, I was soon asleep, and grateful for the warmth. I cannot be certain of the events which led to the man hunt. I suspect the prefect reported me to be missing, and somehow, as night drew on, this became a fear for my wellbeing. Tom and Stephen were sent to search the farmyard. The first I knew of the matter was when Tom prodded me with a pitchfork.

"Ouch!" I popped up like a Jack-in-the-box, a crown of rotted straw on my head. "What did you do that for?"

"I thought you were a rat."

"Well I'm not. I was asleep if you must know. The warmest sleep I have had since I arrived here."

"And the smelliest. Come on, Charles," Tom said. We need to call off the bloodhounds."

That night in the dormitory, and to my surprise, they told me they had been scared.

"Of what?" I asked.

"The trees creaked, like a giant flexing his muscles. The leaves of the yew rustled and sang in mourning." Tom shivered.

"And then a great blast of wind blew out our lanterns," Stephen whispered, "leaving us entirely sightless."

"But then," Tom continued, "the glimmering windows of the house gave an eerie focus as the search continued within. Then Steven heard your rustling in the dung heap. Joe's heavy pitchfork was leaning against the wall, so I took it in both hands and wielded it around. You know the rest."

I could not help but laugh at their fanciful descriptions, never having thought of the night-time as being frightening. I did indeed, know the rest, and against all expectations, I was not punished. Nor was I punished when I wandered off to the woods to collect eggs. I was not punished even when I climbed to the top of one of the stone eagles in the quadrangle, although the following week I was forced to concede that their concern for my safety was not without foundation when one of the eagles came crashing to the ground.

All I desired lay beyond the boundaries. I soon became familiar with the prefects' routine and stole away down the valley whenever I could.

Everyone shivered, teeth chattered, and bones ached with the cold. Joe had stockpiled plenty of wood for the fires, but the fireplaces were much too small to have significant effect. As the frost grasped ever more tightly at our toes and fingers, we closed the doors and shrank our occupancy to three rooms, stuffing the gaps around the windows with straw and rags as the biting wind sought every crack. The frost lasted for weeks, day and night. The sky glowered from the top of Longridge Fell, frowning upon the valley, and sweeping down in all its anger to throw freezing rain at the windows. Starlings fell like stones from the trees, and the hated brown rats infested every building.

"Fazer Stone."

"What is it Hareng? Why do you cry?" We had finished our Latin studies and were looking forward to break-fast. Hareng did not usually come to the schoolroom. We all stared at her.

"Zer is no food, Fazer." Her thin frame belied her strength, both of character and physique. "it is ze rats. They 'ave found ze pantry, and—"

"Nothing?"

Hareng shook her head. "Zey gnawed t'rough ze flour sacks. What little eez left eez fouled by ze droppings. We shall all starve." She sobbed. "All gone. Ze bread I made yesterday—not a crumb."

"Is there nothing at all, Hareng?"

Her wailing grew louder, she sank to her knees, her hands covering her face.

"I am sorry. I—"

"Come, Hareng." Father Stone put his hand beneath her elbow. "Come. Stand up now. You have no need to apologise. Joe will kill a pig, meanwhile, this is an opportunity to show how God will provide for us." I remember how we all looked at one another, with Hareng's news gnawing at our bellies as the rats had gnawed our food. Father Stone's idea of killing a pig was all very well, but that would mean a long wait. We all started to talk at once, stating the obvious about our delayed break-fast, and making Hareng cry even more. Father Stone clapped his hands to silence the hubbub. "Boys! Boys! There are to be no further studies today." Silence spread in a gentle wave, hunger momentarily forgotten by the unprecedented announcement. "We have plenty of vegetables in the garden, and as far as I am aware there is no law that says we must eat bread at break-fast." Laughter followed in the wake of the melancholy silence.

"Where is Master Charles?" I stood up. "You will assist Joe with the pig and ask his advice on the subject of the rats, and while you are about it, ask him about the polecats. I shall ask Father Wright to take the donkey and cart to Skipton for two sacks of flour. He can check at the inn to see if there is any post. We shall not starve, Hareng. God has not brought us to Stonyhurst to be beaten by rats."

I raised a fist to the air, shouting, "Death to the Hanoverians" and ran off to find Joe. I spotted my old friend's unmistakable figure lumbering across the pasture, a long pole slung over his shoulder.

"Joe! Joe, wait for me." By the time he turned around, my spindle like legs had covered the distance between us.

"My, my, Master Charles. What's the big 'urry? And why isn't yous in class a-learnin'?"

"We have to kill the rats, Joe. The Hanoverians. You have to show me how to do it. Father Stone said so, and the polecats too."

"Foumarts I calls 'em. Bin takin' the eggs they 'ave. What's this 'bout 'Anoverians? What's them?"

"The brown rats, of course. They came to England on the boat with Protestant George when he took the throne. My Father told me about them."

"Well I never 'eard no rat sayin' 'is prayers, neither Protestant nor Catholic, but if your Pa said so, it must be true. An' is you tellin' me that Father Stone says it's no learnin' until you kill all the rats?

"No, Joe, but there is no break-fast. The Hanoverians have eaten all the bread, and fouled the flour and—"

"I knows that. 'areng 'as bin wailing in my ear 'bout it. I's on my ways to fetch a pig. Can't 'ave 'ungry boys and fat pigs now, can we?"

"Father Stone sent me to ask you to kill a pig."

"Did 'e now?" Joe grinned. "Now that's all very fine seein' how I says to 'areng we need to—"

"It was your idea?" Joe looked over my shoulder, causing me to turn to see what had taken his attention. Hareng, Thomas and Christopher, were in the vegetable garden, while my friends Tom, Alexander and Stephen were among a group with Father Stone. "Why are they going to the forest, Joe? The oak and elm won't feed us."

"They will be a-foragin'. That's what forests is for. They won't eat nothin' 'til that 'areng cast 'er eye over it. That girl knows all there is to know 'bout mushrooms an' the like. Yous won't 'ave empty bellies for long, I'm thinkin'." He held out the pole. "Know what this is, Master Charles? I'll tell 'ee. See the pole is 'ollow. See the rope through it an' the loop?"

"It's to catch the pig, isn't it, Joe? You will loop the rope over the pig's head and pull it tight. The pig can't bite you and he can't get away either." Joe's shoulders sagged.

"You seen one afore, then?"

"No."

Joe nodded. "Yous is proper clever, Master Charles. Proper clever, not just book learnin' clever." His teeth glinted like shiny brown stones hiding in a thicket. "Come along, we 'ave work to do. You 'ave to sweep up what's left o' the flour. I will show yous 'ow to turn it into bait."

CHAPTER EIGHT

Footballs, Foumarts and Foxes.

With eyes narrowed to the dawning sun, I walked down the driveway with the towering walls of Stonyhurst at my back. I paused to watch the melting of the hoar as bright, thin warmth spread diagonally across the symmetry of the landscape. Waterfowl crowded together in sullen acceptance of their lot, the frost too harsh and the sun's rays too weak to melt the lakes. Reeds and rushes, like brittle and broken skeletons, waited for the order from God to make new growth and stand proud in the breeze once again. The unmistakable whining sound of swans in flight lifted my eyes. I watched in wonder as they glided towards the western lake. Landing with webbed feet thrust forward, a furious flapping of wings slowed them. I shook my head in disbelief as they stopped barely a yard from the end of the lake. They were not designed for ice-skating. When in flight or on the water they are the most elegant of birds, and yet when walking they are just the opposite. The cob and pen muttered to each other as they waddled along, in apparent disgust of their food being below the ice. I wondered how the pair were faring at Walton, and whether they would choose the little island for their nursery.

I first appreciated the value of ivy, yew, laurel, and holly when at Stonyhurst. These evergreen stalwarts provide invaluable shelter for birds. I have planted and encouraged all four in my parkland with great success. But I digress. It is a habit of mine. The once immaculate gardens of Stonyhurst had a beauty of their own, as nature reclaimed the borders and softened the edges of formality. Frost added its own splendour, making visible the invisible, from the tiny hairs on the stems of wraithlike nettles to spider webs in their thousands, forced to give up their secrets until the sun's rays moved like a magician's wand. The yew trees stood proudly in the open ground. Six in all, between the house and the distant gateway, they are still there, giving shelter. Rooks argued like haggling women at a vegetable market, in continuous dispute from the uppermost branches of the naked oaks and elms of the ancient woodland that stretched away to the foot of Longridge Fell.

My role of rat catcher and foumart killer gave me the freedom to access areas which would otherwise have been out of bounds. Father Clifford informed the prefects that I had permission to hunt beyond the boundaries, so long as I stayed within the Stonyhurst Estate. I do not think I would have been more pleased if he had said I was to be the Catholic King of England.

With Joe's guidance, I took to my task with enthusiasm, trapping and poisoning to my heart's content. My first priority being the pantry and kitchen, then the dormitory and the schoolroom before spreading my domain to the nether regions of the buildings. After a month or so it became clear that I would never totally eradicate the Hanoverians. They ran in the walls, they ate the plaster, they bred in their dozens.

Joe gave me some traps, which I used to great effect, but they were almost the death of me. Discounting the many falls suffered in the pursuit of eggs, I can say the incident with the traps was my first real brush with death. I was walking across the cricket pitch with the traps slung over my shoulder when I heard the first rumble of thunder. The weight of the traps slowed me considerably. Storms develop quickly in that part of Lancashire, and black clouds were racing over the hills. Within minutes, day turned to night and the first raindrops hit me with force. I dropped the traps and ran for the shelter of the pig sty. No sooner was I inside than I heard an almighty crack. The landscape lit up with the brilliance of a tropical sun as the lightning found its target. My traps. There can be no doubt that, had I not dropped them and run, I would have been killed. As the storm eased, Joe and I went to inspect, and found the traps to be welded together and the cricket pitch badly burned.

I remember clearly the conversation I had with Joe when I first entered his workroom. At first, the outbuilding appeared chaotic, but Joe soon put me to rights.

"I keeps the chemicals careful, Master Charles. Poisons on the top shelf, see? Don't you goes a pokin' up there without me 'ere, see? I mights not be able to read, like you clever boys can, but I knows whats in all these, an' I knows whats dangerous." It was in this room that he showed me how to make poison biscuits for the rats with a mixture of oatmeal, chopped garlic, arsenic and brown sugar. He showed me how to preserve leather with turpentine, soap, and arsenic, and how to make a football from a pig's bladder. I recall the day I had just finished my first football, and was about to leave, when a prefect arrived.

"Waterton, you are to go immediately to Father Clifford's room."

"Am I in trouble?"

"I don't think so," the prefect said. His desultory tone gave the impression of disappointed.

I knocked on Father Clifford's door.

"Come in, Master Charles. Come in." Unlike Monsieur Raquedal's room, Father Clifford had made some effort to be comfortable. He sat in the only chair, and there was a small rug. He indicated I was to sit upon it. At the opposite end of the room, an arched recess provided a bed in the form of a board and a rough blanket. A small statue of St Ignatius and a Crucifix adorned the windowsill.

"Hareng tells me you are successful in your campaign against the rats."

My shoulders sagged. "I will never complete the task, Father. Joe and I have trapped and poisoned them, but they breed so. I fear the Hanoverians will always be with us."

He leaned forward and placed a hand upon my shoulder. "I am sure they will, but if Hareng says you are doing a good job, then that is good enough. Yes, yes. That's right, it is good enough. "What is it that you have there? Do I see a football?"

"Yes, Father. Joe showed me how to make it. First, I had to clean the bladder, that was the easy part. Then he showed me how to cure skin and use it to cover the bladder. See? Joe says cow hide is better, but that pigskin does a passable job if one uses the flank." My words tumbled out like fish from a net. Father Clifford took the ball and turned it this way and that.

"An excellent job, Master Charles. Yes, excellent. Your stitches are neat and even. I think this will make you very popular with your fellow pupils." He handed the ball back. "I think we should add 'football maker' to your title. How does that sound?"

"It sounds very well, Father. I will make a football every time a pig is slaughtered, and will do my best with the rats."

"If we all do our best in whatever our calling, then we can do no more. Always remember that, Charles. *Quant je puis. Quant je puis.* As I can. As I can. Come, let us show the ball to Father Wright."

Unsurprisingly, the football proved to be very popular, raising my status amongst my peers, and easing my relationship with the prefects. After an inevitable accident, Joe boarded up the broken window, and Father Stone directed the game should be played in the meadow. I was not so very much interested in the game, as in preserving the bladder and skins.

I confess I pushed the boundaries of my freedom, and explored the Ribble valley, and as far as Langdale Fell, where I observed the deer. On the lower land, especially near the river, I saw many species of birds. My collection of eggs now included those of the kingfisher, goat sucker, woodcock, hawfinch, and pied fly catcher.

Nothing has ever given me greater pleasure than to sit amongst the branches of the forests, sharing the birds' sanctuary. My respect for God's creatures extends to all, but my love of birds has always been my ruling passion. There are those who will speak of natural history in derisory terms, saying it is all for bumpkin heads, but I say they are the bumpkin heads, and have everything to learn by opening their eyes to the world around them.

I recall one summer's day, when I was sitting in the middle branches of an oak tree, enjoying the company of my feathered friends, when I heard Father Clifford and Father Stone approach. I tucked up my legs and kept perfectly still, not wishing to disclose my hiding place. I have never been an eavesdropper, but the circumstances meant I was privy to a conversation of which I was the principal subject. Father Stone was a very serious man. His main role was to teach the classics, his knowledge of Plato and Ovid was beyond compare. Much of our school work involved translation of these works, furthering my love of the languages, although Latin has always been my favourite. But once again, I digress. They stood almost directly below me, no more than ten feet away. The overheard conversation went something like this.

"Please, Father. Whatever it is, I am sure we have known each other long enough to discuss anything. We understand one another, do we not?" Father Clifford said. "What worries you so?"

Father Stone twisted his hands, cracking his knuckle bones. "It is the boys, Father. I wonder if we give them too much freedom. I am thinking particularly of Master Charles."

"He completes his studies satisfactorily, does he not?"

"Oh, yes. I have no concerns in that way. He thumbs the books almost carelessly and absorbs everything in one teaching. I have the impression he completes his formal studies as quickly as possible, so he can spend time with Joe Bowren, or go rambling on the Fell."

Father Clifford ran the tip of his forefinger over his lips as he formulated a reply. "And our other pupils, let us not forget them. Do you have any concerns, anything at all, in a more general way?" Once again Father Stone paused, his mouth open, restless fingers twining and cracking. Father Clifford continued, "Please, you must tell me."

"It is the tradition of our school, that many pupils become priests. With this in mind, I feel there should be more religious discipline and less playing of games. I think Father Wright disagrees with me on this point, he takes what he calls a more holistic approach, but I think such things are not good for the soul."

Father Clifford leaned forward. "Maybe you are right, but please stop cracking your fingers. That is not good for you and it jangles my head when I try to think. Please—do stop." Father Stone looked down at his hands in astonishment.

"I—I apologise. I did not know I was—that my fingers—it is not a conscious thing." His head flopped to his chest.

"No. Well, it matters not. As I said, we have known each other long enough to understand one another, and to be honest with one another."

Father Stone's head jerked up, I saw his face flush. "I am always honest with everyone. How can we not be, as men of God? Is that not what we teach? God would know if we lied. I—"

"Yes. Yes, of course. I was thinking more of being open, you know, speaking frankly. The fact is that many of our pupils become priests because there is little other opportunity for them. This is not the case with Charles Waterton, who, like any eldest son, is destined to inherit an estate. Even if an eldest son wished to take the cloth, he *could* not, but I like to think that the younger siblings who do so are truly called."

"Do you really believe that?" The colour drained from his face as quickly as it had arisen. "That priests sometimes take their vows due to an accident of birth?"

Father Clifford sighed deeply. "You said yourself that it is a tradition. It is my opinion that each pupil should be encouraged to develop in his own way, whatever that may be, given the restraints of society."

"And Master Charles? How will he fit into society?"

"He is an extraordinary boy. As with all our pupils, were it not for their families, and therefore their religion, some would be in the army or the navy before the age of fourteen. We agree his intellect is in no doubt, and although those of our faith cannot attend university, I am equally convinced he will carve his own path and lead a meaningful life."

"You do not share my concerns over the footballs?"

"No, Father, I do not. I think the balance is as it should be. Regarding Master Charles, I think his skills against the rats can be extended to the foxes, and in spring, to the fledgling crows."

Father Stone's eyes flew wide. "Really? I think he should be curbed, not encouraged."

"We cannot change him, Father. We should not try to change him—or any of our pupils. We must help them to achieve their potential, whatever that may be, and in whatever direction it takes them. He is not wicked."

"No. I did not mean to infer any wickedness." He pressed his lips together, blinking rapidly.

"Is there something else on your mind, Father?"

"I—I don't know if I am wrong to do so, but I miss the life we led in Liège. I miss the bells of the city, the streets, the bustle—"

"God has guided us to safety, that we might continue our work. Life is certainly different here, I grant you."

"Do you not miss our school?"

"Of course. When I look to the heavens, I see the same sun, moon, the stars as the people of Liège."

"Do you think we might return one day?"

"I think that is unlikely, in my lifetime at least. For my part, I am content."

"Do you think, Father, that Catholics will, one day, be able to celebrate Mass without the need to hide away?" My hearing sharpened at this question, thinking the very notion an impossibility. Father Clifford's reply was astonishing.

"I do. I think that one day we shall have the vote and be permitted to hold office. I believe that those of our faith will be Members of Parliament." I witnessed a smile creeping over Father Wright's face. I mention it because of its rarity. "You are amused at the thoughts of an old man, thinking them nothing but dreams. I will not live to see these changes, but time will prove me right. These pupils of ours will, God willing, live to see many changes in the world. Some good and some not so good, but 'twas ever thus."

Father Stone nodded, "This place is so vast, so isolated." He almost whispered, but the sharpness of my hearing served me well.

"Did you say something?" Father Clifford asked, "did you say, 'this cannot last?'"

"No, Father. I said…" at this they walked away, and when they were safely out of earshot, I made my descent. They say eavesdroppers never hear any good about themselves, but in this experience I was content with the personal revelations, and wiser for the encounter.

When I reminisce about my days at Stonyhurst, I think of the long dining hall. Numbers of pupils swelled with the passing years, but the hall was big enough to seat two hundred or more, and at mealtimes the walls echoed with clattering cutlery. Portraits of the Weld family looked down upon us as we tucked into the simple but wholesome food. Ornate plasterwork on the high ceiling told of the wealth that had built the place.

I can close my eyes and picture the pupils tending the gardens, bringing them back to a more manicured splendour. With Father Wright to direct us, we even helped to repair the building. Desperate measures were sometimes necessary to prevent a floor giving up to woodworm, or the stonework to the elements.

My only regret is that I could not have stayed there longer. If I had had my way I would never have left. Thomas stayed for four years before returning to Walton Hall. The damp air played havoc with his lungs. Christopher and I stayed two years longer than he.

Shortly before our departure, Father Clifford called me to his room. I had been in poetry class when a prefect interrupted Father Stone.

"Father Clifford demands Charles Waterton's presence in his study, immediately." I had no qualms about it, the prefect's tone failed to alarm me because I knew I had done no wrong. Once again, I sat cross legged on the little rug.

"I have long been studying your disposition, and I clearly foresee that nothing will keep you at home. You will journey into far distant countries, where you will be exposed to many dangers. There is only one way for you to escape them. Promise me that, from this day forward, you will never put your lips to wine, or to spirituous liquors."

"What of weak ale, Father?"

"It will not harm you and is often safer than water. You must make your decision as to which is the greater evil, Charles."

I am indebted to Father Clifford for my abstinence from alcohol. I made the promise and kept it. Just think, dear reader, how much money I could have squandered, had I not had the guidance of Father Clifford. I consider this man, more than any other, to have been my true friend, and Stonyhurst to have been the greatest influence upon my life. I suppose it is this which keeps me wearing my old uniform. Never having been one for fashion, the old-fashioned cut of the swallowtail coat does not trouble me.

It may seem odd in these days of fast steam trains that few boys returned home for holidays, especially at Christmastide when the roads were so muddy, or frozen. This was not a hardship, just the opposite in my view. Throughout my life, whenever I have found myself to be in England at Christmastide, I have travelled to Stonyhurst in all weathers, as do many former pupils, to celebrate the birth of our Lord in pleasant sentiment. Tom, Alexander and Stephen also kept the tradition, but they are now departed this life. The journey I took with my father in 1796, with two overnight stops, now takes but six hours by train. That is not to say I approve of the smoke belching engines, because I do not. Nowadays the country is patterned with railway lines, crossing the country like a nest of newly hatched grass snakes. Yorkshire is particularly affected, with a track laid to every coal mine, taking the black stuff to the factories.

In the spring of 1802, Christopher and I returned home, our education complete. I was twenty years of age, and he in his sixteenth year.

PART TWO

CHAPTER NINE

A Huntsman and a Sailor.

My years at Stonyhurst had seen me grow both physically and in maturity, and so it should not have come as a surprise that there had been changes at home. Everyone and everything were six years older. Helen had told me by letter that Dawson had been found dead in his pantry some twelve months previously and had been replaced by Harris. Mrs Bennet suffered terribly from rheumatism but was as sharp as ever in her wit and observations.

Monsieur Raquedal and Mr Bartram were still in situ. Helen, Isabella and William, at eleven, ten and eight years of age, were deemed old enough to join us in the dining room. In total, including Mr Bartram and Monsieur Raquedal, eleven of us sat at the great table. Only Edward was still too young.

I spent many an hour watching the barges on the newly opened canal. As the waterway curved through the village twelve locks took the boats on their way to the River Calder. Small iron wheels attached to stone posts guided the towropes around the long curves. The steady plod of the horses echoed beneath the bridges as they pulled their cargoes of coal or corn. Tow ropes had already begun to carve furrows in the stonework of the arches. To my delight, my feathered friends had adapted well to the changes in their world. The navigation itself posed no difficulty for them, but the ever-ready guns of the bargees by day were as plentiful as those of the poachers by night.

One of my favourite vantage points was, and still is, the uppermost branches of a beech tree which stands a few yards from the avenue. From there I can see the house, the stables and farmyard, many acres of pasture, Stubbs Wood and most of the lake. On one particularly warm day, I watched Father as he rode down the avenue, dismount and hand the reins to a groom. Purposeful strides and a bowed head spoke of his being deep in thought, and not the best of humour. I waited for a while before scrambling down the smooth bark. The drawing room window was open.

"Foul mouthed—thieves—utterly disgraceful—approach to our home..." He could only be talking about the bargees. Thus convinced I was not the source of his temper, I entered the house through the rear door. Father was pacing up and down, his face as red as robin's breast. "Ah, Charles. I was just telling your mother about—"

"The navigation." I interrupted.

"Your father is concerned that the bargees will poach on our land."

"You are right, Father. I know it for a fact. I have seen them shooting where the navigation goes through the woodland. They shoot pheasants, rooks and pigeons."

"Have you indeed," Father blustered. "I will shoot *them* if I see it. Perhaps you should use your gun on them, Charles."

"No, Thomas, you must not say that. Charles would hang if he shot a—"

"I know, I know." He leaned on the mantelpiece. "It just proves I was right in not allowing the course of the navigation through the parkland. Can you imagine what it would have been like?"

"To change the subject, Thomas," Mother spoke calmly, "did you succeed in your business this morning?"

Father looked relieved. "I did, my dear. I have purchased two very fine hunters."

It came as a complete surprise to me that Father wanted me to ride with the hounds. He had been a keen huntsman in his younger days, but had given it up after a severe fall. Like any offspring, I wanted to please my parents and to this effect, I took to the hunt with every bone and sinew in my body.

Father introduced me to Lord Darlington. Not without reason did his Lordship hold the reputation for being the most skilled and daring Master of the Hunt. We became friends, and I did all in my power to emulate him throughout the hunting season, taking part in every hunt in the West Riding of Yorkshire, and beyond. The highest hedges and widest ditches were a joy to behold, their clearing an accomplishment giving satisfaction beyond description. Now in the autumn of my life, I concede we simply shared a lack of trepidation.

Others did the fearing for me. Fortunately, Mrs Bennett did not see me in the field. Two days after one particularly successful hunt, I was summoned to the drawing room. I was expecting congratulation but Father's stern expression told me otherwise. The clock had been turned back to my childhood as I stood before my parents, wondering how I might have offended them.

"You have taken to the hunt too boldly, Charles. Darlington speaks highly of your daring. Praise from such a quarter glides into the brains of young men and turns them upside down." I didn't know how I was expected to respond, and turned to Mother.

"We want you to stop hunting before you break your neck."

I shrugged my shoulders. Clearly, they had discussed the matter at length, and I was being delivered of their resolution. Fait accompli. "You obliged me by commencing to hunt." I saw the colour rising in Father's neck as he continued, "you will further oblige me by giving it up." A silence ensued, so I thought I had better say something.

"You asked me to start, and now you ask me to stop." I bowed my head. "I am your obedient son." My lack of protest seemed to surprise them as neither Father nor Mother said anything. What they could not have known was that a recent encounter had wrested with my conscience, and I was ready to give it up.

During the aforementioned recent hunt when I had been not five miles from home, I became separated from the main body of riders. I could tell from the barking of the dogs that they were now coming around towards me, so I dismounted to adjust a stirrup, and wait. As I sat on a stone, a fox appeared directly in front of me. Panting and bewildered, his tongue lolling out of his mouth. He stopped short and stared me full in the face.

"Poor little fellow, thy fate is sealed." I said, "Thy strength has left thee, and in a few minutes more, thou wilt be torn to pieces." Then he shrank back into the wood again, as if to try another chance for life. A few moments later, he was killed. The hounds snarled and ripped him apart before the huntsmen appeared, and so even if Father had not asked me to stop, I had lost my appetite for the hunt.

In comparison to the days when all England belonged to the True Faith, my family's situation is greatly diminished. The Waterton name being synonymous with high principal, land and title were confiscated and high taxes charged by the bastard Queen Bess and her reformation. Had her father remained true to his wife, our situation and that of the whole country would have been very different.

Nothing had been mentioned of my future. I had certainly not given it a thought, and had been content to explore the woodland and pastures, chat with the tenants, and continue with my rat catching as I had at Stonyhurst. Had it not been for the war in France, I would have been packed off on a Grand Tour, as had been customary for young men. Then in 1802, the Treaty of Amiens, and what turned out to be peace of a little more than a year's duration, provided an opportunity.

All was arranged for my brother, Christopher, to accompany me to Spain. We stayed for one night at the conveniently situated Victoria Hᐥtel, near the docks in Hull. The following morning, we boarded the *Industry*, a fine and sturdy brig under the command of Captain Lettus, our destination being Cadiz, and from there, to Malaga, on the southern coast of Spain. Two of my mother's brothers had settled there. Not having been inclined to join the priesthood, their faith had prohibited any meaningful life in their country of birth.

As I write this memoir, I recognise the loosing of the ropes at the quayside to be the perfect metaphor, the final severance of the umbilical cord and the end of my formative years. Since that moment, my life has been a series of death-defying experiences and adventures, interspersed with both joy and sadness. I have done much and travelled far. There have been regrets and disappointments along the way but, for the most part, I consider myself fortunate, and blessed.

Christopher and I were two young men with the world at our feet. As we cleared the Humber Estuary on that November morning, the cold, grey water roughened, a north wind filled the sails, pushing us along at a good rate.

"Can we not return to port, Charles," Christopher shouted above the roar, "until this abates? Can we not put in to the Wash?" My brother clung to some rigging. He had a dreadful pallor.

"Take heart, Christopher," I shouted back, "the wind is blowing us with great efficiency to our destination." He looked at me with the dispirited eyes of one who feared he would not see the dawn, and then vomited over the side.

In the event, we put in at Margate. Christopher regained his bonhomie and Captain Lettus gave his assurance that things would improve once we had crossed the Bay of Biscay. Hundreds of starlings had roosted in the furled sails, but in the morning as the canvas was dropped, they fell to the deck, frozen stiff.

Once in the notorious Bay of Biscay, with the spritsail set for steering and all square-rigged sails furled, those who took the wheel were forced to work in pairs, such was the violence of the sea. They lashed themselves to the mizzen mast to prevent being washed overboard as they performed their duty. I did what I could to cheer the grey faced Christopher. With his stomach now entirely empty, he retched saliva into the receptacle at the side of his cot.

A week later we were off the coast of Portugal but still being tossed around like rag dolls. A wind, blowing directly from the west, untamed by any land between the Americas and the *Industry*, threw itself at us with the irrational fury of a madman. For two novice sailors, it could not have been worse, but unlike my young brother, I did not suffer the *mal de mer*.

"The wind is warmer, you should come on deck."

"If I were to come on deck, it would be to throw myself overboard to stop this shifting about in every direction. I would rather take my chances to swim ashore. The temperature is of no interest to me, only the cessation of the wind."

"Staying below is the worst thing you can do. Believe me, Christopher, the best cure is to put your eyes to the horizon. Ask any crew member if you will not take the word of your brother. In any event, you cannot swim."

"Just tell me when you can see Cadiz, Charles." He groaned.

"But that is why I told you of the warmer wind. It means we approach our destination, and when we arrive, we shall be cossetted by the Spanish sun."

Poor Christopher did not reply, and I made no further attempts to lift his spirits. Ten days after leaving Margate, we crossed the Gulf of Cadiz, and at dusk, we entered the harbour of that town. Christopher remained below decks. Even in the harbour the *Industry* rose and fell. Waves crashed over the spit of sand that connected the town to the mainland, but despite the stormy weather, I found Cadiz to be alive with revelry, laughter, music and singing. I was a young man, twenty years of age, and impatient to experience everything on offer. Stepping onto the gangplank, I grabbed the hand-ropes to either side and looked along the quayside. Men and women staggered about in drunken oblivion. Cadiz, I decided, would wait until the morrow, when Christopher and I could explore together.

"Break-fast, Christopher. We must find some break-fast."

My poor brother looked down at his feet. "I have no desire to eat until the ground ceases to move beneath me. We may be on dry land, but everything still moves with the motion of the sea."

"You must eat something or you will waste away. What shall I tell Mother and Father if you die of starvation?"

"It's all right for you, Charles. You do not suffer as I do."

"Not entirely true. I too have sea legs, but it will pass. Father said we must present ourselves to Consul Duff, but first of all we must find some fresh food." Christopher groaned as he drudged behind me, holding his stomach.

The sights, sounds and smells of the town washed over me like a giant wave, too much to absorb, other than in one huge gulp made up of a thousand flavours. We spoke no Spanish, but Captain Lettus had given us directions to the Consul's residence.

"The town is heaving with people, Charles. We shall never find our way."

"Follow me, brother. We cannot stay on the quayside all day. I am hungry." After passing through a gateway in the ancient city walls I stopped at a market and bought a melon and two pomegranates. Christopher was less enthusiastic, and we were discussing the best way to set about eating them when I heard someone call our names. I turned to see a tall man in the bright red uniform of the British Army hastening towards us.

"Messrs Charles and Christopher Waterton!" he shouted again, even though he was now standing beside us. "Thank God I have found you." We must have stared at him like codfish. Christopher told me later that he had thought we were to be arrested. "I am Consul Duff. I was at a loss when Captain Lettus told me you had gone into the town. The place is alive with celebration and I feared you would be lost in the crowds."

"What is being celebrated?" Christopher asked.

"Marriage, my dear boy. The marriage of Prince Ferdinand to Princess Maria Antonia of Naples and Sicily."

"Is it not always so crowded?" my brother looked relieved.

"No, but it is a busy port, so there is always a bustle about the place. We must go to my residence at the Consulate where we shall complete the formalities of your arrival and then I shall escort you to your lodgings."

Consul Duff could not have been more accommodating. He arranged for our trunks to be taken from the quayside to our rooms, and then, that very same afternoon, he took us to a bullfight. Thousands packed into the arena, roaring at the spectacle of human versus animal. My brother and I, mesmerised by the skill and bravery of the matadors, were swept up in the intoxicating atmosphere. We cheered and shouted in the heat and dust until our shirts were soaked with perspiration. The Consul sat beside us, smiling benignly and fanning himself, having seen, he informed us, many such performances. As we left, he instructed us to stay close by him, and watch for his red coat, should we become separated.

Once outside the arena, my mind was taken with the city. As a young man who had never been abroad, everything was a new experience. The buildings, the carriages, the market and the shops, the churches, the skyline, the olive skin of the Spaniards, the black skin of the Africans, their clothing and the many languages all added to the maelstrom of the experience. I detected snippets of conversations in German and French which I could understand, and many others which I could not. The styles of dress of various nationalities made for a show such as a grand theatre could not rival. I lost sight of both Consul Duff and Christopher, and the uselessness of his advice was immediately apparent. My dilemma was my own fault of course, and while his suggestion regarding his coat was made in sincerity, it was not so practical as it had seemed to be. Every matador wore a scarlet cloak, and many of the revellers were dressed in red. I was not concerned. After all, I knew the way back to the Consulate, or so I thought. I wandered amongst the throng, eager not to miss anything. Darkness fell, and drunkenness became the order of the night. I was hopelessly lost and unable to ask for directions. I tried to apply logic, and walked to the harbour, thinking to retrace my steps from the morning. I found the spot where Christopher and I had met Consul Duff, but then had no idea which way he had taken us. After trying this way and that along the narrow, twisting streets of Cadiz, I was entirely baffled, passing the same buildings more than once. I tried to take bearing on the churches, but apart from their bells telling me it was now after midnight. Eventually I decided to stay still, and watch for a Frenchman or an American, distinguishable by their dress.

"Excusez-moi, Monsieur. Vous êtes Français?"

"Oui, Monsieur."

To my relief, he was sober. "Je suis Anglais, et ne sais pas où je suis. Pouvez-vous me diriger vers le Consulate?

"Vous êtes au mauvais côté de la ville, mon ami." His words filled me with dismay. I was on the wrong side of town. Christopher would be worried, no doubt, and Consul Duff not pleased at being kept up until this late hour by a subject who had failed to follow him. "Suivez-moi," my French saviour said, "je vais vous prendre."

"Merci beaucoup, monsieur." He must have thought me quite mad. Not only did I follow him, but I held onto his coat as he took me through the still crowded, narrow streets. I do believe we were the only two sober people on the streets of Cadiz that night, and to this day I marvel at the fact that I asked this man for help. Candles burned in every window of Consul Duff's residence. Christopher was standing on the doorstep. He leapt forward and almost knocked me to the ground.

"Charles! You're safe!" I regained my balance and turned to thank my good Samaritan, but he had gone. To my regret, I had not adequately thanked him.

We attended Mass at the Parroquia de San Antonio du Padua. What bliss to be able to take part in a publicly held service, and in such a Cathedral. Over the following two weeks, Christopher and I picked up a smattering of Spanish. We acquainted ourselves with the streets of Cadiz, its fair maidens and all that was for sale in that way, as befits a young man's education. In all, Cadiz provided a very satisfactory start to our travels.

After bidding farewell to Consul Duff, we boarded a vessel bound for Malaga. A fair wind and blue skies persuaded my brother to stay on deck and the short voyage did something to persuade him that not every sea is stormy. We passed easily enough through the straits of Gibraltar and entered the Mediterranean Sea in all its brilliance. Becalmed for several hours, I was like a child in a sweetshop, observing birds that had I previously only seen in illustration. Even Christopher was impressed.

"Look, Charles. Whatever are they?" He pointed towards the coastline.

"Flamingos, Christopher. To see such birds, I am in heaven."

Such was my fascination for the inhabitants of the shoreline, I cannot recall the name of the ship, her captain or crew. We remained on deck throughout the night, marvelling at the profusion and brilliance of the stars. As dawn broke, the ancient walls of Malaga came into view. The gentle curve of the seashore stretched for miles either side of the man-made quayside.

Where Cadiz had been a maelstrom of city life, Malaga had an entirely different pace. Whether the royal nuptials had been celebrated here, I never knew, but if so, they were now finished, and the city was about its normal business.

We hired a man with a donkey cart, my command of the Spanish language being sufficient for the task.

"Calle Molina Lario, por favor. La casa de Senor Bedingfield." He loaded our trunks and we sat beside him as the cart trundled through the streets. The hubs of the cartwheels almost touched the walls of the buildings, but our man and his donkey were of indisputable experience as dogs, cats, and chickens made way for us. We were clearly of some novelty interest. Children stopped their play to stare, and womenfolk paused their gossip. The carter reined in the donkey and pointed to a doorway. The building was on the junction of two busy streets. Our trunks were set down at the roadside, and I paid the carter. Christopher pulled the bell handle and we waited. When no response came, I tried my luck, but to no avail.

"What shall we do, Charles?" Before I could formulate a reply, we were approached by a priest. He spoke rapidly, the incomprehensible interspersed with our names, and those of our Uncles Edward and Martin as he waved his arms about in gesture. I gathered his name was Father Bustamante, and that our hosts had another house a little way off. The priest looked around and gave a loud whistle, waving to a man with a mule-cart. Father Bustamante hefted our trunks into the cart.

"La Casa de Campo." He instructed the driver as we climbed aboard.

Away from the shadows of the streets, I reflected upon the practicality of the carter's clothing. His loose, linen apparel and the broad brim of his hat looked far more comfortable than our fashionable clothing and top hats. His eyes were shaded, and there was no sweat about him. Neither the wheels nor the mule's hooves raised dust in the baked, red earth as we left the city and headed slowly towards the mountains.

CHAPTER TEN

La Casa de Campo.

If I were asked to describe my uncles' house in one word, I would say *idyllic*. They had chosen well, La Casa de Campo was in the foothills of the Montes de Malaga, a short distance from the busy, crowded streets of the city where they had the smaller residence in Calle Molina Lario, from which they conducted their business affairs.

The arched cloisters of La Casa de Campo surrounded a courtyard where a deep well provided cool, clean water from the mountains. On the ground floor, one room was designated as their office, and the others gave spacious living accommodation. The bedrooms were on the first floor. My uncles employed two maids, a cook, a manservant and a stableman. Beyond the walls, views of Malaga, farmlands and coastal plain, dotted with white-washed houses, spread like an artist's canvas. But an artist cannot reproduce the sounds and smells, the drift of a gentle breeze, or the scurry of a lizard.

Uncle Edward, the elder brother, stood at six feet and four inches, and with a character to match, he cut a powerful figure. They were agents to the British Government. As such, and within their self-imposed exile, my uncles were able to serve their country of birth, and practise their religion in a way that was not possible in England. They had taken Spanish citizenship, such was their love of their adopted country. Business often took them into the city, especially when there was need to oversee the loading of a ship. Harvests of almonds, pomegranates and oranges were exported under their watchful eyes. Their greatest responsibility, however, came from the export of the local wine, along with the accompanying paperwork.

We lazed away our days, Christopher and I, beneath the olive trees, for over a year. My only criticism of this idyll was that the trees, although attractive and productive, were not tall enough to be worth a climb.

In the spring, I observed the quails and bee-eaters as they arrived from Africa, a land so exotic, and yet not so very far away. No man-made borders affected the birds, no passports or paperwork to beset their travel. More plentiful than sparrows, flocks of goldfinches, with dancing flight and twittering voices, red faces and yellow wing feathers, were such a cheerful sight.

Our forays into Malaga gave opportunity to practice the Spanish language. Anyone who is fortunate enough to know the joys of Latin and Greek can pick up most tongues. Father Bustamante became our friend, and we regularly celebrated Mass in the Catedral de la Encarnación.

Towards the end of the summer, my uncles had a visitor, Mr Wilsher. He arrived on a particularly hot day, riding a donkey. When I first saw him, I thought him to be a big man, but when he dismounted, he was no more than five feet tall, due to the shortness of his legs. My uncles greeted him warmly, which is how I knew he was no stranger to them. For all his peculiar shape, Harold Wilsher was smartly and fashionable dressed, complete with a top hat, making his appearance on a donkey somewhat incongruous. Only his buckled shoes and white stockings bore the dust of the road. The stableman took his donkey, and a maid brought orange juice and almond biscuits to the shade of the courtyard. Later, over supper, he told us many amusing tales of his travels throughout Europe, laughing as he did so. I think I can say both Christopher and I were truly fascinated, he certainly whetted my appetite for further travel on the continent. Then, quite suddenly, as we had finished our meal, he took on a business-like persona, suddenly standing up, as if to attention.

"And so, Messrs Bedingfield, now we are replete—to business." My uncles led the way to the office. Christopher and I never saw them again that day. It transpired that our visitor was a travelling salesman, and knowledge of European wines a prerequisite of his occupation. He stayed for three nights and during our conversations he told me of the Barbary apes of Gibraltar. I expressed a desire to see them, and as this was his next destination, my uncles agreed I should accompany him.

The stableman saddled both Mr Wilsher's donkey and another for me, and we set off before the sun could beat us too harshly. As we neared the highest point of the mountain path, we turned to look back at the bay of Malaga. From here, the old city walls could be truly appreciated, and the skill of the Moorish people of ancient times brought into true focus.

"Observe, Charles, not only the city walls, but the farmland. See the lines of the irrigation canals, so perfectly constructed. This, too, was the work of the Moors."

"Seen from above, it is hard to think how such engineering was possible. You say all this was the work of the Moors?"

"Indeed, it was, and a thousand years ago at that. The ancients are to be admired are they not? Without them, there would be no wines of Andalucia, and no melons or oranges, indeed they were the creators of all farming here. The people of Malaga would simply be fishermen, which they are of course, and there is nothing wrong with that, but the Moors enabled the farming of the land on a grand scale."

We watched the harvest workers moving between the vines, throwing the pale green fruit over their shoulders and into the baskets strapped to their backs. "Uncle Martin told me that the white grapes produce a dessert wine."

"Ah, yes, my friend. You speak of the Moscatel. It suits the palette of the English and enjoys a good demand. Further north, in the mountains above Cadiz, the Palomino grape dominates, and produces the even more popular sherry, the soil and the sea giving it a unique flavour. Jerez cannot, to my knowledge, be reproduced anywhere else in the world.

"It is a science, is it not?"

"Indeed, it is. There are those who would tell you that anything which is not art, is science, but I say this. Wine production is both. Yes, my friend, art and science mingled in a glass."

Our journey took five days, but because he was so well travelled, we were never short of conversation. When we stopped for our daily siesta, I would lie on my back beneath a tree, and observe the griffon vultures as Mr Wilsher dozed. As they soared from the mountains in constant search for food, I estimated their wingspan to be anything up to nine feet. The vulture is a little loved bird, unpopular for its perceived ugliness, but to my mind there is no such thing as ugliness in nature. The griffon is a large bird, even by the standards of other vultures. The white head, broad wings, dark flight feathers and a short tail make him easily recognisable, even when soaring at height. At ground level, red legged partridges scuttled in the undergrowth in their quest for food. Snakes made silent passage across our path, ants were everywhere. We always chose our spot carefully when stopping to rest.

The high-pitched buzz of crickets filled the air day and night. After siesta, we would travel on until dusk when Mr Wilsher would head for a farmhouse or taberna. Without exception, he was welcomed as a friend. I find it impossible to think how anyone could fail to like this dapper little man. Before he would accept even so much as a glass of wine, he made sure the donkeys were well stabled, fed and watered, which said much about him.

"I am no lightweight, Charles, as I am sure you will agree. My hosts always want to feed me and it would be churlish to refuse when they offer such delicacies." He patted his ample girth. "The result is that my donkey has to work harder than yours, but with care, the donkey is not the stubborn animal he is reputed to be."

"Not stubborn at all, sir." I replied. "He carries you as if you were a sack of feathers." Mr Wilsher laughed, shook his head, and patted the donkey's neck.

My companion had seen the sights of Gibraltar many times and as he had business to conduct, he gave me a letter of introduction to the Consul, Mr Glynn. A most amiable man, Mr Glynn insisted that any friend of Mr Wilsher was a friend of his, and that I stay in his residence. My bag was soon unpacked, and we set out to find the apes.

"They like the highest and steepest parts," he informed me.

"Shall we go up there? Are there paths?" I craned my neck to the height of the rock, excited at the prospect of such a climb.

"Paths of sorts, yes. But you are in luck," he smiled, "the wind has changed, we shall not need to climb very much."

"How so?" I asked. "What difference does that make?"

"They will be on the move. The Barbary ape likes to shelter from inclement weather. All we have to do is watch and wait. Come, follow me.

If I know anything at all about these creatures, I know where they will be headed." He led me to a path, and we climbed no more than a couple of hundred yards before he held out his arm, signalling me to stop. To my astonishment, some fifty or sixty apes passed within easy view. Some had young on their backs as they moved along, sometimes stopping to stand on their hind legs and sniff the air. I observed them for an hour or more, fascinated by their clear family groups and community behaviours.

A day or two later, Mr Wilsher and I continued to Cadiz, our journey ending far too quickly for my liking. I think I could have enjoyed this little man's company for ever. He spoke of Malta, and his description of Valletta and the history of the island set my mind to make it my next destination.

He sold his donkey, and we parted on the quayside as he boarded a ship bound for London. We vowed to meet again, but when I made enquiries of him upon my eventual return to England, I was told he had fallen in love but that his passion for the young lady in question had not been returned, and he had hung himself. I was shocked and saddened that we would not meet again, making the memory of our little journey all the sweeter.

Rather than return overland, I decided to sail back to Malaga. Mr Wilsher had advised I visit Malta before the winter, as the Mediterranean could be fickle.

Mother Nature, however, in all her fury and power, had different plans for me. With the donkey and my few possessions unloaded, I set off for Calle Molina Lario, eager to ask Christopher to join me. Even before I left the quayside, I sensed that all was not right, as if an invisible fog had descended, enveloping everyone and everything in melancholy. I saw a badly stained mattress slung across a balcony to dry and heard the most terrible cries coming from within. It was not difficult to conclude that Malaga was in the grips of a plague. I knew my uncles and brother would not be in the city, and so made my way straight to La Casa de Campo.

Christopher ran to greet me as soon as I was within sight of the house. I dismounted and led the donkey to the stable.

"Thank God you are here, Charles." He grabbed me by the shoulders and held me closely.

"What is it? Are our uncles sick?" I gently pushed him from me.

"No. No, we are safe enough here, so they say. It is terrible, just terrible. People are dying in their hundreds."

"Calm yourself, Christopher. Such agitation is not good."

"Agitation cannot kill me, Charles. You cannot imagine—"

"Let us walk to the house, Christopher. I am tired and thirsty, are there any biscuits?"

Later that day, I mentioned my desire to visit Malta. "Mr Wilsher recommended it."

"I agree," Uncle Martin said, "you should leave Malaga as soon as you can. Both of you. I have to go into the city tomorrow on business, and I know of a Maltese ship in port. I will endeavour to see the captain."

"What do you know of this illness, Uncle?" I asked. "Is it the black death? How does it affect its victims?"

"It is known as the black vomit, *il vomito negro,* in the tongue of Spain. The name describes just one of the dreadful symptoms. Some say it is cholera, others the yellow fever. It kills quickly, that much I do know. Few recover once it has taken hold."

"I have been away for a little over a week. How has this happened?"

"You must ask God about that." I detected annoyance in his tone. "I have no idea, but it is affecting business. Father Bustamante prays constantly, perhaps you should ask him."

"Do you think God punishes in this way?"

My uncle sighed deeply. "I am a businessman, Charles. No expert in the Almighty, I'm afraid."

"I'm sorry. I did not mean—"

"I know, I know. I feel a responsibility for you and Christopher, that is all. What would your parents say if you were to fall victim to a plague whilst in my care?"

Until that moment, I had not given a thought to the possibility that Christopher or I might become ill. We were fit young men.

"If it is God's will, how do you think He chooses who will die?"

Uncle Martin threw his arms wide. "Charles, how can I answer that? I see it as a question of faith. What I believe is up to me. You must decide for yourself."

"Then I believe it is God's will, although I will never understand how He chooses who should die and who should survive."

The day after this perplexing conversation, Uncle Martin went to Malaga, returning in the afternoon with a Maltese captain. "This fine captain is to dine with us, Charles. He sails for his home port on the morrow, and both you and your brother are to be his passengers."

The captain was a fine fellow. I regret I cannot recall his name, but he entertained us with the most wonderful seafaring tales. We dined at one o'clock, and he drank a copious amount of wine. Uncle Edward persuaded him to stay for supper, after which Uncle Martin helped him into the cart and the stableman took him back to his ship. That evening, one of the maids packed a trunk for us. We rose before sunrise, ready and eager to commence our voyage. The cart was loaded and we set off. The journey to the quayside was not a pleasant one. Bodies had been left in doorways, ready for the dead-carts. I saw a dog laying across a body, howling at the loss of his master. The stench of death was everywhere, gloom and horror permeated the foul air. People scurried about their business, heads bowed. A man and a woman, each of them carrying the lifeless body of a small child, staggered their way along, blindly making their way to the graveyard.

The usual bustle surrounded the ship, or so we thought. When I hailed a member of the crew to load our trunks, he shook his head.

"Por favor, el capitàn està muerto. El venició en su sueño. Damos gracias a Dios por su misericordia."

Christopher stared at him as he voiced the words that were upon my lips. "How can a man be so energetic, and within a few hours, be dead?" The sailor shrugged and boarded the ship.

"You heard what he said, Christopher, the captain expired in slumber, and we must thank God for his mercy. What I can say for certain is that we will not be sailing today."

We watched as the sailor, along with three others, carried the captain's body and threw it on a pile of corpses. We sent for Father Bustamante to pray for his soul, but word came back that he was too busy tending the sick. I made enquiries as to whether any other vessels were leaving for Malta, but there was none, and so we had no choice but to return to La Casa de Campo.

Three days later we heard that the government had declared a state of pestilence, the port of Malaga was closed, and travel from the city forbidden. Weeks passed. The death toll now ran into tens of thousands, although who was counting, I could not say.

With a visit to Malta quite impossible, Christopher and I stayed out of the city. From time to time, however, business matters took our uncles to the house on Calle Molina Lario. On one such occasion, Uncle Edward was told that Father Bustamante was ill. Naturally, my uncle went to see the man who had afforded him many kindnesses in the past, and sat with him through his final hours. This act of kindness, so typical of Uncle Edward, cost him his life. He never returned to La Casa de Campo. As soon as I heard he was ill, and not wishing even to wait for a donkey to be saddled, I set off on foot for Malaga. Uncle Edward's previous good health and strong constitution meant he fought the plague for five days. Then, at sunset, he slipped into a slumber from which he never awoke. Some victims died with very little pain or bad symptoms, and if there is any crumb of consolation to be taken from his death, it is that he did not suffer, as so many did. He died in the town house, with Christopher, myself and Uncle Martin at his side.

Not wishing to leave his corpse for the rats, we got him a coffin. At around midnight, he was conveyed to the great burial pits, dug by galley slaves in endless rotation of dig and fill. We were told there was no room for his coffin, and so we had to take him out and throw him in. He landed on top of a Spanish Marquis who, Uncle Martin informed us, had once dined with them. Before returning to La Casa de Campo, we took a walk along the Alameda, thinking to take some sea air before passing back through the fetid streets. The wind had freshened and, coming from the east, felt kindly enough, but it brought a cargo of corpses which had been dumped at sea, and was now washed ashore. Vultures tugged at an easy meal, some standing atop the bodies as they gorged on the flesh of men, women and children.

Shortly after Uncle Edward's death, I was seized with vomiting and fever. I recall the most dreadful spasms, but little else. Christopher told me I had been given up for lost. I felt a little stronger each day, but the ache in my lungs confined me to the house.

"You are a fortunate young man," Uncle Martin said. We were in the courtyard, enjoying a glass of cool well-water. "Not many recover, you know."

"Christopher tells me that the plague has retreated from Malaga."

"Indeed so, but the government has not lifted the restrictions. The port is still closed."

"Plague and pestilence," I said, "is a greater enemy than the gun. Napoleon himself could not have wreaked greater havoc."

"Quite so, and it could yet return. The government could be proved right to impose this quarantine. Only time will tell."

It had not occurred to me that this could be the case, and I determined to visit the harbour as soon as I was sufficiently recovered.

"Will you come with us, Uncle, when we return to England?"

"No, Charles, this is my home. I am content here, and as you know, I have many friends."

I could make no argument.

Two weeks later, my brother and I took the cart into Malaga, hoping to speak with the governor regarding our departure. We arrived at the gate of his residence at one o'clock, just in time to see him ride out in his carriage. A lackey advised us to return the following morning, when he was sure his excellency would give us audience. The harbour was packed with ships. Two Spanish brigs, each heavy with cannon, blocked the exit, herding all the vessels together like sheep. The officers had been rowed ashore and were heading into the city for some amusement.

"What do you think, Christopher? Could one of these ships slip away?"

"What? Now?" My brother sounded frightened. "You do not intend—"

"No, of course not. There is no wind."

"Wind or no wind. How could a ship get past those brigs without being blown apart?"

"Quite easily, I think. Their officers have become bored with nursery duties and prefer the fleshpots of Malaga to their harbour watch. The difficulty will be to find a captain with a sense of adventure."

The French would have nothing to do with us because we were at war with them, the Treaty of Amiens a forgotten hope. Others simply shook their heads and pointed towards the brigs. Darkness was falling, the officers had returned to their ships, and we made our way to Calle Molina Lario for the night. I was tired and needed a good sleep, but once again, Mother Nature had a different plan.

My first thought was that there had been a most terrible carriage crash, and then the sound raised to a crescendo, growing to that of a thousand carriage crashes. The house shook violently, and I was thrown from my bed. We dashed into the street in our unmentionables, not having time to dress properly. The earth shook beneath our feet, and we were thrown around like rag dolls, staggering about with the screaming crowds, trying to keep our feet. To see a fellow human being die of the fever is a fearful thing, but to see the streets, buildings and people of a great city like Malaga swallowed up by a yawning earth is terrifying. Screams were drowned by the roar of the earth and the crashing of walls which had stood for a thousand years. The helplessness of man against the forces of nature is never more evident than when an earthquake shatters with indiscriminate destruction. Even the city walls of the Moors could not entirely withstand the vibrating rocks upon which they stood. Masonry fell like rain. People walked about all night on the Alameda, keeping as far as they could from the danger of being killed by falling stonework, or of being buried alive. Others huddled together, some almost naked, not knowing where to turn or what to do. When the shuddering stopped, we returned to the town house to retire for the rest of the night and I was soon asleep, dreaming of being on board a ship, rocking with the waves.

"Charles! Charles!" Christopher had hold of my shoulders and it took a few moments for me to realise that the rocking was, in fact, another earthquake. Once again, there was no time to dress. The shaking of the building left us in no doubt that such a delay could be fatal. We made our way to the sea front where the Mediterranean raged, thrashing the shoreline with waves thirty feet high. Ships jostled together in the relative calm of their overcrowded gaol. The city walls and the Cathedral fared better than many other buildings, but none were left unscathed. Many sea birds perished that night, their tattered corpses strewn about on the shoreline. Smaller tremors rumbled as Mother Nature waved her hand at the arrogance of man—but she did not shake her fist.

Upon our return to La Casa de Campo, Uncle Martin greeted us as if we had survived a hundred plagues. We recounted our experiences, and I told him of my determination to find a captain who was prepared to make an escape. "You will need papers, Charles." He turned to my brother. "I assume you also wish to leave, Christopher."

"I do, Uncle. Charles is still weak and I would not have him travel alone." I was touched by such sentiment from my young brother. Christopher had such a kindly nature.

"No vessel from Malaga will be allowed into an English Port without written guarantee that there is no plague. You do realise that, Charles?"

"I do, Uncle. Malaga *is* free of plague, we all know that."

"Indeed, we do, but the Spanish Government is the one who has the final word and those in charge still leave the quarantine in place. If the governor gets wind of your seeking a captain who is prepared to run the gauntlet, you will be thrown into gaol."

"Fear not, Uncle," I assured him. "I shall be discreet."

The following morning, we bade farewell to Uncle Martin, assuring him we would send word of our safe arrival in England.

A man stood on the far reach of the harbour wall, staring out to sea. I made my way to join him. There was no-one else around.

"The wind is from the west," he said. "No good at all." I assumed he was talking to himself until he suddenly turned towards me and shook me by the hand.

"Captain Bolin, sir. At your service. I understand you and your brother wish to leave this Godforsaken place."

"How did you—?"

"—know you wanted to leave? A port has more whispers than a King's court and I have a hold full of fruit for the markets of London."

With no clearance to be had at the Custom House, the queue to petition the governor of Malaga stretched for a hundred yards or more. Christopher and I agreed that he was unlikely to be sympathetic. His duty was to his government and having no special cause other than our desire to go home, we came to the conclusion that he would not assist. Captain Bolin was Swedish, and made petition to his Consul, but without luck. As a last hope, we made our way to the British Consulate, where a little bribery persuaded Consul Laird to issue a document stating that Malaga was free of sickness, and had been for some time. A simple truth. I showed it to Captain Bolin.

"Good. Very good," he said, "we shall need this when we reach the shores of England." I liked Captain Bolin, he was made of sterner stuff than most and his command of the English language gave for easy conversation.

"The Spanish will fire their cannon at us, be sure of it, Mr Waterton, and if we are foiled in any way, we shall be imprisoned or shot."

"I have observed the habits of our custodians, Captain. They are bored and lazy. They leave their brigs each afternoon with no more than three men on watch and come ashore to enjoy the delights of Malaga."

The captain looked me in the eye, as if seeking my character. "I think you are a man of courage, sir."

"Thank-you, Captain," I replied, "I assure you the sentiment is reciprocated."

Three days later, Christopher and I boarded the *Anna Elizabeth*, she was a square-rigged ship of modest size. Mindful of the fact that England was now once again at war with France and Spain, the captain had obtained false papers for my brother and me. I was listed as a Swedish carpenter, and Christopher as a passenger. My boyhood instruction from Grainger in making cabinets for my egg collection would have stood me in good stead had my status been challenged. We slept on board for five nights, awaiting favourable wind. Each morning, Captain Bolin walked out on the harbour wall and looked to the sky. As he returned on the sixth day, I observed a spring in his step.

"There's the start of an easterly, Mr Waterton. I think we may be in luck."

As the sun arced, the wind increased. With whispered orders from their captain, the crew of the *Anna Elizabeth* manoeuvred the ship to give us a clear run, and when the officers of the brigs were safely ashore, and without a shout, the crew dropped the sails and we were off. To say I admired Captain Bolin would be an understatement. As we left the constraints of the harbour a great cheer rose behind us. We were at sea in a cloud of canvas, the topmasts straining under the force as we cleared the surge and were beyond the firing range of the Spanish well before the officers were back aboard their vessels.

In all my travels, and of all my brushes with death, I have never seen or experienced anything that came close to the horrors of Malaga, nor have I ever been so happy to leave a place. We passed Gibraltar at eleven knots and were quickly free of Spanish jurisdiction. Christopher did not complain of sea-sickness, even when the wind changed and we were beset by cold and stormy waters. Captain Bolin's composure inspired us all. Even the surliest of sailors quickly obeyed his every command as sails were positioned in response to the wind. We tacked against a northerly for thirty days before the coast of England came into sight and the wind shifted to a chill from the east.

We anchored off Brownsea Island, near Poole, in Dorset. The easterly prevented our sailing up the Channel, and so our papers were sent ashore, for delivery in London. As we awaited their return, I convinced myself that they would not be accepted, and that we would be pariahed wherever we went. Captain Bolin disagreed, and I can now say with impunity that I have never been happier to be proved in the wrong. Consul Laird's certificate had done the trick and circumnavigated the diktat of the Spanish. With permission to sail up the Thames and right into the heart of London, Captain Bolin landed his cargo and we bade farewell on the quayside. We had no luggage. To have stowed a trunk would have alerted the Spanish guards of our intentions to sail.

My brush with the plague had left my lungs vulnerable to the cold, and without any warm clothing, the inclement weather had taken its toll. We hired a hansom cab to take us to Uncle John Bedingfield's house, where we stayed for a week or so. His joy at our safety was entirely countered by the news of his brother's death. I recovered a little and we continued our journey to Yorkshire. Mother found it difficult to believe that her skinny eldest son could survive a sickness that had taken the life of such a big man as her brother.

Back in the bosom of my family, my strength slowly returned. Mother insisted Doctor Hey examine me. He declared my lungs were still affected, but it did not stop me from climbing trees and generally tramping about in the parkland. He suggested a warmer climate might be of benefit.

The following spring, we had word that the plague had returned to Malaga with even greater virulence, taking a further thirty-six thousand souls, including that of Uncle Martin. The news forced me to admit the Spanish had been right to continue the quarantine.

I have never been to Malta. It was not meant to be.

I rode with Darlington a couple of times. Mother didn't object. Perhaps she thought it would do me good, but my appetite for the hunt never truly returned. Father was against it, presumably because he feared losing his heir. He had sold the hunters while I had been away and none of the horses in the stable matched them, further dulling my interest. Curiously, I had also lost my appetite for ale. Prior to my travels I had enjoyed a glass at dinner, but after the milder and more palatable Spanish beer I found the English brew to have a bitter flavour, and never again has a drop of alcohol passed my lips.

CHAPTER ELEVEN

Demerara.

Father purchased two sugar plantations, a popular investment in those days. His brother-in-law, Michael Daly, had recommended it, being the successful owner of two such in Demerara, South America. With the pressing need to provide an income for my brothers, Father had taken his advice, and Uncle Christopher did likewise.

Demerara was a political football between the Dutch, Spanish and British. They had all taken a chance on this inhospitable land, fighting over it for centuries in a half-hearted sort of way. There was money to be made from the European addictions to sugar, coffee, and tobacco. Cotton was also grown.

Although I was content enough at Walton Hall during the summer months, the ache in my lungs increased in direct proportion to the falling temperatures.

"I think Doctor Hey may have been right, Mother. A warmer clime may suit me."

"Do you have anywhere in mind, Charles?" We had finished breakfast but were still sitting around the table. A glance through one of the windows caused me to shiver. A sharp frost decorated the trees.

"Perhaps I could superintend our estates in Demerara."

She turned to Father. "What do you say, Thomas?"

"I shall write to my sister and her husband. Charles could stay with them."

Within the month I was on my way to London with all arrangements having been made.

"Good to see you again, young fellow, and I must say you look a darn sight better than when I last saw you." Uncle John's voice boomed above the cacophony of the coaching station. He was not so tall as my late Uncle

Edward, but nonetheless taller than I would ever be. He slapped me on the back with force. I staggered a little.

The fact that my uncle had been knighted said much for his character. In 1796, he had saved the king's life. Our mad king was not popular at the time, and the mob crushed forward as he left a theatre. A man wielded a gun, and Uncle John put himself between the would-be assassin and the king. In thanks, and despite his Catholicism, he was knighted. Mother was very proud of him. His portrait hangs in the dining room at Walton Hall, on his breast the ribbon and badge of the Guelphic Order, presented to him by King George III.

"There is someone you need to meet, but firstly you must rest after your arduous journey. I cannot imagine being jostled about for hours on end. The post-coach may be fast, but they are an uncomfortable ride, are they not?" Uncle John signalled a carter to take my trunk. We were driven to his residence in his carriage and four. That he was permitted to own such a thing right in the middle of London being a further indication of the high regard in which he was held.

I think the servants had been told to look after me as if I were a china doll. My every whim was anticipated. They seemed to know my desires before I did, producing a kerchief if I sneezed, or a file for my nail before I knew I had snagged it.

My uncle took me to the home of Sir Joseph Banks, President of the Royal Society. Sir Joseph, as everyone knows, had travelled widely, and with none other than Captain James Cook. I enjoyed his company very much, and I believe he enjoyed mine, despite the difference in our ages. He had sailed to South America, Tahiti, Australia, New Zealand, Canada and many more places, collecting plants previously unknown in Europe. His experience and knowledge of tropical trees and plants knew no rival. At the time of our first meeting he had recently been employed by the king to design his garden at Kew.

He impressed upon me the need to take care of myself. Had I not experienced the horrors of Malaga, I might not have taken his advice so seriously.

"The low, swampy countries within the tropics are insalubrious and fatal to the European constitution." He looked me directly in the eye and prodded my chest with his forefinger. "I tell you this, young Mr Waterton. You may stay in the tropics for three years or so and not suffer much. After that period, fever and ague,[4] and probably a liver disease, will attack you, and you will die, at last, worn out, unless you move from time to time, to a more favourable climate."

"I shall follow your advice, Sir Joseph, because it comes from experience. May I ask if you have any further words of wisdom regarding travels within the tropics?"

"Be friendly towards the natives—it is their country, not yours."

I followed his admirable advice with great success, proven by my longevity, although I believe I ran less risk of perishing in the swamps than most Europeans. I never found the weather too hot and could go bareheaded in the heat of the day. By having my hair cut short, I was far more comfortable than those who followed fashion. Being a teetotaller, I survived where so many perished, falling victim to one of the many tropical diseases that so love to take the white man.

Uncle John made much of my departure, insisting he accompany me to Portsmouth.

"I shall be able to write to your parents and tell them I saw you depart England in good cheer, and good health."

The latter was something of an exaggeration, but it is fair to say I was much recovered. I boarded Captain Brand's ship, *Fame,* on November 29th 1804, bound for Stabroek on my first crossing of the Atlantic Ocean. I slept on deck unless the weather prevented my doing so, enabling me to observe the stars above, and the night fishing skills of the sailors.

The Bay of Biscay kept up its stormy reputation, much to the joy of the petrel. A true harbinger of a storm, and lover of the buffeting wind. I watched these agile birds as they swooped around us. Captain Brand knew his ship, and I never once felt myself to be in danger. Once passed the Tropic of Cancer and on our way towards the equator, *Fame* sailed in

---

4   Malaria

gentle rhythm across the ocean with the gentle breeze of the trade winds filling her sails. The shouts of the topmen as they ordered the sailors to heave and loose the ropes, the cracking of the canvas as the wind shifted, and the splashing of the water on the bows all became the sounds of my world. For the first time, I sailed without sight of land.

Sea birds told of the proximity of South America, and within a day of sighting a pelican, high mountains broke the horizon.

Along the coastline, hundreds of miles of mud flats dissolved into the sea, with the silt of the Orinoco turning the sea the colour of pale flesh. Stabroek lay further south, a little way past the Essequibo, on the estuary of the smaller River Demerara. When I say the Demerara was smaller, I do not mean it was a little river, but small by South American standards. Our passage had taken six weeks.

"We are fortunate," Captain Brand said, "the river is not in flood and the tide is with us." At the time, I took his words to be nothing more than conversation, having no knowledge of the dangers of a tropical river. Only the ingenuity of the Dutch engineers, a hundred years before, made our mooring possible. Indeed, Stabroek owed its very existence to their sea wall, their canals, dykes and sluices, all built to trap the fertile mud as it was washed down from the rivers.

Captain Brand moored alongside one of the many landing stages in the estuary.

The carriageway between the moorings and the town is a mile of mud, edged with stones, and a narrow brick footpath. High tides and frequent flooding make any further attempts at roadbuilding a waste of time. The traveller has no choice but to accept this tiresome part of his journey.

Unsurprisingly, the town had a distinctly Dutch air about it. Ever conscious of the need for drainage, the colourfully painted wooden houses all had ditches to the back of them. These were dug to take away the filth of the town, as well as flood waters.

Aunt Anne and Michael Daly lived at their plantation, *Belle Vue*, seven miles upriver. Living quietly, they stayed away from the swamps, and the town, as much as possible. This is why, in my opinion, that despite living in Demerara for long periods, they enjoyed good health.

During my stay, they told me the delightful story of their meeting by chance in Wakefield, when she was out walking. They fell madly in love at first sight and, against the wishes of the family, married soon afterwards, and left England. I would have been around eleven years old at the time, and away at Tudhoe. Michael Daly was already established in Demerara, owning two estates, producing cotton and sugar.

Uncle Christopher visited infrequently. He lived at Woodlands, near Doncaster with his wife and five children. His estate, *Fellowship,* grew cotton and sugar. Father's estates were called *La Jalousie* and *Walton Hall.* This may appear to be an unimaginative name, but it was common practice to name a foreign estate after one's home in England. *La Jalousie,* named after the French style of ventilation which had been installed prior to my father's purchase, grew coffee and sugar. The pine louvres helped the flow of air remarkably well, and in the South American climate, the slight breeze thus created was much envied by other Europeans. *Walton Hall* was given over entirely to sugar, and was not far away from *Belle Vue* and *Parklands,* the latter being Michael Daly's second plantation.

Because Uncle Christopher was an absentee landlord, I found myself to be in charge of over four hundred slaves.

Slavery can never be defended. Those who do so have hearts of iron. The very notion should have been stifled at birth. I looked upon our slaves as fellow men and made all the kindnesses that were within my power. My principles were echoed in sycophantic lip service in the drawing rooms of English society by those who reaped the benefits of the trade. Most of my neighbours had a different view, unable to conceive the thought of conducting their business in a humane manner. For my part, I could never say I owned a man, and in my defence, I would say I was kind to them. The Waterton slaves were well fed and accommodated, and when necessary, tended by a doctor. All this was incumbent upon anyone who had slaves in their care. I can say I was more generous than most and made sure they were looked after in their old age, but all my efforts were a poor substitute for freedom. For this I was denounced as a fool by many, and from a hard-hearted business point of view, they were correct.

The Dutch have been the most reluctant to give it up. To my dismay and disgust, they still own slaves in South America.

The social life was not to my liking. As a teetotaller, I was looked upon as a curiosity, add to this my being more interested in the waterfowl of the shoreline than wild women of the town, I simply didn't fit. Against the fashion of the day, I had my hair cut short and shaved my face. My appearance gave much amusement to the debauched young of Stabroek, but these measures were simply a practicality in such a climate. The long-haired followers of fashion (wigs having been ditched by all but lawyers and judges due to a tax on powder) were the ones who suffered in the heat and humidity, not I.

"Will you not join us for a game of cards, Mr Waterton?" The question came from one of the dandies of the town. There were plenty of them. Young men, that is, of about my own age and with too much money and too little to do.

"You mean, do I wish to gamble?"

"If you care for a wager, sir, I am sure we can accommodate you." He filled his glass, draining the last of the rum from the bottle. One of his company signalled a serving girl to bring another.

"Sarcasm does not suit you, sir," I retorted, "any more than I am suited to your idea of pleasure."

"I hear, sir, that you take an interest in the birds. Maybe, if you do not care for the cards, you would like a little wager on the cock fighting."

"No. I would not. God's creatures may squabble amongst themselves, but not for my pleasure. I should rather see a bare-knuckle fight if you care for one." He laughed as he leaned back in his chair with such force that he and the chair toppled backwards, breaking the spindles. He looked around in astonishment, as if not sure how he came to be upon the floor. "Perhaps you should curb your habit of alcohol, sir."

He rolled to his stomach and then heaved himself to all fours before grasping the remains of the chair and standing up. "I do not have a drop of rum before three in the afternoon, sir. I am no drunk." Sweat poured from him as his face grew redder and redder.

"And before three? What do you drink for break-fast?" His companions banged their fists on the table, cheering their hero. Another drinker joined in the banter.

"He is an Englishman! He has Madeira and water for break-fast. We all do, unlike the Dutch. Now there is a people who can drink. It's gin for them, morning, noon, and night."

Michael Daly introduced me to Charles Edmonstone, a Scottish Presbyterian and timber merchant who had lived in Demerara for twenty-four years. His home, Warrow's Place, stood on the banks of Mibiri Creek, a tributary of the River Demerara, and some miles inland. The journey to this haven was via a narrow channel of deep, black water. The overhanging trees of these waterways block even the midday sun and turn the brightest of days into night, as if lit by a reluctant glimmer of the thinnest moon. Further along, Mibiri Creek narrows, making rowing an impossibility, and the boatmen are forced to dig their oars into the bank to push the boats along. After some distance the creek opens quite suddenly into a wide savannah and Warrow's Place comes into view, it being on a slightly elevated site.

During my visit, Mr Edmonstone showed me the value of bichloride of mercury, or mercuric chloride as it is otherwise known, as a preservative. He was a keen taxidermist and his willingness to share his knowledge motivated my life-long quest to perfect the art. I cast my mind back to Stonyhurst. If only Joe Bowren and I had had the stuff! Mr Edmonstone assured me that with care, it could be used perfectly safely, and I began experimenting with this excellent chemical, so beloved of the hatters. Mercuric chloride is used in their manufacturing process, and never more put to the test than by those who wear a top hat in the tropics.

"If it can preserve a top hat here, Charles, it is a substance of some use to the taxidermist." Mr Edmonstone joked, "Its ability to stiffen and harden knows no equal."

I am forever indebted to my friend's generosity in sharing his knowledge and expertise.

His wife was the daughter of Princess Minda, an Arawak Indian, and William Reid, who lived in nearby Camouri Creek. Mrs Edmonstone taught me the basics of the Indian language. At the time of my first visit they had one son, Charles, and Mrs Edmonstone was pregnant with their second child.

Mr Edmonstone had arrived in South America in 1781 and I can say with impunity, that he was the most valued friend I ever had in the world. Some years before we met, he had accidently been shot whilst assisting in rounding up runaway slaves. He survived, but the bullets lodged inside him for the rest of his life.

There was nothing I liked better than to spend time at Warrow's Place, and I ventured upriver whenever my duties permitted me to do so, or when the ague determined I was too ill to work. Standing a hundred yards or so from a curve in the creek, the house was of traditional Indian construction, that is to say, on stilts. Servants' quarters had been built in the same manner.

Charles Edmonstone was at an advantage as a timber merchant, his wife's maternal relatives having passed on their expertise and shown him where to find the best trees. His nephew, Archibald, was his business partner. Being younger and more able bodied, he spent a lot of time in the woodland and was therefore very knowledgeable. Nobody was better acquainted with the forest trees than Archibald Edmonstone. He gave me a catalogue of over sixty types of tree which grew in the vicinity of Mibiri Creek, giving their Indian names, rate and height of growth, their quality and uses. I still have it. I call it, 'The Science of the Forest.' Archibald showed me the fruit bearing trees where the finest birds in all of Demerara could be found.

No country in the world can offer a more extensive and fertile field to the ornithologist. Not only the shoreline birds had my attention, sea water and freshwater swamps behind plantations drew me like a magnet to the sights and sounds of the interior, but this delight had to wait.

I had been in Demerara for a little over a year when I had word of my father's death, forcing me to return to Yorkshire. There had been Watertons at Walton Hall since 1473, and it was now my turn to take up the responsibility as custodian of the acres. I left the plantations to the care of managers. I took with me some preserved birds and other creatures of the forest which I had worked on with Mr Edmonstone, stowing carefully my first specimens from South America. I was twenty-two years old.

CHAPTER TWELVE

The Twenty-Seventh.

Father had been laid to rest in the family vault at St Helen's Church, in Sandal. I would have liked to attend his funeral, but he had been buried for some four months before I was home. Word of his death had not reached me for some weeks, and then I had to wait for a ship to take me home. My sister, Helen, and I took a walk.

"I thought," she said, "that Father would like to have been buried near his father, here in the parkland."

"Was that Mother's idea—him being taken to the vault?"

"She said not. Apparently, he wished to be with his ancient ancestors."

"I didn't know anything about that. When did she tell you?"

My sister shook her head. "So many questions, Charles. She told us about his wishes the day he died."

I noticed for the first time that my sister was becoming a very attractive young woman. She linked her arm in mine. "I don't know, but come, Charles. Let us walk back to the house. You look half frozen."

"Only half?" I countered. "I believe I am entirely frozen to the bone. South America is much kinder to my skinny frame."

We walked in silence for a while, my head being occupied with the specimens I had brought home with me, and the challenges of taxidermy. Helen brought me back to more mundane matters.

"I understand Father's will is the cause of some concern," she said.

"For Mother, yes. Thomas has been telling me. How much do you know?"

"Nothing, really. My brothers just tell me not to worry."

"And they are right, but of course telling you not to worry is unlikely to satisfy you."

She laughed. "You know me too well, Charles." Turning to me as we walked, she gripped my arm a little more tightly. "You will stay here, Charles, won't you? I would rather you did."

Helen tugged my heartstrings. Responsibility for my family, and the Estate, fell to me and contrived to keep me in England, but the forests and birds of Demerara pulled me in another direction. I stopped and stared at her as the dilemma went to war in my head.

The legalities necessary for foreign travel should have prepared me for the tedious complications of inheritance. In my ignorance, I thought I merely had to sign a few papers to officially become the present incumbent of the estate. In a manner, this was true, but the lawyers have no rush in them. Twelve months passed before all was signed and sealed. Helen need not have worried about an imminent departure on my part. The worry was entirely my mother's when she learned she was completely reliant upon her children. Father had bequeathed her just one guinea, and a small income.

"This is unbearable, Charles. How can I live like this? I had expected things to be much the same for me, but without your father's company. How can I suddenly be so dependent upon you?"

Thomas was now nineteen years of age and destined for the priesthood. Christopher, at seventeen, was eager to accompany me when I returned to South America. Helen was thirteen, Isabella, twelve. William, aged ten, had just started at Stonyhurst. Edward was seven.

"I can only think that Father thought to live a little longer and see his offspring independent of their mother."

"You mean he thought to outlive me?"

"How can I possibly know what he thought, Mother. You are the one who was married to him."

She huffed out of the room, followed by a timid looking maid.

The lawyers made much of it. Mother was greatly displeased in this shift of authority. Our every conversation ended in her shouting and wailing that if my father were alive, she would make him change his will. Her difficulty was that the person she should have been shouting at was dead. As his heir, I was the next best thing, and so she vented her spleen upon me. This all meant for delay upon delay at the behest of the lawyers. Only Helen and Isabella gained from it all insomuch as we rowed on the lake and tramped the paths of the park together, whenever the weather permitted them to join me.

I employed a gamekeeper by the name of John Coe, and could only hope that in my absence he would keep the rats, poachers and foxes at bay. Christopher reluctantly agreed to stay at home with Mother until he was twenty-one.

Before returning to South America, and as promised, I visited Sir Joseph Banks, spending many an hour in his company.

"I would be obliged, Charles, if you would procure for me a sample of wourali. It is thought to be the principal ingredient of a strong poison used by the Indians when hunting. Some has already been procured and experiments have been undertaken on a rabbit and other small animals regarding its effects upon the heart and lungs. More is needed. I am given to understand it has great effect and would like to know exactly how the poison is prepared. The strength can vary. For my part, I doubt it could kill a large animal but I, and other men of science, seek knowledge in all such things. We do not know how it works, and whether there is a scientific use for it."

Naturally I was only too pleased to have such a purpose and readily agreed to his request.

His enthusiasm whetted my already voracious appetite for Mother Nature and all her mysteries. "I would be delighted, Sir Joseph. To have a specific goal, rather than casual observation, will give my explorations a true purpose."

"Also, I shall give you a list of plants, and would be grateful if you would try to collect some seeds. It will depend upon the season, of course."

Naturally, I agreed. This man had given his advice so freely, and it was a small request.

I returned to Demerara, and although I could not have known it at the time, more than three years would pass before I was able to fulfil my promise to Sir Joseph, being kept busy in the plantations.

It must be remembered that England was still at war with Spain, and Napoleon was yet to be defeated. The militia were based in Stabroek, and as the result of a conversation I had with Colonel Nicholson, I became a Lieutenant in the 2nd Regiment. This, I am at pains to point out, was bestowed upon me without my having denounced the Catholic Faith in any way. Had this been pressed upon me, I would have declined. I still have the papers, they are dated September 11th 1807.

Privateers from the Orinoco perpetually sailed the coast of Essequibo and Demerara. They would come ashore and raid the properties of the British, taking anything that they could carry. Such actions did not go unchallenged.

One morning, upon sighting a Spanish ship, a North American citizen and five English gentlemen set forth in a schooner to challenge her. They left with good intentions, but without a commission or any authorising papers, and as such, it would have been better if they had stayed on shore. Their schooner was soon in the possession of the Spanish. I was not alone in my concern for these gentlemen, for they were in serious danger of being taken to the Spanish settlements in the Orinoco and imprisoned as pirates. I, and I alone, of all the British in Demerara, could speak Spanish. Added to this, my being a Lieutenant of the 2nd Regiment, I was ideally placed to perform a rescue. Naturally, I volunteered, and the friends of the captured men quickly acquired a vessel for me. On October 24th, Colonel Nicholson gave me written instructions to sail to Barbados, the wartime headquarters of the navy and the army, where I was to take further instruction from Admiral Sir Alexander Cochrane. Perhaps all this seems unimportant, but my reason for writing of this is that I was the first Waterton, and indeed the first Catholic, to receive a commission since the days of Queen Mary's reign.

The voyage was a worrying one. The sailors were continually pumping sea water from the hold. I made no comment, as they were doing their best, but took the precaution of keeping my Daniel's life preserver with me at all times, sleeping with it under my pillow.

Upon arrival in Bridgetown, I immediately sought Admiral Cochrane, that I might serve my duty. To my dismay, I was told by the navy's agent, a Mr Maxwell, that he was not in residence, but at sea around the islands. His absence lead to my being heartily entertained as I awaited his return. Mr Maxwell gave a dinner party at his country house, and I break-fasted with Captain Beaver aboard the Acasta, a frigate of forty-four guns. A few days later, a messenger asked me to attend Mr Maxwell's residence.

"Lieutenant Waterton. I have good news for you." He shook me firmly by the hand.

"Am I to sail? Is Admiral Cochrane here?"

"Not at all. No. He has not yet returned, but you may return to Stabroek."

"How so? I have not—"

"Your commission is redundant. The men you were to free, are free already. I have word from Tobago that they have landed there, having overcome their captors."

"They are all safely landed?"

"All but one, it seems, who was washed overboard in the scuffle. The others were in a bad way, having had no fresh water they were all but dead of thirst when they landed, but are now recovering."

"Then I am glad, but disappointed not to have had the opportunity to serve."

"You were willing to do so, Lieutenant, and that is all that you can be."

I was reluctant to leave Barbados. The presence of our serving soldiers and sailors meant Bridgetown was perpetual fun.

'Nunc est Bibendum, nunc pede libero Pulsanda tellus.'

Now is the time to drink up, and dance to the lively beat.

Although I did not drink, I did plenty of dancing and had a wonderful time of it.

The hospitality at Warrow's Place knew no bounds, with local delicacies of fish and meat always on the menu. The Warrow Indians were frequently about the place. Their willingness to show us their skills in the forest and their customs showed no reticence or shyness. On one occasion, I think it was my second visit, they performed an entertainment. Mr Edmonstone sat with his wife, who was heavy with child, to his right, and myself to his left. Their sons, Charles and Robert, sat on the ground before us. The Indians gathered between their little audience and the shore of the creek.

"They play an instrument called a wanna, and their dance is called the Warrow Dance." Mr Edmonstone explained. "The wanna is constructed entirely of bamboo, one length inside another with a slit at one end, like a clarinet."

Their powerful music increased as they began to dance. The larger instruments had a deeper sound than the smaller ones, together making a most melodious sound. Mr Edmonstone tapped me on the arm.

"The bandmaster's headdress is a Warrow's passie. I will ask him to show it to you." Their dance appeared to tell a story, but I confess I did not understand it. Sometimes the movements were slow and shuffling, and at others, fast and exciting. All came to a climax of celebration, with great shouts of whooping joy.

As the natives settled to light fires and cook on the shoreline, Mr Edmonstone, having knowledge of the language, asked the bandmaster if I might inspect his passie. I was immediately struck by its heavy weight. From the crown, two rows of white heron feathers were fastened by basketwork, holding them upright in the centre. Above this, a bird's head, carved in wood and painted, was fastened to two further pieces of wood, fitting either side of the wearer's head. This was covered in colourful cotton thread, with hundreds of hummingbird feathers attached to it. Parrot feathers were suspended to dangle around. Anyone could see that such a thing would take many, many hours to make. I smiled and shook him by the hand to indicate my admiration. The bandmaster said something, and Mr Edmonstone translated that he wanted me to have it.

"Surely I cannot. How can I take it?"

"You must, or he will think you do not like it." It is one of my most treasured possessions.

Soon after my visit, Mrs Edmonstone was delivered of a daughter, whom they named *Eliza*.

No man of conscience can be without political opinion. I have already written of my opinion on slavery, and so to my delight, in 1807, the first significant step was taken to abolish this cruelty of man on man.

First, America, and then Lord Grenville's government in England, banned the import of slaves. Those who profited from this trade had fought abolition for years. This was no less than the twelfth bill to be put to Parliament. But conscience won through, and the bill became law. Although significant, it was not the end of it. Illegal traffic continued, with trading between owners and prices rising higher and higher for a strong male, or a female of childbearing age. They were valued as if they were cattle. I had no stomach for any of it.

The following year, a second opportunity to serve my country arose. I was commissioned by Governor Ross to carry despatches from the Commander of the Fleet, Admiral Collingwood, to Don Felipe de Ynciarte, the Spanish Captain General of the Orinoco. His headquarters were at the Spanish capital, Angustura,[5] some three hundred miles up the River Orinoco.

I requested that Mr Edmonstone be included in the commission. He had been unwell for some time, having succumbed to the ague, and I was convinced a change of air would do him good. Governor Ross agreed, and we sailed in the *Levina*.

All went well whilst at sea, but as soon as we entered the estuary of the mighty Orinoco, it was clear that this force of nature was in wild mood. Large trees coursed downstream like twigs of hawthorn in a rushing beck.

Mr Edmonstone and I were of the opinion that we must wait for the river to disgorge its temper, but our captain was experienced. He let the strong currents push his vessel to the eddying waters of the riverbank and had her lashed to an overhanging tree. The crew hauled by means of a capstan, then set out a second rope to repeat the process. By this laborious method, we made our way to the fort of Barrancas. When I informed the Spanish officers of our important mission, they provided us

---

5   now Cuidad Bolivar

with a long, narrow vessel, rigged like a schooner. Whilst much smaller than the *Levina,* she was more suited to the wiles of the river.

The crew were fearful of the creatures both in the water and on land, but they had no objection to my going ashore at the end of the day's sailing to hunt for our dinner. I would shoot maroudies and accouries, the former being much like pheasants and the latter a close relative of the guinea pig. On these expeditions, I had no choice but to return the favour to the leeches, which made free with my legs.

Keeping to the bank where the flow was less rapid gave greater opportunity to observe the parrots, scarlet arras, and many more birds of the forest, as well as the innumerable waterfowl. The horned screamer could be heard far and near and I saw several in the trees, but never got a clear shot at one. At night, jaguars could be heard. We saw many caymans, so easily mistaken for a passing log.

One day, when a Spaniard was at the tiller and we were particularly close to the bank, I spotted a labarri snake coiled beneath a bush. This venomous species is a master of disguise, being a dirty brown with some speckling. Being keen to study his fangs, I shot him, and leaned out of the boat to recover his body. He was mortally wounded, but not yet dead and so I needed to grip him just behind his head. With one hand grasping a bush, I almost had him when the helmsman took fright and put to port. Still gripping the branch, I toppled head first into the water, my weight taking the bush below the surface. Twice more was I dragged beneath the surface. The first time I came up I saw the helmsman being pushed aside, and another man seizing the tiller. He put hard to starboard as I went down again. As I gasped to the surface, I saw the boat coming back for me. Still clinging to the bush, I reached for the bank, but the branches were of no great strength. I was submerged for a third time and convinced of being an easy meal for a cayman. As I came up, and to the horror of my rescuers, I grabbed the labarri.

"*Señor, usted no puedo traer a bordo!* Sir, you cannot bring that on board!"

I held onto my prize. After such effort, I had no intention of leaving him.

"Puedo, y lo haré. El es demasiado herido para hacer daño. I can, and I will. He is too injured to do any harm." I replied.

Once safely back on board, I realised my shirt and trousers had been ripped to shreds. I was anxious to start dissecting, but before I started the operation, I changed my clothes, that I might perform in more comfort. My sharpest knife did the job. The snake was fully grown at eight feet long. Once the labarri was well and truly slain, the crew gathered a little more closely as I dissected the head, revealing the fangs that had caused such fear. I was able to show them the oblong hole on the inner side of the fang, and the little bag of poison that is situated at the tip of the root. I pressed the tip of the fang with a stick, causing an upward pressure on the bag. A small quantity of thick, yellow liquid oozed from the oblong hole. My audience stepped back, gasping in horror. A short while later, we saw an alligator pass by. He was at least thirty feet long, but too late for an easy meal.

At last we arrived in Angustura. After listening to the sounds of the forest for three weeks or more, the noise of the town jangled me. If I had had my way, I would have delivered the dispatches and set off straight back down the Orinoco, but this was not to be. I was received by Don Felipe, and handed over the despatches. He was a large man, with a girth to match his height, a shape that reminded me of Joe Bowren, but here the similarity ended. The governor was all ceremony and splendour. He informed us that we were to attend a dinner every evening during our stay, and that I was expected to wear my uniform. Not so much an invitation, as a command. This was all very well, except that I did not have a uniform.

The spread of food was nothing less than obscene. Forty dishes of fish and meat were laid out, not as choices, but as separate courses, giving some explanation for the size of Don Felipe's belly. Our host wore full military dress with enough gold braid for ten uniforms, and which appeared to have been made before overindulgence had wreaked havoc with his waistline. Before he had finished his soup, he was dripping in sweat, to the point when I feared he would liquefy and turn into a blob of jelly. For my part, I would have been happier with one dish, nicely cooked, but courtesy and diplomacy demanded I tried a little of each. We were not long into our dinner, maybe on the third or fourth dish, when Don Felipe turned to me.

"This is more than I can bear. Pray, pull off your coat, and tell your companions to do the same. I shall lead by example." He then stripped to his waistcoat. Mr Edmonstone and I, and all the officers at the table were grateful to do the same, but I am sure none more so than Don Felipe himself. The following night, he wore a blue uniform of much lighter cloth, with a little gold lace at the cuff.

My first impression of this man was not my last. It transpired that we had much more in common than I first thought, and I have fond memories of my stay in Angustura.

"In my younger days," he told me, "I mapped the coastline from the Orinoco to the Essequibo. I dressed as a common sailor and enjoyed every moment."

"May I see your map?"

"Come to my offices tomorrow," he said, "I shall be delighted to show my humble effort."

His humble effort was a thing of beauty, a superb map, beautifully finished by his own hand. Don Felipe had been something of an explorer and knew the importance of detail when reporting to the uninformed. Where map making was *his* passion, the observation of nature is mine. He told me of a dreadful incident he had witnessed when walking along a stretch of the riverbank. A large cayman had rushed from the water and taken a man, plunging back into the Orinoco with his victim firmly between his jaws. Although this had taken place some years previously, Don Felipe trembled as he described the screaming, the terror and the pain, and the helplessness of both the victim and the witnesses, who were unable to assist in any way. The beast, Don Felipe told me, had been hiding in the shallows before making his move.

"*Monstrum horrendum, informe.* A terrible form of monster." I said.

Don Filipe nodded. "They can move quickly, very quickly when there is something on the menu."

Angustura, despite its remote location, had everything one would expect of a civilised town. Man had stamped his footprint in this remote part, and made sure he wanted for nothing. Mr Edmonstone's health improved as a result of the luxury he enjoyed. After a week of luxurious entertainment, we bade farewell to our host and sailed with the flow of the river back to Fort Barrancas, and from there to Stabroek, my commission completed.

CHAPTER THIRTEEN

Enough is Enough.

Between these episodes of duty, I continued to manage the estates to the best of my ability, and as my conscience would allow. In 1812, Stabroek became Georgetown, and in 1814 the political situation became formally settled, with Demerara, Berbice and Essequibo forming British Guiana[6] and becoming part of the British Empire.

Mother wrote to me informing me that my brother, Christopher, and cousin, Robert were on their way to Guiana. Uncle Christopher had died at his home in Doncaster. His body had been brought to Walton Hall, and from there he had been laid to rest in the family vault at St Helen's Church, alongside Father. I prayed for his soul.

Christopher and Robert were far more interested in the estates than I could ever have been and took to the management like a duck to water. I wished they had come sooner. Christopher stayed with me at *La Jalousie* but was eager to extend the estates. Along with Robert and three other like-minded plantation owners, he hired a vessel and set off up the River Paumaron. I wish he had not. One month later, only Robert and two of the three returned. Christopher and the other fellow had succumbed to yellow fever. Poor Christopher. We had seen and survived so much together during our time in Malaga.

Perhaps this was the final blow, I had had enough of plantations, and of slavery. I resigned my position. My remaining brothers were happy to leave the management of the estates to Robert. From that year, I never again set foot on a plantation.

Having minutely studied the haunts and character of the birds of the coast for some time, there was not one that had eluded me. My collection

---

6 now Guyana

of the different species of preserved birds ran into hundreds and I was eager to increase it with the birds of the forest.

I spent some time at the Edmonstones' house prior to my first foray into the forests. While I was there Mrs Edmonstone was delivered of her second daughter whom they named Anne, quite the prettiest infant I had ever seen. All was well, and little Eliza was delighted with her baby sister.

One afternoon, the peacefulness of Warrow's Place was suddenly disturbed by the arrival of Mr George Faye, an English gentleman whom I had met in Georgetown. He was rowed to the shore by two slaves, who then helped him along a log which had been set in the mud as a sort of path. He appeared to be in some distress and his attempt to hurry caused him to stumble. The slaves helped him to his feet and I met him at the shoreline.

"Mr Waterton, I have been seeking you for three weeks, for you are the man who can save me." He took me by the arm, desperation flowed from his eyes. "My liver is in a poor way, and your skill with the lancet is well known. Bleed me sir, I beg of you. If I were to go to any other surgeon, I would be betrayed."

Some years previously, I had been instructed in the valuable skill of blood-letting by the able Doctor John Marshall of Georgetown, a man known equally for his skill as a surgeon, and his righteous attitude to the law. Naturally, I did as my visitor requested and took eighteen ounces. As the blood flowed into the bowl, he told me of his other troubles.

"You know me, Mr Waterton, I am not a bad man, and yet I am hounded. Old Hercules has put five hundred pounds on my head."

I must explain here that 'Old Hercules' was the nickname of Governor Carmichael, the new Commander of Georgetown. He was a man of small stature, known for both his generosity and quick temper. While his temper was quickly up, it was also quickly down. He soon earned his nickname for two separate, but comparable reasons.

Firstly, his namesake Hercules was a demigod associated with commerce in ancient Rome as the protector of the cattle market. Governor Carmichael was determined to rid Georgetown of corruption. Unscrupulous Dutch lawyers had long held more power than the governors of the past, assisted in their wrongdoing by many an officer who put personal gain above righteousness.

Secondly, the filthiest of stables could not have produced a greater stink than the streets of Georgetown. Under the command of Governor Carmichael, all the litter, both human and animal, was wheeled out within two weeks, just as Hercules had done in his fifth labour.

I cannot think of a more appropriate nickname. Governor Carmichael was a man of great experience, being almost seventy years of age when he took the post. His loyalty to the Crown of England knew no bounds. But to return to George Faye and his fear of betrayal.

"How so?" I asked.

"My accuser holds high office, and Governor Carmichael has taken his side without giving me audience. It is true that I owe money, but—"

At this point, a slave came into the room to inform me that a tent-boat was approaching. Bearing in mind our remote location, this was an unusual occurrence. I looked out of the window and saw four officers of justice on board. I quickly bound up my friend's arm and directed him out of the back door.

"Take the bridge to the field, hide in the sugar cane." Such was his fear of capture, he ignored my advice, and jumped out of the window into a filthy trench, landing up to his armpits in water. I went to the front of the house where the officers were making their way along the log.

"We have a warrant for the arrest of Mr George Faye." He waved a piece of paper.

"He is not here, Officer." I said.

He pointed to the canoe and the two slaves who had brought my friend. "This is his canoe."

"I fear you are mistaken and have had a wasted journey. That is my canoe." He pushed past me, and the four officers searched the house, much to the chagrin of my host. The officers' curses would have made a whore blush.

After they left, I sought Mr Faye, calling out his name for an hour or more. I do not know what became of him, but I never saw him again.

The next day, a warrant arrived, ordering me to appear immediately at Government House. I had had it in mind to visit Governor Carmichael, in order to request the necessary paperwork for my intended travels, and now wished I had done so. At that point I knew him only by reputation.

On my passage down-river I had time to contemplate my tactics and decided to appeal to his generous side. I went straight to Government House. The waiting area was crowded with men whose bored countenance told me they had been there for some time, and I expected a lengthy wait. To my surprise, I was called within minutes, and suffered the glares of those who shuffled on their backsides as I was ushered into the governor's office.

"And so, sir," he banged his fist on the table, shouting, "you have dared to thwart the law, and to defy me."

"General," I replied, "you have judged me rightly, and I throw myself upon your well-known generosity. Mr George Faye is a friend of mine, I have many times enjoyed his hospitality, and so when he sought my help, I could not refuse him. He is a good man, who has fallen upon bad times, and if you ever were to find yourself in a similar position, I would do the same for you, and take my punishment accordingly."

He stared at me for some time, his eyes narrowing and widening as if assessing my honesty. Eventually he said, "That's brave." He shook me heartily by the hand. After that, we chatted for two hours or more. He told me he knew he would never complete his cleansing tasks.

"I do not have enough time on this earth to finish the job, but I have made instruction that I am to be buried under the flag-staff, and so not be entirely forgotten." Before I left, he gave me written permission to go freely in the whole of Guiana for any length of time. I still have the document, dated April 16th, 1812.

I returned to Warrow's Place where Mr Edmonstone advised me to hire at least eight Indians to accompany me on my planned journey up the River Demerara. Before I left, a priest visited, and the baby Anne was baptised.

I left Georgetown shortly before the rainy season. Not the best time of year for such a venture, I admit, but I was eager to explore beyond the plantations and travel through the wilds of Guiana. I had no other objects in view, other than natural history and to at last fulfil my promises to Sir Joseph Banks. At the age of thirty, blinded by the imprudence of youth, I thought myself a mature, experienced traveller and a man of wisdom.

I packed a sheet, twelve feet long and ten feet wide, with looped holes on each side to shelter me from the rains. A gun, a pocket telescope, a lancet, a towel, a hammock and a quantity of rectified spirit were all neatly stowed along with my little knives. Other items, which are usually considered necessary for a man to travel, were not necessary in the forest. I speak of shoes, a top hat, stockings and the like. Thanks to my practical hairstyle, I had no need for brush or comb. I wore a broad brimmed hat, a thin flannel waistcoat under a loose shirt, wide canvas trousers, and braces.

After purchasing a sturdy, masted canoe and food supplies, and hiring six Indians, I set off for Warrow's Place, my first port of call. Supplies consisted mainly of cassava bread, this is a staple food made from the grated root of the cassava tree. In its raw state, it can be mixed with herbs to stop bleeding, and as an antidote to snake bites. As a food, it is not really a bread at all. The juice is squeezed out, and the remaining mixture baked over a fire before being cut into biscuits and dried in the sun. It is rather tasteless, but a hungry man does not care. Mr Edmonstone lent me a slave, who went by the name of Billy.

My aims were threefold. Firstly, to reach the Macoushi Indians' settlement, a tribe known to produce the strongest wourali poison, and to be the most accurate with the blowpipe.

Secondly, I intended to travel on to Fort São Joachim, held by the Portuguese, and to establish the existence or otherwise of Lake Parima, and the fabled Eldorado.

My third aim was to collect as many specimens as I could, including the seeds for Sir Joseph. If I were to assist in educating my countrymen of the natural history of Guiana, I would need evidence.

To my delight, Mr Edmonstone agreed to accompany me and my little party as far as the post-holder's house. We travelled in the same canoe, with two slaves sailing a separate craft for his return. We passed by the plantations, and the sugar works at Amelia's Waard,[7]*after which there was nothing to suggest that anything had ever been planted. Once abandoned, any attempts at cultivation are rapidly overgrown in the damp heat of Guiana.

We reached Saba Rocks within three weeks. My Indians informed me that this was good progress. Saba simply means stone. The rock at the riverside is remarkably smooth and slopes into the water. The Post-holder's role was to report to the government any suspicious travellers. I showed him my papers. As he perused, he said,

"You will not see a white man past here. Only Indians, and free men of colour." He looked at me as if I were a curiosity in a fairground.

"I am not looking for white men," I said. He thrust the papers back at me.

"You will probably die, but I expect you know that. If the savages don't kill you, the ague will, or the yellow fever."

Having no desire to continue the conversation, or spend any time in the man's company, I bade him farewell. Mr Edmonstone had a more a more encouraging outlook.

"I look forward to your return, Charles," he said.

"It is good to know that you think that to be a possibility."

"The post-holder does not know you as I do." He smiled and shook me firmly by the hand.

"He is correct on one point. I shall not see another white man for some time."

"You will see the Portuguese at Fort São Joachim."

From Saba Rocks to the point at which we would leave the River Demerara was two weeks away if the weather was favourable. I was eager to travel on before the rains started.

---

7   now Amelia's Ward

There were five habitations of Indians between Saba Rocks and the Great Fall, and it was at the first of these that I met a family of Acoway, and their chief, Sinkerman. The day was drawing to a close, and they were happy to have us stay and share their food. From the notes I made at the time, I can pinpoint the date exactly. May 1st 1812. A distant rumbling interrupted our meal of maroudie, cassava and a pot of vegetables. The forest fell silent, with the exception of the crickets, but their incessant chirruping was soon drowned out by a deep roar, and the fearful screaming of the Indians as they huddled together beneath a mora tree. Had I not experienced the earthquake of Malaga, I too would have been in fear. The shaking lasted a minute or so. Anyone who has not experienced an earthquake will dismiss the incident as trifling unless there is loss of life, but what they do not understand is that at the time, there is no saying how long it will last, or how severe it will become. Upon my eventual return to Warrow's Place, I was told by Mr Edmonstone it had been centred many hundreds of miles away, at St Vincent's Island.

We travelled on. Beyond the known waters, a gentler landscape with sloping hills is interspersed with higher land. At a turn in the river, an almost perpendicular rise towered above us. Trees overhung the river in a kaleidoscope of spring, summer and autumn with the dead strewn among the living, victims of old age or lightning. Magnificent specimens of the green heart tree, known for its hardness and durability, the hakea renowned for toughness, and the ducalabaliu, which surpasses mahogany in its versatility, were all in abundance. Hayawa and olou trees delighted our nostrils with their sweet-smelling resin.

All these, and more, are documented in my humble scribblings. I refer here to my published works, 'Wanderings in South America,' and 'Essays on Natural History,' I feel no compunction to re-iterate the beauty of the forests. If, dear reader, you would like to learn about the flora and fauna of Guiana, then I suggest you buy a copy. I seek only to inform those who cannot see such things for themselves. Whilst I hope my writings have encouraged others to travel, I concede that the terrain and climate is not to the liking of everyone. My 'Wanderings' or to give the title in full, *Wanderings in South America, the North West of the United States and the Antilles,'* have been translated into French, Spanish and German and proved popular in America where, I am told, it has been read by Theodore Roosevelt.

The mosquitos, itch insects, chegoes, guinea worms, whip worms and the tiny but extremely irritating, bête rouge, all sampled my blood.

At the next settlement, I procured my first sample of wourali. None of the women folk were allowed anywhere near the hut where the poison was stored. Through sign language and my increasing knowledge of their tongue, I asked what they had killed with their poison.

"Monkeys, mostly," their chief said, "but also wild hogs and once, a tapir, but it did not taste as good as the hog."

One of the Indians seemed particularly keen to demonstrate the effectiveness of wourali, and a medium sized dog was brought forward. The dog was injected in the leg, using an arrow head. From a scientific point of view, the location of the wound was of relevance, as no vital organ could be directly responsible for the effect. The dog turned his head, looked at his leg in a wistful manner, and then sniffed at the ground. After three or four minutes, he staggered, and lay down. He barked once, rather weakly, before putting his head between his forelegs. He fell to one side with his eyes open and shuddered a few times, each shudder lasting about five seconds. I put a hand between his forelegs and felt his heartbeat flutter. He stopped breathing, but still his heart beat a little longer. He was quite dead within a quarter of an hour. I thanked the Indian profusely for the demonstration, this being my first observation of the effectiveness of the poison. A most peaceful death.

As we continued up river, the rains commenced, hampering our speed. The river was bubbling like a cauldron as it rushed by. Some days later we heard the falls in the distance, and diverted away from the Demerara, and towards the Essequibo.

Four of the Indians rowed the canoe via a circuitous creek, taking with them the specimens I had shot thus far. Billy and I, along with the other two Indians, travelled overland and I experienced the true forest for the first time. Away from the river, my eyes adjusted to the all-enveloping darkness, and the shadowy world where the sun is only permitted to penetrate at the behest of a fallen tree. Such a fall would be caught by the ropes of the prolific vines, where the tree might die or live again at a new angle. Tiredness, rather than sunset, told of the end of the day. Even the incessant rain could not directly penetrate the cover, but the steaming atmosphere soaked everything, including our hammocks. Like the sailor who does not see land for weeks on end, I lost all notion of the world beyond the forest. Never silent, the sounds and sights, the light, or lack of it, created an unimaginable beauty. I found that one of my bites had ulcerated, causing me to limp. All four of us were suffering from dysentery.

We reached the Essequibo at sunset, its dimming light causing me to screw up my eyes. Too tired to hunt, we ate cassava bread which was less than good, being a little mouldy, and slung our hammocks. I closed my eyes as I ate, trying to conjure the flavour of gingerbread, but alas, it was not possible.

We relaxed, awaiting the arrival of the canoe, which arrived two days later. In a short respite from the rain, we dried our hammocks. The canoe was launched and we proceeded in the swollen Essequibo. Lower branches of the riverside trees were dragged in the flow and the midstream islands were covered in swirling water. Our journey slowed in direct proportion to the quickening of the river. When it became impossible to progress due to speed of flow or waterfalls, the Indians, assisted by Billy, had to take everything out of the canoe and drag it, and its mast, overland. I would have helped, but by this time I was considerably weakened by the ulcerated bite, and dysentery.

There were no settlements. We lived on cassava bread, maroudie, and pacou, the fattest and most delicious fish in Guiana, killed by the Indians with their spears.

Leaving the Essequibo, we joined the Apourapoura river and after two weeks we reached a settlement of the Macoushi Indians. My relief knew no bounds, and I set about curing my ills, having developed a method whereby I could tap the claret without assistance. I applied a compress to my upper arm and then used the lancet on a raised vein. When my blood started to flow, I released the compress, and let free twenty-four ounces. It then remained to bind my arm, which I did using my other hand and my teeth. I became practised at this, and the end result was quite neat. Thus, I rid myself of the fever in my blood without troubling my native servants, who did not understand it. A mixture of calomel and jalap, with a little laudanum took away the poison from my gut and I was much improved. I had collected many specimens, and had an occasional glimpse of a jaguar, but by reaching this tribe, I was able to accomplish an important goal.

At first reluctant to reveal their secret recipe, the Macoushi eventually permitted my witnessing the preparation of wourali. I felt privileged. The preparation took place in a cave, with ritualistic ceremony. No female members of the tribe were permitted inside.

Here is their recipe.

Ingredients.
Wourali vine leaves, tied in a bunch.
Two types of green, bulbous plants.
Some large, black ants. (These have a strong sting, which produces fever.)
Some small, red ants. (Their bite gives a sting, like that of a nettle.)
Some strong peppers.
The pounded fangs of the labarri and couanacouchi snakes.

The Macoushi had cultivated the peppers near their houses. The snake fangs, I was informed, had been saved from a previous kill. The method is thus.

Scrape the wourali vine and its root into thin shavings.
Make a colander from leaves and put the tied wourali in it.
Hold this over an earthen pot and pour through some hot water.
The liquid which comes through will be dark brown, like coffee.
Discard the shavings. Bruise the bulbous stalks and squeeze out the juice into another pot.
Add some of this to the brown liquid.

Add the ground fangs, ants and pepper.
Place over a slow fire, adding more juice as the pot boils.
Remove any scum with a leaf.
Reduce to thick brown syrup.

The poison was stored in a little pot, and covered with deerskin. I was told that they took the poison out from time to time to boil it up and thereby keep out any dampness. To my everlasting gratitude, they gave me not only a pot of this powerful poison, but also the separate ingredients, each carefully wrapped in a leaf, as was their custom. I suspected from the start that the wourali vine was the active ingredient, and the others simply fearful additions to the concoction. They also gave me some blowpipes. All were carefully stowed in the canoe.

Two days after leaving the Macoushi, we came to another settlement. Here, in a mixture of sign language and Indian words, an old man told me he had seen Lake Parima.

"It is a lake of fresh water, the purest water a man will ever taste." I waved my arms in a circular motion, indicating I wanted to hear more, and being too willing to oblige, he took his tale too far, and lost his credence. "I have seen large ships there, with sails like clouds." Much as I would have liked to believe him, I could not.

We travelled on through sparsely populated areas with settlements of no more than ten people. Eventually, we came to the source of the creek, where we abandoned the canoe. From this point, the baggage and my specimens were all carried by the Indians.

Without any gradual thinning of vegetation, we found ourselves quite suddenly on the edge of the forest, gazing at thousands of acres of savannah. It took half a day to march across this wetland. For the first time, I saw the jabiru, the largest bird in Guiana. Despite the lack of human population, this wily bird knew to keep out of gunshot. We waded through wet ground, and tramped across bare hills, where sharp stones cut my feet. Vultures soared over distant mountains.

Symptoms of the tertian ague (which show on alternate days) reared, teasing me with its intermittent presence. I had felt unwell for a few days before it hit me with full force. I instructed Billy to drench me in cold water and rub me down vigorously with a towel. This, followed by further application of the lancet and purgatives, had some positive effect. It occurred to me that I was most often smitten after being in a swamp, and suspected there may be a connection between the tropical waters and the ague, but this remains mere conjecture.

Our journey was lengthened as we were forced to divert around floods, eventually coming to a wide creek. With no option available other than turning back, I ordered the Indians to make a raft to transport my specimens across the water. The venture took a day to complete. Before we could push the raft across, prudence dictated we beat the bank of the creek half a mile each way with long sticks in order to chase away any crocodiles. This done, the strongest of the Indians swam across and did the same on the opposite bank. We then took to the water, pushing the raft, whilst all the time looking out for crocodiles. That night we slept at the waterside, and the following day I saw spur winged plovers, an egret, and flocks of scarlet and blue aras. I shot one of each, adding them to my growing collection.

The tertian ague weakened my body, accompanied once again by dysentery, forcing us to stay a while at the little settlement. I performed with the lancet, but not the purgatives, as my bowels were too much in a state of flux. One of the Indians prepared a draught of cinchona bark, insisting I drink a cup of it each day. He also informed me a great flood plain lay ahead, and that several rivers flowed into the south west corner.

"It will take four days to walk around the flood, and then four days after that, you will reach Fort São Joachim."

As luck would have it, we chanced upon a group of Portuguese soldiers on the bank of the River Pirara. They were busily making canoes with the help of some Indians. My command of the Spanish language enabled us to converse.

"As you can see, gentlemen, we are in a bad way. May I ask you to take me to the fort?"

"We dare not, sir," the captain said, "no-one is allowed in. We have strict orders on the matter, but we will take a letter, if you would pen one."

Respected Sir,

Since I do not have the honour of your acquaintance, I thought it more proper and fitting to wait here until I have received word from you. Having travelled thus far, I do not wish to return without having seen the Portuguese Fort, and beg your permission that I might be allowed to visit it. My motives are honourable. I am not a man of business, nor am I a soldier or official. I am a Catholic man, with a country estate in England. Many years of my life have been spent in Demerara.

I have not spoken with a fellow European for some weeks, and would relish the opportunity to do so. I can give you news of the battles, such as it was when I left Georgetown.

Valencia has fallen, and General Blake, along with his brave troops, is a prisoner of war. Despite this, it is plain to the world that the British are gaining strength every day.

Lord Wellington has taken the city of Rodrigo.

We must give thanks to the Almighty for the punishments he has served upon our enemies.

Please forgive my writing this letter in Spanish. I do not speak Portuguese, and can only hope that you understand this communication. Please forgive, also, that this letter is not written in ink. An Indian servant dropped and broke my inkwell.

May God grant you many years of health. Meanwhile, I have the honour of being,

Your Obedient Servant,
Charles Waterton.

My shaking hands folded it as best they could, and I handed it to the captain.

"God speed you, sir," I said, "for I fear my usually robust constitution is failing."

"Do not wait, sir," he said, "travel slowly along the riverbank. I shall bring the commander's reply in a day or two."

By this time, every member of my crew had dysentery. Some were fevered, all of us were severely bitten and had ulcers and pustules on our bodies and limbs. The nights were cold and stormy, it rained in torrents and there was no sun to dry our hammocks. My strength of constitution failed, and all hope lay with my letter, and with the Waterton family motto.

'Better a stranger become a friend, than a friend become a stranger.'

As promised, the captain returned with a reply from the commander.

Sir,

Please accept that my orders are that no-one enter the frontier as established by my government. I hope with every sincerity that you do not think me uncivil. I have ordered a soldier to land you at a certain distance from the fort, where we can consult together.

I could not read on, because my eyes would not focus, and I could not write a reply, such was my shaking. I can only assume that on his return to the fort the soldier told his commander of my advanced illness, because on the following morning the commander himself came and took my pulse.

"I am sorry, sir," he said, "to see the fever has taken such a hold on you. You shall go directly with me to the fort, and though we have no doctor there, I trust we shall soon bring you about. The orders I have received forbidding the admission of a stranger were never intended to be put into force against a sick English gentleman."

It is fair to say this demonstration of common sense, a characteristic lacking in many, saved my life. I was taken to the fort where, for six days, I was nursed and fed. The fever subsided, and I was once again able to stand. The commander would have had me stay longer, but I was eager to return to Warrow's Place before my health failed again. A soldier rowed me back to my crew, all of whom were in their hammocks where I had left them. Every man still had dysentery, and many of their bites were now angry and weeping with vile pus. The ague affected each man in varying degrees of severity, but all were able to travel.

No explorer would ever retrace his steps through choice. He desires to go on, to find another way, but my desire was crushed by the instinct to survive, and to prove the post-holder to be wrong. I considered it high time to take the advice of Sir Joseph Banks, and return to England as soon as I was strong enough to undertake the voyage.

Before we reached the first settlement the ague attacked me with renewed force. We settled for the night. Billy drenched me and rubbed me down, but I had not the strength to use the lancet.

"Billy," I beckoned him closer, that he might hear my whisper, "do you think I will last the night?"

"Ah, Massa, you go dead in four hours more, then you stop a shakin'."

"Then in four hours more, you must throw my body out of this hammock and try to get back to the settlements."

"We not take you back?"

"No, Billy, leave me here, for there is nowhere I would rather be, and carrying my corpse would lessen your chance of survival." He stared at me, his eyes dulled by fever, his body shaking. Billy held the cup as I swallowed a draught of the cinchona before retiring to his hammock.

You know I rallied, dear reader. The little raft awaited us at the creek side, and once again we foiled the crocodiles. Every mile through the jungle felt like a mountain to be conquered. Our canoe was a welcome sight, and we took to the water. The rapids were now twelve feet wide at the uppermost, and conversation entirely impossible, such was the roar of water. The Indians disembarked and tied the boat to a fallen tree with a length of bush vine while Billy and I remained on board. The lead Indian held his paddle in a vertical position, indicating his intention to steer down the centre line of the falls. He then signed for the vine to be cut. The crew piled in, we began our descent. Due to the skill of our oarsman, we touched not one rock all the way down the rapids. Then, having made it down the most dangerous part of the falls, we hit a rock and capsized. Many specimens were lost, including the individual ingredients of wourali poison and the seeds I had collected for Sir Joseph. Perhaps it is more astonishing that anything at all was salvaged from the dousing, but all crew members, the pot of poison, the blow pipes and my notes had survived, having been stowed in the very far corner of the bow.

The weather tried us sorely with crashing thunder storms of greater force than any I had hitherto experienced, accompanied by heavy rain. I shivered but could not tell if the air were cold or the fever blasted me. My entire body was like an earthquake insomuch as I did not know when it would stop. I thought perhaps Billy was right and only my death would stop it, but I managed a wave to the post-holder.

I had the Indians take me to Mibiri Creek, where the ministrations of Mrs Edmonstone revived me. I had been away for four months and was tired and sick. Barely recognisable and no longer the spirited young enthusiast, I had changed, or better to say, my experiences had changed me. Three months would pass before I had the strength to carry a gun. Within the peace of the interior, where the sun rose and set on a landscape unchanged, where man was yet to destruct in the name of progress, commerce, and so-called civilisation, I had experienced indigenous civilisations unfettered by greed and jealousy.

In my absence, an epidemic of yellow fever had run riot through the plantations of Guiana, taking many hundreds of souls, including that of my cousin Robert. The plantations were once again without a Waterton, but I did not feel obliged to take up their management.

On a more positive note, Mr Edmonstone had heard from Governor Carmichael that he had written to Lord Bathurst with regard to my explorations, and his Lordship had requested I visit him upon my return. I sent word to Georgetown that I would require a passage, but until I could stand without shaking, I was not fit to undertake the voyage to England.

I used this time to instruct Billy in the art of taxidermy. Whilst peaceful, life at Warrow's Place was never dull. Mr and Mrs Edmonstone's reputation for hospitality ensured there were often visitors. Old Hercules was still trying to rid Georgetown of corruption, and as a result of this, a Dutch captain by the name of Lauwens arrived one day. No longer a seafarer, the captain was deskbound in Georgetown.

"Captain Lauwens is agitated." I said. My host and I were walking by the riverbank, well out of the captain's earshot. "Do you know the cause of his distress?"

"His story will soon come out, Charles. There is no need for me to question him."

Later that day, when we had all finished a meal of fish and cassava bread, Captain Lauwens began to talk of his troubles.

"I admit I cannot balance my books. I fear Old Hercules has been informed by those who would see me removed from my position and thrown into gaol. The governor's reputation tells me he does not want to hear how I came to this impasse."

"What do you intend to do? Can I assist you in any way?" Mr Edmonstone asked.

"Only that I may be allowed to stay here until I have made arrangements to travel to Brazil."

"But," I said, "if you are innocent of any corruption, why do you not stand your ground?" Before he could respond, a slave brought a letter to the table. There was no mistaking the seal of Governor Carmichael. Mr Edmonstone read it slowly.

"It appears the general is on his way to visit." Captain Lauwens leapt to his feet, upsetting the table. Mrs Edmonstone called for a slave. I followed the captain out of the house, catching up with him on the edge of the forest.

"Where are you going, Captain? You cannot just make off."

"He must have heard of my plans and is on his way to arrest me. He will have me in gaol."

I grabbed him by the arm but was too weak to force him to return to the house, and so I pleaded with him.

"Come back, Captain. You cannot know that is the case, and you will not last long on your own in the forest. We will go to another house in another creek, until the general has gone. I am sure he will not stay long if Mr Edmonstone tells him you are not here."

Within half an hour we were being rowed by two slaves, making our way up Waratilla Creek, towards the home of Mr Beaumond, another friend of the Edmonstones. We left in haste, but the slaves had had the foresight to put some large troelly leaves in the canoe as makeshift umbrellas, should it rain. Otherwise we had no provisions. We passed the night at the home of Mr Beaumond, though I fear Captain Lauwens did not sleep. In the morning, we thanked our host and set off back for Warrow's Place.

Upon our approach to the junction of Mibiri and Waratilla Creeks, an unmistakable tent boat came into view. I managed to catch Captain Lauwens before he jumped overboard.

"Quickly, Captain, lie in the bottom of the canoe." I ordered the slaves to cover him with the troelly leaves as Governor Carmichael's boat drew alongside. He was accompanied by the Captains Eyre and Dawson, and Commissary Pittman, all of whom were known to me as good and reputable fellows. I could not imagine for one moment that they were here to arrest anyone. The governor would have sent soldiers for such a task.

"Have you seen Captain Lauwens lately?" I asked, as if a polite enquiry.

"No. I have not, I fear he may be unwell." The governor said.

"I believe Mr Edmonstone is expecting him." I said, as if in casual conversation.

"I think I can speak for my companions when I say it would give us all great pleasure to see him, he is such an excellent fellow." Captains Eyre and Dawson, and Commissioner Pittman agreed, nodding their assertion.

Captain Lauwens lay quite still under the troelly leaves until we arrived at Warrow's Place.

"Stay here, Captain," I whispered to him, "remain in the canoe, and when we are in the house, go and hide in the wood hut. I will come for you in a couple of hours."

When I brought him out Governor Carmichael shook him by the hand. "When did you leave town, Captain?"

"I have been visiting a friend in a nearby creek, and now intend to stay a day or two with Mr Edmonstone."

All was entirely congenial, and Captains Lauwens' perceived troubles a thing of the past.

Three months later, I could stand for five minutes or more without shaking and deemed myself well enough to travel home. I had packed a hundred and fifty birds, many from the coastal regions and some from the interior, along with the precious wourali and blow pipes.

The night before my departure, Governor Carmichael insisted I attend a grand ball at the Union Coffee House. He had entrusted me with some colonial despatches which I was to deliver to Lord Bathurst, along with a letter of introduction and recommendation, should his Lordship require a person to conduct an exploration.

An ox was to be killed for the feast, and I persuaded the butcher to allow me to slay the animal with wourali. He clearly found this to be a strange request, but nonetheless he indulged me. The beast weighed nine hundred and sixty pounds. I injected him in the large muscle of a rear leg and waited for the poison to take effect. After four minutes he began to waver and was dead within twenty-five minutes. As with the dog, he died peacefully. His flesh was the sweetest and most tender I have ever tasted.

The following morning, I visited Captain Lauwens. He insisted on giving me a watch. He told me he had had it made by Keating of London and it cost £40. I declare it the best watch a man ever wore. He accompanied me to the quayside, where I once again boarded the *Fame* of Liverpool, this time under the able command of Captain Williams, who insisted I slept in a cabin.

Thanks to the generosity of Captain Lauwens, and with little to do during the voyage, other than survive it, I was able to study my bouts of the tertian ague. Without fail, it set about me on alternate days at noon, shaking my meagre body as if a giant had hold of me. The times between attacks were marred by the dread of return, and I could only think of the brief respite as a calm before a storm, the advent of further shaking. This obstinate and persistent malady brings nightmares of bizarre nature, so much so that sleep is feared by the tortured sufferer.

I remained in my cabin, fearing that any venture on deck would result in my being swept overboard by a puff of wind. My only companion was a marjay kitten, given to me by a Dutch farmer's wife shortly before sailing.

"My slave found it in a field, apparently deserted by its mother."

"But it is a wild cat."

"And it will be a dead wild cat if you don't take it, Mr Waterton. They are excellent ratters. If anyone can tame one, that person is you."

With this assurance, I accepted with gratitude. I suspected the Hanoverians of Walton Hall had run riot during my absence and that I would need all the help I could muster to rid my home of the unwelcome rodents. During the voyage I had limitless time to observe Miss Marjay and compare her to my domestic cats. The most obvious differences were her larger size and distinctive markings, although also known as a tiger-cat, her markings were more like those of a cheetah. Her ears were rounded, whereas domestic cats have pointed ears, and her tail was extraordinarily long. If my memory serves me well, it was about three quarters of the length of her body. Less obvious was the shape of the main pad of her paws, which was long and oval, rather than the rounded shape of the domestic cat. Within the confines of my cabin, she climbed everywhere she could. By the time we sailed into the River Mersey, Miss Marjay and I had become friends.

My enforced rest on board ship did nothing to aid recuperation, and I was unable to proceed to London. I sent the despatches to Lord Bathurst on the post-coach, with a letter of apology, and proceeded to Walton Hall. I was thirty-one years old, but on looking in a glass I saw my reflection to be that of a wizened old man. I went straight to the drawing room. Mother held me by both hands, her eyes welling with tears.

"Thank God you are home." She took a 'kerchief from her cuff. "I could not bear to lose two sons. Does your brother have a decent grave?"

In truth, I had no idea. He had died upriver on the Paumaron, and it was unlikely that anything more than a shallow grave had been possible.

"Yes, Mother. He is at rest in a peaceful place." At this, she seemed to recover herself a little, looking at me as if examining a curiosity in a fairground. The tropical sun had turned my skin the colour of mahogany, and the ague had painted dark rings under my eyes.

"You look like a monkey," she said, and I could not disagree. "Cook must feed you up before you disappear altogether."

Little did I know at the time, that Cook would be 'feeding me up' for three years.

CHAPTER FOURTEEN

Poachers, Vermin, and a Missed Opportunity.

There was much to occupy me. The ague pestered, but what cannot be cured must be endured, and so I set about as many tasks as I was able.

Game laws had been passed which permitted unbridled shooting of all species other than those for the table. Keepers shot everything that moved, other than the robin, who escaped the gun for superstitious reasons. Added to this, the enclosures of common land had robbed the birds of much of their hunting ground, so there were thin pickings, especially for the birds of prey. The kite had disappeared from the skies of Yorkshire, the last one having been shot by my neighbour, Lord Pilkington. He was proud of it.

I was at the grotto, enjoying the morning sunshine of early summer when young John Winn of Nostell Hall, as it was known in those days, approached from the northern gateway. He had a dead buzzard slung over his arm.

"Do you expect thanks?" My tone must have told him I was not pleased.

"I thought you might want to stuff it."

"Stuff it? I stuff nothing. But I will stuff you with shot if you ever bring me a bird again."

"It's the last one, Mr Waterton. Are you sure you don't want it?"

"I suppose you have already killed its mate."

"I have that," he grinned.

"Then you have murdered generations of buzzards." He frowned, shrugged his shoulders, and slunk off. Had I been stronger, I would have wrung his neck, but he was a sixteen-year old, with no interest in birds other than shooting them, his lack of years blinding him from his folly.

The ague conceded a longer respite, and after a week without shaking I travelled to London, eager to visit Sir Joseph Banks and to make the acquaintance of Lord Bathurst who had replied to my letter, saying that as soon as I was sufficiently recovered, he wanted me to explore the island of Madagascar. I could barely believe my luck. My Catholicism notwithstanding, Governor Carmichael's recommendation had set me up for a government commission of life changing proportion. I was to be an international explorer, financed by the British government. As such, my views would be taken seriously. Not only *my* name, but that of the Waterton family would be restored to its proper place, thanks to this opportunity. The ague would have to take its chance. I was to sail in October, giving me the summer to further regain my strength.

I dined with Sir Joseph. Gout had confined him to a wheelchair and he preferred to stay at home, away from the bustle of the city. This suited me well, for after the peace of the jungle, city life jangled me more than ever. I was not yet ready for London, although London was apparently ready for me.

He entirely forgave my failure to supply his seeds when he heard the circumstances of their loss.

"I could hardly expect you to go back and collect some more, and as to the wourali ingredients, I am sure it will one day be proven that the vine is the poisonous element."

"It is my belief that the amount of poison required to kill a creature is directly related to body weight, and strength of the lungs."

Sir Joseph nodded. "A logical conclusion in respect to weight, I grant you, but why do you mention the lungs specifically?"

"I am not sure. What I do know is that there is more to learn, and I intend to conduct further experiments. I have told you of my observations regarding the dog and the way his heart fluttered after he had stopped breathing. The killing of an ox required a higher dose. In both cases, the poison did not enter via a vital organ. I am sure I can find out more, and when the ague permits, I shall be busy with it."

"For any experiments to hold credence, they must be carried out under scientific conditions, preferably at the London Veterinary College. It is my advice that you give some wourali to the people there. I am sure they would be delighted to hear all your reports, and for you to be present when any experimentation takes place. But tell me, Charles, have you made any progress on the preservation of quadrupeds?"

"I regret I have not. No matter what solution I use, the nose, lips and ears shrivel up like a mummy. Within a short time they look hideous, and all I can do is cut off these extremities and substitute them for wax ones, which look little better."

"Some problems cannot be resolved, my friend, and I believe it is impossible to remedy this defect." He paused, and then smiled at me. "But I will say this, if anyone can come up with a way to satisfactorily preserve these parts, it is you, Charles. Promise me that if you ever resolve the matter, you will share your discovery."

"Of course, I will. Why ever would I not?"

As suggested by Sir Joseph, I gave several samples of different strengths of wourali to the college, each duly labelled and encased in wax. They thanked me profusely and invited me to be present whenever they experimented. The most interesting of those which I attended was performed on four she-donkeys. Six scientists were present, as well as the college president, Lord Percy of Northumberland. The first donkey was injected in the hind leg and expired within twelve minutes. A tourniquet was applied to the foreleg of the second animal, and the poison administered below this. The donkey was unaffected until the tourniquet was removed, and then died ten minutes later. The third donkey was given a smaller dose in the shoulder and revived but was very disorientated. A fourth donkey was also injected in the shoulder, this time with the same dose as the first two. She fell to the floor, apparently dead. At this point, an incision was made in her windpipe, and a pair of bellows used to inflate the lungs with artificial respiration. I took my turn at the pump, as it were, and after two hours, the donkey lifted her head and looked around. The bellows were set aside and the donkey expired. The bellows were taken up once again, and after two hours more, she revived, stood up, and walked around, showing no sign of distress or pain. We were all delighted with this result. It proved beyond doubt that wourali did not affect the heart, although what use this might ever be, no-one could say.

I returned to Walton Hall. Lord Percy gave me his word that he would keep me informed with regard to further experimentation, which he did. About a month later, he wrote to tell me that the third donkey had died three days after the experiment and that the fourth was still alive, but in poor health.

Hanoverians were everywhere. In the walls of the house, in the roof, and behind the skirtings. How everyone in the household had put up with it I do not know. The cats worked on the problem but could not solve it alone. Miss Marjay followed me around the house, taking her position on the staircase each evening, where she would wait for a rat, seizing her prey without fail in one lightning pounce. Nothing could surpass the dexterity with which she disposed of the rats. Had it not been for her successes, I doubt that Mother would have tolerated her presence. Due to the constant scrabbling, I was quite unable to sit and read, or write a letter, and so I resorted to a cunning method, as learned from Joe Bowren. I set a trap that would not kill, but merely imprison my enemy. It did not take long for a large male to be tempted by a morsel of bread. I dipped his hind quarters in tar and let him loose in a pantry. He disappeared within the walls in a trice, where the smell of the tar soon had his compatriots on the run. I repeated the process in various parts of the house, and within a month or so, I could relax in my home, free from their noise.

Having mentioned the successes of Miss Marjay, I feel obliged to tell of her time at Walton. She never truly fitted in with the domestic cats, preferring her own company. Her excellent climbing abilities were due to her elongated paw pads and tail, and she was happier in the woods than in the house or stables. Miss Marjay could run up and down a tree with the agility of a squirrel. However, and unsurprisingly, the Yorkshire winter was not to the liking of a tropical cat, and the first harsh winter saw her demise. Her body was found in the woods, too decayed for preservation.

My observations in the forests of Guiana, particularly of the symbiotic relationships between all flora and fauna, gave inspiration for the future of my small patch of Yorkshire. First to be helped was the barn owl, a species that had been targeted by superstition as well as being perceived as an enemy of the farmer. Working on the island, next to the footbridge, I made a stone box, about four feet square, and wedged a stick of oak inside as a perch, designing and constructing it in such a way that it could be taken apart and moved. Upon its completion, I instructed Coe to move it to a quiet spot behind the stables, but my feathered friends had a different idea. Before the lazy scoundrel of a gamekeeper had obeyed my orders, a pair of barn owls had moved in. To say Coe did not share my enthusiasm for the birds does not begin to explain my difficulties with the man.

"Mark my words, Coe," I wagged a finger at him, "if you so much as touch those owls, or their young, I shall strangle you with my bare hands."

Mrs Bennett was as bad in her own way. Superstition over magpies, and an unshakable belief that hedgehogs suckled from cows and turned their milk sour, were but two of her misconceptions of nature. Upon seeing a magpie, she would bob him a curtsey, genuflect, and say, 'Good day to you, Mr Magpie. How is your lady wife today?' She believed this would appease him, and the bird would not open the door to evil, provided she did not look him in the eye.

Word of my encouraging the birds to a safe haven spread quickly. Some thought me odd, I know, but this did not trouble me in the slightest. My difficulty lay with the poachers, for my parkland became a magnet to them. Many a time, I would chase them off.

On one occasion, a would-be thief had the nerve to make for my pea fowl as they roosted in the sycamores on the island. No doubt of the opinion that he was invisible in the fading light, I recognised him as the man who had stolen pheasants' eggs from me in the past. He was well known in the area for his ways, but even if this had not been the case, his demeanour gave him away. He looked about him in all directions at once, hunched shoulders over a coat too big for him, and drooping with many pockets. Without a doubt, his was a poacher's coat if ever I saw one. Rather than chase him off, I approached slowly, and engaged him in conversation, pretending to be a gardener.

"Are you the new keeper?" I said. He turned quickly.

"Aye, I am. The Squire has asked for a pea fowl for the kitchen."

"Then you had better come with me, for there is a fine fat one roosting in the ivy on the old water-gate."

Within two minutes I had enticed him onto the step and shut the great oak doors behind him.

"What's your game?" he shouted, banging his fist on his prison door.

"My game, you thief, is exactly that. Mine."

"You cannot imprison me," he wailed, "I shall jump in the water and drown myself. Let me out and I will never come back. Never."

"Am I to believe the word of a poacher?"

"Let me out, I say."

"I will let you out in due course, thief, but not for a while. You need a little time to reflect upon your ways."

I released him at daybreak, sentence served, and never saw him again.

All birds are welcome here, with no detriment to the orchard or the garden. Contrary to the belief of farmers, the starlings do not trouble the pigeons, which breed most successfully here. Pheasants can be heard in all parts of the wood, and the presence of carrion crows and chattering magpies gives me no cause for concern. The fact that my woodland teems with birds can be attributed to my banning all firearms.

Lord Bathurst wrote to say I was to explore the interior of Madagascar, visit Monomotapa, and the Seychelles Islands. A suitable ship had been found, and all was arranged for me to sail in October. Sadly, the self-same day as I received this letter, I fell to a virulent recurrence of the ague. I never acted so much against my own interests as when I declined the commission. I ought to have gone, and let the ague take its chance, but I made my decision, and have regretted it ever since.

On the days when the ague released its grip, I would take myself onto the lake aboard *Percy*, going ashore here and there to observe the trees and the condition of the woodland in general. This, after all, was key to my desire to encourage the birds. As an experiment, I cut down a willow on the south eastern shoreline of the lake, splitting its stem into twelve.

The consequence? I will write of it later, for it took some time to come to the present result.

Soon afterwards, I received a letter from Mr Edmonstone.

Warrow's Place,
Demerara,
Guiana.
4th September 1812.

My Dear Charles,
I trust you and your family are well, and that your journey was not too arduous. Your decision to leave was a good one, for the difficulties of living in this climate do not change but seem to grow worse. My wife is once again with child, and I wish she would agree to remove to Britain, if only for the boys' education, but feel I cannot force her from her home. Charles and Robert, Eliza and Anne are well, and bring us great joy, although Eliza's weakness of the chest continues to be of concern.
Please write soon and tell me of the experimentation with wourali.

Your good friend,
Charles Edmonstone.

I replied the same day. Perhaps by committing to the pen, I was forced to accept some truths which I would rather have ignored.

Walton Hall,
Walton,
Wakefield,
West Riding of Yorkshire.
1st November, 1812.

Dear Mr Edmonstone,

Thank-you for your letter which arrived today, and for your enquiries regarding wourali. I have deposited an amount with the Veterinary College. Their experiments will be conducted under scientific conditions, and thereby hold credence.

Regrettably, the ague still has the upper hand, and dictates my future. For the time being, I must be content to stay at Walton Hall, and tend the acres here.

You enquire of my family. Mother weeps daily for Christopher, I think he must have been her favourite. Thomas is settled in France where he can freely practise his faith, lucky fellow. He has the double advantage of good health and no responsibilities. William and Edward are still at Stonyhurst. I have it in mind to visit them but fear I would not want to leave.

My sisters, Helen and Isabella, remain under Mother's wing.

The summer has been fair, but I do so miss the warmth of Guiana. Only on the warmest days have I been able to wander barefoot. Now the winter is upon us, we bank the fires up to a roar to compete with the icy blasts.

Please give my regards to your wife. I trust she will be delivered of a healthy child.

I struggle to understand why you would want to leave. Naturally, you are most welcome to come to Walton Hall, but would I prefer that I was at Warrow's Place.

Your friend,
Charles Waterton.

As winter began to release her grip, and the ice slowly melted from the lake, I realised the enormity of the task before me. If the wildlife were to be restored to the numbers of my father's days, there was much to do. The birds were persecuted everywhere other than within my acres.

I could do nothing for the buzzard, the sea eagle or the kite for they would never nest within my acres, but my success with the barn owl encouraged me to assist in other areas. I expected it to take time for the birds to know they were safe within my parkland, but in the event, they came quite quickly. The key was not difficult to turn. All I had to do was provide nesting sites, and my feathered friends were happy to join me.

The birds of Guiana have a great advantage over their English cousins. With no winter chill to strip the trees, any predator, especially *homo sapiens,* has a hard time to spot his prey. My observations, both in the tropics and in the grounds of Stonyhurst, led me to plant yew, holly and laurel, the evergreen stalwarts of England. Within the foliage the blackbird, thrush, sparrow and starling could perch, quite undetected were it not for their singing.

Spring came slowly that year. The thin sunshine of April prompted a frenzy of nest building, nowhere more so than at the lakeside. I have consulted my notebooks, and see I recorded frost remaining in the hedge-bottoms until the 2nd of June. For the first time in many years, the coot, wild duck and goose could raise their chicks with no more than the pike to worry them.

I missed Guiana. Thinking the ague would confine me forever, I missed the freedom of travel, and I missed the hot sun. When the battle rages, the soldier does not know who the victor will be, only that he must fight on. When inclement weather forced me indoors, I had my specimens to work on, my goal being to find the best formula for preservation. Meticulous removal of all the innards and skeleton, be it a bird, mammal, crustacean or insect, was my starting point. Little did I know that it would take me over thirty years to perfect a method to my satisfaction.

Many things had not changed. Old More still chimed the hour, the stables and farm buildings continued to fall into dilapidation. Monsieur Raquedal and Mrs Bennet continued to preside in their respective roles, albeit more slowly than in their younger days. Mother, Helen and Isabella would occasionally travel to Leeds, to visit their dressmaker, or to Wakefield, to make a social visit. Upon their return, Mother would harangue me and the exchange between us would have little variety.

"I found myself apologising for your absence yet again, Charles. You should make more effort in society if your sisters are to find suitable husbands."

"I am sure my presence would detract from the objective, Mother. I am not one for social pleasantries."

She would then flounce off, shouting, "I know!"

The following winter was a harsh one, with frosts day and night for fourteen weeks. I walked to the little island on ice a foot thick, and more. Wild ducks flew around, almost landing, and then taking another circuit, and then another before finally putting their feet to the ice with a great beating of wings as they put the brakes on their skidding. They reminded me of a preacher in church. You think he has finished his sermon, but no! He takes another round, and then another.

Only where the water flowed into the lake could the birds find a place to bathe, or drink, prompting me to instruct my mason to create a stone bath for them near the house, and a maid to fill it with warm water each morning. When spring came, I turned my attention to the lake.

Centuries of sludge had built up and the water quality was suffering due to the flow having become inadequate. Silt, and vast quantities of mud and weed, meant the fish were having a hard time of it, especially the larger species. The water egressed the lake over a weir and by-wash, so I opened the sluice and drained off thousands of gallons in the hope that by changing a percentage of the water, the problem would be solved. I employed Mr Rhodes of Horbury to remove the mud, paying him sixpence a yard to remove 45,000 yards of the stuff.

When walking in the parkland, my mind would often drift abroad, and to the time of day in different parts. Old More was good enough to tell the time in England, and since the men of longitude had set the meridian in Greenwich, the time could be calculated easily enough for any part of the world. The same sun shone on us all, and it struck me that a sundial could be moved to show the time at different degrees of longitude. Father had told me of a garden in Liège where, hundreds of years ago, several dials had been set by Father Francis Line, to do this very thing. With this in mind, I visited George Boulby, a skilled mason who had a workshop in the neighbouring village of Crofton. I had heard he was a craftsman, and not a simple builder of walls. His fine touch could carve the most intricate pattern or statue.

"I can make as many dials as you like, Squire. It will be the setting of the gnomons that will be the clever part."

"I thought, perhaps they could be set atop a millstone, all around the edge. What do you think?"

He scratched the back of his neck as if to concentrate his thoughts and beckoned me to follow him outside. "Come with me if you will, Squire, out the back. I have some dials already made. We could have a go at setting them up."

Fortunately, the sun was shining, enabling us to set six dials. We had been positioning for Paris and Rome, Malaga and Demerara when he suddenly sat down and threw his cap to the floor.

"What is it? Are you not well? I asked."

"I think I have it, Squire."

"Have what? Are your innards out of sorts? I could let you have some—"

"Pardon my interrupting, but there is nothing wrong with my innards. 'Tis my head that is slow."

"How so?"

"What I need to do, Squire, is to make one sundial, like a big ball, but cut with triangles. Each facet will face the sun at a different angle."

"Is that possible? I mean to work the times onto one piece of stone?"

"I reckon it is. Leave me to work on it."

"Tell me, Mr Boulby, who taught you your craft?"

"No-one, sir. I am self-taught."

"Surely man, you must have been to school."

"No, sir. My father taught me to read and write, but I am not educated. I just work things out in my head." I took a liking to the man, I even felt an affinity with him, despite the differences in our lives. His skill and pride in his work was evident from the intricately carved pieces in his workshop. George Boulby was a very intelligent man.

"You will understand, Squire, it being set, the sundial would not give the different times all at once. Those parts to the north side will never *cast* a shadow, for they will be forever *in* shadow."

When I say that Boulby was intelligent, I feel it does not adequately describe the man. He was a genius. He hewed the sundial from a great globular stone, facing it with twenty perfectly edged equilateral triangles, each set with a gnomon and carved in the neatest fashion with the name of a place I had either visited, or hoped to visit. Not only place names, but the points of the compass and the equinox are all neatly displayed. It is a handsome piece and stands on the island. He asked for five pounds, but I paid him twenty guineas.

Word of my sundial created much interest locally, and I was happy to show it to anyone who cared to make an appointment, especially if it were a sunny day and I could properly demonstrate its value. On one such occasion a local solicitor, Mr Robert Carr, visited. After admiring Boulby's work, we took a walk across the fields, each armed with a gun in the hope of bagging a rabbit or two. I showed him a beech tree where a woodpecker had been feasting on some grubs, foolishly reloading my gun as I talked. I had rammed the paper down on the powder when the ramrod, which was armed with brass at both ends, passed right through my forefinger between the knuckle and the first joint. I could tell it had not broken the bone, but the paper had ignited the powder and followed through. It did not hurt in the slightest, despite being as black as soot. The bone, now perfectly visible, was still intact. We went to a nearby cottage where my tenant, Jane Price, stood in the doorway. "Mistress Price, do you have a pot of water on your fire?" She saw my blackened hand and bid me enter.

"Sit you down there, Squire," she pointed to a chair. She poured water into an enamel jug from a simmering pot, adding sufficient cold to avoid a scald. She put a bowl under my hand and Robert poured water through the wound until it had washed away the marks of the gunpowder. Ruptured tendons were hanging down like tangled string.

"Do you have a strip of linen?" I asked. "I need to bind it up." Mistress Price provided the necessary. I collected up the ruptured tendons, giving the finger its original shape as best I could, and with Robert's assistance, bound up the wound. Under my instruction, he bound a tourniquet on the other arm. Using my penknife for a lancet, I let 22 ounces of blood as a precaution against a fever.

Upon our return to Walton Hall, I introduced Robert Carr to my mother and sisters. Mother could not leave a stranger alone with her daughters, and so I was able to escape her fussing, and employed the assistance of Mrs Bennett to apply a very large poultice. I renewed it twice every day and am pleased to report that the inflammation never extended beyond the knuckles, and in time I recovered full use of the finger. With hindsight, the entire matter had a most fortuitous outcome, for some years later Robert Carr married my sister, Helen.

A visitor arrived that year, sent to Walton Hall by Earl Percy of Northumberland. She stayed for twenty-five years. I write of the fourth donkey, the Jill who had suffered so much in the name of science. A year had passed since the experiment at the London Veterinary College, and her health had suffered as a result of her contribution to science. The Earl, in his wisdom, thought she deserved a peaceful retirement, and had her sent to me at his personal expense. I named her Wouralia, and she lived on the island.

As well as planting the evergreens, I had planted two acres with saplings of the oak and larch. They were healthy specimens and had put down their roots. As spring warmed the air of their third year, they budded, and some had burst their first leaves when disaster struck. Thanks to my neighbours' wanton destruction of the birds of prey, the balance of nature was all awry. A plague of field mice, a staple food of the owls and hawks, killed all but a few of my saplings. The mice gnawed the bark so severely, that the trees bled to death, their sap running as if cut by a lancet. Many holly bushes and the apple trees in the orchard also suffered badly. The mice were everywhere despite the efforts of the cats. Then they were gone, as quickly as they had arrived, their battle won, and the devastated battlefield deserted.

I spent Christmas with William and Edward at Stonyhurst. Oh, the joy of those walls, and oh, the sadness at leaving. I spent hours with Father Clifford, sitting cross legged on the rug, transporting me back to the hallowed days of my youth, telling him of my travels, and how I had followed his advice.

"The rats are still with us, Charles," he smiled.

"The rats will always be with us, Father."

"Do you remember your official title?"

"I do. Rat Catcher, Foumart Killer and Football Maker."

He told me of the sudden death of Joe Bowren, the year before. Edward and William had not thought to tell me, but then, they would not have known of my friendship with Joe.

I confess a tear welled as I left. The sight of Longridge Fell brought memories of my ramblings, of hiding in the pig litter, and other adventures.

William told me of his intention to join the Society of Jesus and remain at Stonyhurst as a Master. My youngest brother, Edward, was drawn to botany.

"Charles Bernard, do you not know how it grieves your mother?" Mrs Bennett ranted. She had ambushed me on my way out. Over break-fast, I had told Mother that I was now quite free of the ague, which naturally pleased her, but then told of my intention to travel to Africa, and she burst into tears, running from the room.

"Mrs Bennett, she does not understand my need to explore."

"Neither do I. You have an estate to run. Why do you need to go off to these dangerous places? Is it not enough to be almost killed by the ague? Do you have to try your chance again?"

"So many questions, Mrs Bennett. I am touched by your concern." She strutted away, her stick tapping on the stone flags as she disappeared into her rooms. I no longer expected any family member to understand my wanderlust. Sir Joseph Banks had invited me to join an expedition that was to sail up the River Congo, and I set off for London later that day.

Preparations were well advanced when Sir Joseph received a letter. I happened to be present at the time, sitting opposite his desk. His face darkened as he read.

"I am informed," he said, "that the steam ship that is to take the expedition up the Congo is not powerful enough to make its way upstream."

"Is there no alternative vessel? No other ship at all?"

"It seems not." He lay the letter on his desk, sighing deeply. "I fear the expedition will be a total failure." Seeing my disappointment, he wheeled his chair around to me, and put his hand on my shoulder. "My friend, you shall not go to Africa. The entire enterprise is doomed."

"Will it go ahead?"

"It seems so." He paused, his eyes narrowed in thought. "I wonder, Charles, would you stay in London for a few days? I would like you to speak to the scientists who are to make this journey."

"What would you have me say to them?"

"Tell them of the dangers of the tropical climate, and how to survive it."

Naturally, I agreed. In my little speech, I warned against sleeping in wet clothes and to avoid standing in swampy water, telling how these circumstances often precipitate an attack of the ague. I impressed the need to abstain from any form of alcohol, and of my tried and tested remedies. Having fulfilled Sir Joseph's request, I bade him farewell, and returned to Yorkshire.

CHAPTER FIFTEEN

Further Explorations.

Mother was as delighted as I was disappointed, but not for long. I told her I was going back to South America.

"Can you pay no heed to what happened to your brother, your cousin, and your uncle?"

"I pay every heed, Mother. That is why I have survived all that the tropics can throw at a traveller."

"But you have responsibilities here, Charles. There are your sisters to consider, and myself. Walton Hall Estate is your home."

"This is my ancestral home, that is true, but it is equally true that I feel more at home in the forests of South America. You are more able than I to run this house, Mother."

The battle raged on. Mother pleaded with me to stay. My sisters were more understanding.

"Go, Charles," Helen said. "Mother will calm down eventually."

"Are you sure?" I don't really know why I asked this question, because I was going to go, no matter what. "Write to me at Mr Edmonstone's address. No doubt I shall call there at some time."

"I shall. It will placate mother a little if she thinks she can contact you."

On the 2nd of March in the year 1816, I sailed from Liverpool on board *The Indian,* under the command of Captain Balberney, for the port of Pernambuco, Brazil.

I passed the time in concentrated observation of the inhabitants of the water, most particularly the hundreds of little flying fish. These creatures can enter the world of birds for two or three hundred yards at a time, after which they must dip back into their other world for a moment, the intense heat having dried their scaly wings. Shooting from the water with fantastic speed, they do not flap their wings, but glide. The stronger the wind, the longer their flight. They are pursued by the cunning dolphins, who watch their flight from below. On several occasions I saw the dolphins propel their body out of the water, never once missing their prey, and sometimes awaiting the moment when their flying food dropped beneath the surface. One unfortunate flying fish landed on deck and I was able to observe the wings, which are not wings at all, but fins, and quite out of proportion with the body. Stunned by the fall, he beat the deck with his tail, and died, quite unable to sustain himself for any time without water. This particular fish was quite large for the species, about fourteen inches in length. To describe the taste, I would say the flying fish is much like herring.

Dolphins were often with us, as if enjoying the company of the ship. The sailors, having set the sails to the fair breeze, set about fishing. This is no idle feat. The sailor has no rod and line for the strength of a dolphin, but a staff, weighted with lead at one end, and barbed with five spikes at the other. He then goes to the limit of the bowsprit, where he awaits the moment when his dinner passes beneath him. He heaves the staff, and if successful, a great shout goes up, and his fellows help him haul a meal of fresh fish aboard. In death the dolphin is like no other creature I have ever observed. A rapid shimmer of all the rainbow crosses and re-crosses his smooth body in a myriad of colour, right up to his last moment.

Naturally, I was relieved to see the equatorial coastline of South America. The shout of 'Land-ho!' is music to the ears of sailor and passenger alike. We sailed past the estuaries of the Essequibo and Demerara to our destination. Pernambuco lies on the easternmost point of South America, and was a delight to approach. Coconut trees lined the shore, softening the landscape. Wooded hills behind the town beckoned me to explore beyond. Ships of all nations crowded the harbour, its position naturally protected by a reef. The narrow entrance posed no challenge to the experienced Captain Balberney, and we were soon safely sheltered from the buffeting waves.

The town had at that time a population of some fifty thousand souls and was a chaotic place. The view from the ship did not match up to close inspection. The houses were an eclectic assemblage, reflecting the tastes of many nationalities. The palace of the Captain General had once been the Jesuit College. I learned to my horror that the priests had been ordered out by the Portuguese, whose flag now flew from its rooftop. As a result of this short-sighted decision the poor had lost their only opportunity for an education. Animal and human litter fouled the streets, and nobody seemed to care, accepting it as inevitable. A few houses had been recently white-washed, but most were stained and mouldy, adding to the neglected air. Due to its exposed coastal position, Pernambuco was never without a breeze whipping around the corners, blowing the aforementioned unsavoury matter every which way to irritate the eyes and nose. I suppose the people had become accustomed to it, and after I had been there for a week or so, I admit I noticed it less.

With little desire to stay in the town, I took myself to the village of Monteiro, which lies a mile or two from the coast on the banks of a river. Having secured lodgings with an Irishman by the name of Dennis Kearney and his good lady, I spent a pleasant few weeks in the hinterland. On the very first day I bagged a very fine specimen of the troupiale bird, well known for its rich colours and delightful song.

One of my favourite haunts was an abandoned orchard. The long grass and neglected trees were a haven for wildlife. One day, when I was walking through the orchard, my attention was drawn to a group of six or seven blackbirds, all bobbing and fluttering on the lower branches of an orange tree. The high-pitched tone of a grasshopper competed with their fussing. I approached quietly and stretched out my hand, hoping my stealth would ensure a specimen without breaking its delicate legs. Imagine my surprise, on realising my mistake. This was no grasshopper. A rattlesnake raised his head, and only an instantaneous spring backwards prevented fatal consequences. I withdrew to a safe distance and after a while the snake emerged from under the tree and made off towards a wooded area. He passed over an area of scrubland, showing his length of eight feet.

I have encountered many snakes, both before and after this incident, and can say with absolute authority that they do not bite unless accidently touched, or otherwise provoked, as I had unwittingly done on this occasion.

The environs of Pernambuco are very pretty and there is much to commend the area. Country houses abound, giving evidence of the profitability of farming. Sugar plantations, palm trees, coconut trees, orange and lemon groves, and all the fruits peculiar to Brazil are there in the greatest abundance.

During my stay with Mr and Mrs Kearney I shot fifty-seven specimens, but it was time to move on and leave behind the orange and lemon groves. The rainy season was about to commence, and the birds were beginning their moult, making poor showings for the taxidermist. I bade farewell to my hosts, thanking them for their kindness and attention.

At any other time of year, I would have hired a horse, and enjoyed the forty days it would take to travel along the coastal road. The rains, however, dictated a more pragmatic view. My personal comfort was not the deciding factor, but the risk to my specimens was too great, and I therefore turned to the sea, bringing difficulties of a different sort. Many ships sailed the coast, but the vast majority of these were slave ships. The law had prevented importing Africans from their own country, but trade between owners remained unrestricted. I eventually secured a passage on board a Portuguese brig destined for Cayenne.

A drunken captain makes for lack of discipline. My preference for remaining on deck kept me away from the worst conditions I have ever seen. With ropes scattered around to trip the unwary and deck boards that had not seen a scrubbing brush for years, I was obliged to take up residence on top of a hen coop. Bitten by fleas and other flying bugs, the fourteen-day voyage was a testing endurance.

Whilst not impressed by the seamanship of the crew, I will grant they merited their countrymen's reputation for fishing, and I ate well. One evening, four sharks were sighted in the wake of the vessel. The sailors caught them all, and they tasted very good.

As the town of Cayenne came into sight, an island known as the Constable took my attention. Too small and rocky to be of commercial value, it offered a safe haven for birds. Never before had I seen so many nests on such a small acreage. The island is no more than half a mile in diameter with a central, tower-like rock. Egrets, spoonbills, scarlet curlews, rosy flamingos, the pelican and the phaeton all knew the value of the Constable.

Cayenne is very different to Pernambuco. The inhabitants were hospitable enough but there was no gaiety, no balls, no laughter rang in the streets of this once flamboyant town. Its charm seemed to be mingled with a perpetual sadness, a loss, as if it grieved for itself. Buffeted between the rule of France, Portugal, Holland and England for long enough, Cayenne had been settled under the flag of Portugal for seven years when I visited. Their navy had, in a joint effort with Captain Yeo of HMS Confiance, put paid to French rule.

Victor Hugues, the once iron-handed and haughty French governor, lived quietly with his four daughters. Having been stripped of all his honours and under arrest in his own house, he could only hope for the day when the tricolour would once again be raised.

During my stay, I called at Cayenne's most famous plantation, La Gabrielle. At the time of my visit, this most prosperous of all the plantations in the region boasted no less than twenty thousand clove trees, along with those of the nutmeg and cinnamon. The neat rows, with each tree set thirty feet from its neighbour and topped at twenty-five feet in height, stretched as far as the eye could see, but I did not tarry.

When I left the shores of England my plan had been to sail up the Amazon, towards the source of the Essequibo, here to examine the Crystal Mountains, and search for Lake Parima. Once again, Mother Nature had other plans. Firstly, the lack of a suitable ship had forced me to Cayenne, and secondly, a strong current forced me to make another compromise. A Portuguese sloop had left four weeks previously and was still a mere half way to the Amazon. A traveller is forever at the command of the weather. Deciding against such a tedious and uncertain voyage, even if I had found a ship, I boarded an American vessel bound for Georgetown.

Years had passed since my ague ridden body had left this town, and much had changed, but unlike Pernambuco and Cayenne, there was an air of prosperity. The streets were wide and elevated, made of brick setts, with brick lined trenches to take away the effluent. A refreshing sea breeze added to the very pleasant atmosphere. The shops rivalled those of London for choice and quality of goods. Cleanliness and luxury shone from the well-patronised hôtels.

However, not everything had changed for the better. Old Hercules was dead, mourned by the honest, and buried under the flagstaff in accordance with his wishes, and where the Union Flag now flew. Many said his efforts to rid the town of corruption had worn him out, and with the job only half done. Chaos and misery reigned in the market place, with slaves being bought and sold with no more respect than was shown for a carcass of beef. The import ban had made things worse in many ways and had put up the prices. Blinded by the monster they had created, the owners plundered on. Any man with a modicum of intelligence could see that it would not last, that the economy was built on slavery. There were 70,000 slaves in Demerara in 1816. These sons of Africa had produced, in that one year, forty-four million pounds of sugar, two million gallons of rum, two million pounds of coffee, and four million pounds of cotton.

I acquired a masted canoe and other essential supplies, and as before, I hired six Indians.

Naturally, I called at Warrow's Place. There were letters waiting for me from my sisters and mother, the latter predictably demanding my return to Yorkshire.

Mr and Mrs Edmonstone were their usual genial selves. Their delightful daughters, Eliza and Anne, and the new addition, Little Helen, were the sunshine in their lives. Anne would not leave my side and with her tiny hand in mine we walked to the creek each morning to watch the waterfowl and feed them with little pieces of softened cassava bread.

As on my previous expedition, Mr Edmonstone lent me a slave, and I set off for the interior with no objective other than to indulge in the delights of nature.

Further to my list of essentials as described in chapter thirteen, I offer the following advice to the would-be traveller in the forests of Guiana.

Do not expect to eat as one would in a city.

Forget high seasoned dishes, wines and delicacies, depend on your Indian or yourself for fish and game.

Take cassava bread, but do not eat it after a week, or if it has been wet.

Depend upon the skill and diet of the Indian. You are in his world, so eat his diet, and adopt his lifestyle.

I always found the Indians to be kind to their children and extremely mild and gentle in temperament. A primitive race, they wear no clothes. Some travellers and colonists call them lazy. This is because the Indian has no desire to adopt the European lifestyle, being content to live his own simple life. Once he has hunted sufficiently to feed his family, the Indian has no thought of killing for entertainment. He has no need for money, for there are no markets or milliners' shops for his wife and daughters to frequent. There are no roads to maintain, no poor to support, no army or navy to supply, and no taxes to pay. During daylight hours, if he is not hunting, he will be making his arrows and performing repairs to his bow or fishing tackle whilst lying in his hammock.

In contrast, once an Englishman has come into fortune, he ceases to work, and lies in bed for half the morning. A servant helps him to dress, and he spends his day eating to excess, with perhaps a drive in his carriage in the afternoon.

Now tell me, dear reader, who is the lazy man?

The Indians were happy to show me how to use the blow pipe. My command of their language had improved to the point where I was able to question the leader of my little group on the subject of an antidote. Various theories had come to my attention, such as standing up to the mouth in water, or a generous dose of rum or sugar cane juice, or a mouthful of salt.

"I had a brother," he said, "who aimed his blow pipe at a monkey. He missed it and the arrow descended and hit him."

"What became of him?" I asked, although I knew he must have died because he spoke of him in the past tense.

"He lay down, and said, 'I shall never bend this bow again.' Then he put his poison box and bow and arrow beside him and died." There was no point in my asking how long it took him to die. The Indians do not count the minutes of the day, such accuracy is of no matter to them. "If there were a cure," he continued, "we would carry it with us all the time." To this day, all we know of wourali is that it kills quickly, and very gently, and that there is no antidote or proven medical use.

Each night I suspended the sheet between two trees, at a sloping angle. The fabric had been painted to make it waterproof, and thereby provide protection from the pelting rain and the heavy dew. When the inevitable ague returned without the companionship of dysentery or other internal inflammation, I did not take to the lancet, but relied upon the cinchona bark. When these annoyances presented as a pair, I would treat the internal matter first, this being potentially fatal, and not to be trifled with. I admit this gave the ague full leash, but after I had let twenty ounces or so, and the internal inflammation had subsided, I would take the cinchona bark, and soon be back on my feet, albeit somewhat unsteadily. Only when the partnership of the two became unbearable, did I resort to laudanum.

Experience taught me to tread lightly over rough ground and through the briars. Snakes were certainly to be considered and although defensive rather than aggressive, only constant scrutiny, both of the ground and the branches above, prevents the traveller from accidentally offending these creatures of the forest.

Insect bites are inevitable and can cause fever. Otherwise they can be irritating and even painful to a greater or lesser degree. Scratching is to be avoided, as it can turn the merely irritating into a pustule.

I stayed in the forests and savannahs for six months, the happiest of men, observing the habits of the birds and collecting specimens. I didn't use my gun, preferring to hone my skills with the blow pipe, which caused little or no damage to my quarry, and thereby procured the best chance for a perfect result in preservation.

Upon my return to Warrow's Place, I was not so badly affected by the ague as after my previous wandering. I stayed only long enough to preserve my collection of birds and mammals sufficiently for the journey. Mr Edmonstone was a great help with this, and we discussed our latest experiments with bichloride of mercury, and the perfect state of his top hat!

Further letters from Mother all demanded my return, and as I was due a short respite from the tropics, I left on the 6th of April with more than two hundred excellent specimens.

The journey passed pleasantly enough, until winter seas forced me below deck. All sails were furled, with the exception of a staysail. The captain and first mate took turns at the wheel as the Atlantic threw her weight at us and heavy clouds glowered. Palpable relief on entering the River Mersey resonated throughout the ship, but the damp chill of the English winter combined with the ague to rattle me with the shivers.

CHAPTER SIXTEEN

My Method, and a Friendship Renewed.

During the summer of 1817, I conducted further experiments on skin preservation using a variety of chemical and herbal preparations. Most proved ineffective as I suspected they would. My determination to develop a method to create specimens in a life-like manner dominated my work. The stuffed product looked just that. Stuffed. In other words, not at all life-like, and therefore not to my liking. I wanted to preserve the birds and mammals in such a manner that anyone who looked upon them would see them as I had, when they were alive and bobbing about in the forests. I needed a method that would enable me to create the shape and pose of a creature, be it a bird, a snake, a mammal, fish, crustacean or any other. I pondered the matter for some weeks. In the end, my old friend Joe Bowren came to the rescue. Not literally, of course, but his instruction in transforming a pig's bladder into a football, and Mr Edmonstone's knowledge of bichloride of mercury, provided the inspiration for what became my preferred method.

Unlike many taxidermists, I have dedicated many hours observing and noting in detail the habits of wildlife. Poorly preserved specimens, totally unrepresentative in appearance of the living creature, abound in the drawing rooms and museums of those who purport to be experts. In criticising such shortcomings, my intentions are to inspire improvement, but my comments are badly received. Over the years I have written articles for journals and given lectures at scientific meetings, all with the intention of improving standards. Sadly, my technique, although accepted as superior, is too lengthy a process for those who stuff for a living.

My method is thus.

Firstly, I thoroughly clean the specimen. No trace of flesh or bone must remain. The skin is then immersed in a solution of equal quantities of highly rectified spirit and water, together with half a tablespoonful of finely powdered bichloride of mercury to each quart of the spirituous solution. Depending on the thickness of the skin, it must be soaked for between three and nine hours.

Next, I place the skin before a fire, and partially dry it, turning it regularly to make sure it dries evenly. When still pliable, I fill out the body and head with finely cut chaff or sawdust to a roughly natural shape. All incisions are finely sewn up, and I put the specimen in a cardboard box of suitable size. Within the box, I support the specimen with packing to make it adopt the natural attitude of the living animal. Daily manipulation is essential. I also use a board with threads attached to the creature, especially the little birds, until a natural posture is attained. Depending upon size, it must be allowed to dry slowly over weeks or months, until such time as it is entirely stiffened.

When completely dry, I remove the chaff by a small window flap incision, thus leaving the skin entirely hollow and self-supporting. The process is simple, but requires patience. It is my belief that my specimens will still be bright, and pleasing the eye, long after I have departed this world.

The summer passed pleasantly enough. Mother complained bitterly about everything. I blamed her rheumatism.

"Please remove your stinking dead bodies from the house, Charles. There is such a mess everywhere."

"Not everywhere, Mother. And they do not stink."

"Then what is that awful smell?"

"That is when they are drying, and it is not that bad."

"There are boxes all over the place, bottles of poison, and pickling birds. Why don't you take them to the stables?"

"Because, there is no fire in the stables." She glared at me as if I had said there was no fire in hell. "A matter which I intend to rectify."

My lack of punctuality and my going barefoot were the cause of great irritation to her. Helen and Isabella felt the lash of her tongue for equally trifling matters, but I took the brunt of it. Only Monsieur Raquedal was able to calm her. The old priest held his place in the household like woodworm, burrowing into every corner of our lives. He had asked about my travels, and the state of religion in South America. When I told him of the way the Jesuits had been ousted from Pernambuco, he suggested I request an audience with Pope Pius VII, to pass on the news.

"I expect His Holiness knows, don't you think?"

"Perhaps. But first-hand knowledge is always welcome. You could tell of the state of religion as a whole, or the lack of it."

He was right of course. The native Indians had no religion, and yet their lives were more peaceful and content than any I had known, notwithstanding the European invasions of their lands. I could hardly expect Monsieur Raquedal to understand, let alone the Pope.

Since my days at Stonyhurst, I had corresponded somewhat infrequently with James Alexander. He had followed a career in the Royal navy and become a captain, the rank being as high as a Catholic could rise. Along with Stephen Clothier, Tom Lorrimer and Percy Fitzgerald, he had been one of my closest school friends and I was delighted to hear from him.

Dear Charles,

I trust you are well, and not suffering too much from all the tropics have to offer. I too am to travel, but only within Europe. An Italian winter is much more pleasant than an English one, and with the war finally over, I shall make the journey that I would like to have made some years ago. If you are not in some distant forest, maybe you will join me. I sail from Hull on October 28th and will look out for you at the quayside.

Your friend,
James.

His short letter rescued me from the winter frosts. At Monsieur Raquedal's suggestion, I scribbled a few pages about the treatment of the

Jesuits of Pernambuco, with the intention of delivering my observations to the Vatican in person.

I left instruction with Coe to the effect that there must be no boats on the lake until after May Day. He frowned at me.

"May I ask why not, Squire?"

"The birds and fish will need a chance to breed. I want no fishing from the banks either. I expect I shall be back by then, but if not, remember what I have said."

"In my opinion, it is the pike that do the fishing."

"You miss my point," I said, "the pike don't take fry."

He took off his cap and scratched his head. "If you say so, then that's it then. No fishing."

I had not been to Hull since sailing to Malaga with Christopher. We had been so young, so inexperienced. The tide had ebbed and flowed many thousands of times since that day. On the one hand, it did not seem so long ago, and yet on the other, it was a lifetime since my brother had stood at my side. James greeted me as if I were *his* long-lost brother, grasping my hand and shaking it until I thought my shoulder would be jolted from its socket.

"Charles! I am delighted to see you. The journey will be a joy. I know it will," his face suddenly dropped, "but you have travelled so much. Maybe it will be a chore for you."

"An adventure, James. The furthest I have ever travelled by road is from Yorkshire to Southampton."

"Really?" The years fell away, and we were a pair of schoolboys set upon adventure.

"Yes. Sea voyages are a different thing altogether."

"What do you do all day? On board ship, that is. I am always on duty when sailing, so to be a passenger is something new for me."

"I look out for dolphins and flying fish, but enough of that. Are you game to sleep on deck? What does the captain say of our chances of a smooth passage?"

We sailed to Rotterdam and stayed for one night. James availed himself of a brothel. I had no interest in spending money on women and so rather than take advantage of the carnal offerings, I found a stable and hired a comfortable carriage and four in readiness for the following day.

"Damn this frost and fog, Charles." James rubbed the window with his handkerchief. "I can't see a thing."

"We can only hope it will clear, at least for our return journey." Thus thwarted of any appreciation of the landscape, we were thrown into reminiscing about our years at Stonyhurst. Games of cat and mouse with the prefects, Hareng's cooking, football and rats dominated our conversations as we rattled along. At my behest, we visited Liège, where we walked the Rue des Jésuites Anglais, and up the steps to the entrance door of the former monastery. The building had been transformed into a hospital, but thankfully we had no need of its services. Three sides of a square surrounded a central garden, although perhaps it would be more accurate to call it a stretch of grass. This was the garden of sundials which my father had told me about. James and I made close inspection.

"They were designed by Father Francis Line." I said.

"He didn't go to Stonyhurst did he?"

"No, no." I laughed. "He was a priest here before it was a college. At least I think that is what Father told me."

"Look, Charles, the stonework is crumbling."

"Genius, pure genius," I said, "these dials show the time in different parts of the world."

"Well, they would if the sun were out. Clever though, I agree with you there. He must have been quite a mathematician."

"I had thought to replicate the idea at Walton Hall, but a local mason designed an alternative. I'll show it to you when you visit. You will visit Walton Hall, won't you, James?"

"Certainly, I shall, and thank-you, Charles."

"You will have to meet Mother, but my sisters will compensate." He thought it amusing, but I was serious.

We dallied in the town for a week or so before continuing on to Nancy, Dijon, and Lyon, travelling in more sturdy but less well sprung post-coaches. Every town and village boasted a pretty church, as England had before the days of the Old Goat. I attended Mass whenever and wherever I could. James was less interested.

"Once a week is enough for me."

"What about the Confessional?"

He shook his head. "We would never get to Italy." I could not help but laugh. We were such opposites, and I see now that that is why we made such good companions.

The landscape of the Alps is like no other. Snowstorms threatened to prevent our passage, but we were in expert hands. Our driver screwed his eyes to a cloud-laden sky, licking his lips, as if tasting the air.

"Deux jours, Messieurs, et nous allons traverser les Alpes sans trop d'encombres."

In two days we would set off and, according to our driver, would cross the Alps without too much difficulty.

"Just think, Charles," James said, "in less than two weeks we shall be in Rome, and feel the warmth of a Mediterranean winter."

"If I survive this freezing weather." I pointed to the mountains. "Can you imagine how cold it must be up there?"

He slapped me on the back with force, causing me to stumble. "We're not going over the top, Charles."

I took little comfort from his words but in the event we were well serviced with blankets, and Mount Cenis Pass had as good a road as could be expected. Other than birds of prey, I saw no wildlife, and found it hard to imagine how anything survived in such inhospitable terrain. Before descending to the coastal plain, we spent a night at Lake Cenis where even I could not help but admire its frozen beauty.

Our hôtel in Rome was most conveniently placed in the Via Appia. James and I set about exploring the city while our trunks were unpacked by a valet. A visitor to Rome can do no other than enthuse about the ancient architecture, while statues, fountains and memorials vie to be the most elaborate.

The busy markets teem with every sort of foodstuff. Vendors of pots and pans, knives and other kitchenware all bear witness to the Italian love of food. There is no distinction between birds for the table and the birds of the air. Italians eat everything from a sparrow to a swan.

Our second day stands out in my memory. I had delivered my missive to the Cardinal Secretary, and we were admiring the dome of St Peter's Basilica, when I felt a tap upon my shoulder.

"Shall we climb it? There must be a wonderful view. I am told there are five hundred and thirty-seven steps." I turned to see a man wearing the uniform of a captain in First Royal Lancashire Militia. He spoke with the confidence of a man used to giving orders. I didn't recognise him at first, and then a boyish grin spread across his face. I had not seen Edwin Jones since the day I left Tudhoe. Gone was the stammer and all trace of shyness. We pretended to box one another.

"Any chance of an introduction?" James asked, bringing us back to the present.

"Apologies. May I introduce Captain Edwin Jones, a friend from my first school in County Durham. Edwin, this is James Alexander, a friend and fellow pupil from my days at Stonyhurst." They shook hands. "I am well defended, it seems, but before you two start talking of military matters, I return to your question, Edwin. "We don't climb steps, Edwin. We climb!" He paled a little. "Are you game for it?" We were fit young men, with our nerves in excellent trim, ready for a challenge.

"I think you misunderstand me, Charles. The steps only go to the base of the dome."

"Then what?"

"Then there is a little door, through which there are the most wonderful views of Rome."

"I think we could climb a little higher, Edwin."

"I'm game! When you taught me how to climb trees at Tudhoe, I never thought—but if anyone can do it, we can!"

"You don't mean...?"

James looked incredulous. Edwin and I exchanged a conspiratorial look.

We did our best to look interested in the interior of St Peter's. The three of us ascended the steps with other tourists, and the view from the base of the dome was indeed wonderful. Edwin and I, however, were more interested in the structure of the roof.

"Come Edwin, before we change our minds."

"Don't do it, Charles." James' voice was full of anxiety. "I beg you, as a friend." He grabbed my sleeve. Edwin and I laughed.

"Surely you know Charles has never turned down a challenge?"

"I didn't know it was a challenge?" James hissed.

"Neither did I," I said, "but it is now. Come, Edwin, there is bound to be somewhere we can make a start."

The climb was not so difficult as might be imagined. The ribs of the dome provided plenty of hand and footholds, and we were soon at the top, where we ascended the cross. Not satisfied that we had reached the highest point, I then climbed thirteen feet higher, up the lightning conductor. I don't know why, but I placed my gloves there, as if a calling card. No-one had had such a view of the city, other than the builders of the dome. The River Tiber, Ancient Rome and the Colosseum, the Pantheon, and the entire city spread beneath us. The crowds in St Peter's Square were staring and pointing at us. I tried to identify James, but without success.

After our descent, we employed another skill learned at Tudhoe, outwitting the Papal Cabinieri Corps as we had outwitted the prefects. Mingling with the crowds, James caught up with us as we headed towards the bridge.

"You're mad! The pair of you. You'll never have an audience with the Pope now, Charles."

"Why not? We haven't been caught."

James gave a great sigh of exasperation. Edwin and I fell about laughing.

"Where to now, Charles?" Edwin asked. I cast my eyes about, and they fell on the Castel de St Angelo, sitting there in all its fortified history. The statue of St Angelo broke the skyline with wings spread, ready for flight.

"No, Charles, you mustn't." James had read me like a book. "If you are caught, I shall deny any association with you."

"Just like St Peter, then?" Edwin was helpless with laughter, while James was fit to burst with frustrated rage.

"Come on, Edwin. As long as James threatens to be Peter, and does not turn into Judas, we stand a chance."

The brickwork of the Castel made for easy climbing, and we were soon sitting on the guardian angel's wings. We waved to the crowd, and to give an extra show, I stood on St Angelo's head, balancing on one leg. A great cheer went up.

Pope Pius II, it transpired, did not appreciate our humour. He was concerned that the gloves might diminish the effectiveness of the conductor and ordered they be removed, but Edwin and I had the last laugh, because no-one could be found who was prepared to retrieve them. Upon the orders of the Pope, we climbed up again, further entertaining the crowds.

James had been right in one respect. I was denied my audience with His Holiness, but not because of my climbing. I refused to wear any jacket other than my blue swallowtail coat. I argued that my coat had significance and I would not be dissuaded from wearing my uniform from a Catholic School in Protestant England.

"Are you not terribly disappointed? James asked.

"No. You know I am not one for pomp and ceremony, and there is enough of that in the Vatican to fill the heavens. Although I am slightly disappointed insomuch as His Holiness is unlikely to read my essay. It took some writing."

Not all of Rome shunned us. We were invited to a society dinner as 'The Famous Climbing Duo.' James and Edwin tried and failed to persuade me to buy a dinner jacket for the occasion. I have never owned one, and never will, but James and Edwin were equally obstinate in their view that my school uniform was not acceptable.

"What about this?" I showed them my jacket from my commission in Guiana.

"What do you think, Edwin?" James said.

"Well, I suppose he *is* entitled to wear it."

"Do you have the epaulettes?" James demanded, speaking as if I were a child who had lost his gloves.

"No. Does it matter?"

"Of course it matters, Charles. You look half dressed. I have some spare ones you can borrow."

I don't think anyone gave two hoots as to what I was wearing. Edwin and I were stared at in equal measure, our daring having made us famous for a day or two.

I preferred to rise early, before the streets became crowded. I have never had much need for sleep, and Mass was celebrated at the Church of the Gesù at half past four o'clock each morning, which suited me well. Afterwards, it became my habit to watch the stall holders set up the markets, and then I would meet with James and Edwin for breakfast in a little restaurant just off the Piazza Navona. Despite his military career, Edwin was still an artist at heart, and frequently had his sketch book with him. He left Rome a week or so later, being due back with the Lancashires. James and I travelled south to Tuscany, and beyond. In the Cascini Gardens of Florence the sheer numbers of nesting birds, right there in the hustle and bustle of the city, was a sight to behold. Even pheasants, that species so much the target of the gunman, were there in number. It dawned upon me that the reason for their success lay in the ivy. It trailed everywhere, providing shelter and camouflage in abundance. I think I could have wandered there forever. The climate of an Italian winter suits a skinny frame like mine. When it rains, it does so with force, and is over and done with. There is no such thing as damp air or drizzle.

I was in no hurry to leave, but James had to return to his naval duties, and so by the beginning of February we were homeward bound. I bought a black cloak of great quality and have ever since taken it on my travels, using it as a blanket as well as a garment. James and I were the only passengers in the coach, and all was going well until Mount Cenis Pass. My trunk had become loose and we stopped at the roadside for it to be secured. I stood on the wheel to assist the driver. There being no moon, we were working by starlight and a lamp when the horses took fright. I lost my balance and my knee went through the window. James brought a second lantern from the front of the coach to inspect the damage. Just above my kneecap, two pieces of glass were stuck in my leg. My breeches were ruined. The blood flowed in a continuous stream, and not by jerks, so I knew no vein or artery had been damaged. Using my forefinger and thumb, I squeezed hard to each side of the shards, forcing them out. The driver fainted. James helped me to bind up the wound with my cravat to stem the bleeding as best we could. A light glimmered at the window of a nearby dwelling, about a hundred yards from the road. I ripped a pocket from my coat, and despatched James with instructions that it be filled with whatever could be procured to make a poultice. He returned with a pocketful of hot bran and herbs which was duly strapped to my leg. We journeyed on, although I do not remember much of it. I recall a cold draught through the broken window, the jostling of the coach and the throbbing of my leg. James was as attentive as a midwife, insisting we stop and rest each night on account of my increasing fever.

Oh, the irony of it. I had climbed to the top of St Peter's and the Castel St Angelo without incident, only to be foiled by inadequate brakes.

Further poultices were procured, but by the time we reached Paris, the wound was looking very angry. I have often thought that I would have laid my bones in France, had it not been for the exertions of Captain James Alexander. Fortunately, Doctor Marshall was in Paris. With his exquisite skill in changing the poultice and dressing the wound three times a day, he saved my life. He advised me to remain in Paris to recuperate, but I was impatient to get home, or at least to London.

I freely admit I should have taken Doctor Marshall's advice. The journey to London set me back, and I was forced to seek further attention. Thanks to my Italian cloak keeping the worst of the shivers at bay, and the knowledge and expertise of Mr Carpue, a surgeon of repute, my leg, and quite probably my life, was saved. He held the knife in a flame, cooled it in ice, and then cut away the rotting flesh, before stitching together the healthy sides of the wound.

Bedingfield House
Brooke Square,
London.
1st March 1817.

Dear Mother,

As you will see from the address above, I am back in England and staying with Uncle John. I trust you, and my brothers and sisters, are in good health. It will be a few weeks before I am home, as I am taking the opportunity to meet with the Royal Society. Sir John and Sir Joseph have asked me to attend several lectures, and I am keen to do so.

Your affectionate son,
Charles.

If she had known the true reason for my remaining in the capital, she would have fretted over the Waterton heir being in such a perilous state.

I visited Sir Joseph on several occasions. His gout worsened as my knee improved. By April, the birds were singing from every tree. Spring arrives three weeks earlier in London than in Yorkshire, but it was high time to commence my plans for the further improvement in my parkland.

I did not tell Mother the true reason for my limp. I told her I had slipped and twisted my knee when alighting from a carriage, which was not entirely untrue. The scar is still there, and two years passed before the stiffness left me alone, the glass having penetrated deep into the muscle. During that time, I gave my leg plenty of exercise, and refused to employ a stick.

By copying the example of the Cascini, I planted ivy with an unsparing hand and was delighted to see the birds respond to my efforts by taking up residence by the score.

The ague visited me from time to time, but with less vigour. Shortly after my return from Europe, as I was recovering from such a bout, I received a letter.

Cardross Park,
Dumbarton,
Scotland.
May 22nd 1817.

Dear Charles,
I expect you will be surprised to see my address. The decision to remove the family to Scotland was forced upon us if we were to escape the hazards of Guiana. With the plague worse than ever, and many of our slaves dead, I feared for my family. Mrs Edmonstone finds the climate here very testing and will not go outdoors. I cannot blame her, nor disagree with her when she says her blood is too thin for Scotland. Our sons attend school in Glasgow.
I hope you will visit as soon as the snow has melted and the roads are improved.

Your friend,
Charles Edmonstone.

I told Mother of my plan to visit Scotland. Predictably, she fussed.

"You must not go, Charles. It will still be cold there. What if the ague attacks?" My sisters stood behind her, trying not to laugh.

"Then I shall suffer in Scotland, as I would have suffered here. What is the difference? I won't be caged, and it cannot kill me. *Non-di ponti cadit qui cum sapientia vadit.* He falls not from the bridge who walks with prudence."

Mother stamped her feet and bustled out of the room, shouting over her shoulder,

"You must be back by September, for your sister's marriage."

I had rather fallen out with packing for a journey, especially for what seemed to me to be a very short distance overland. As previously stated in these pages, travelling by canoe in a tropical forest focusses the mind upon essentials. I didn't give a thought to packing, but on the day of my departure, a large trunk appeared under the portico. Grainger, with the help of a young groom, put it in a wheelbarrow and took it over the bridge. With hind-sight, I am grateful for Mother's intervention. Her collusion with Mrs Bennett met all my needs for warm clothing, and included a generous supply of gingerbread.

The birth of rail travel was still some years hence, and my journey to Cardross took some time. Cardross House stands close to the water's edge, with a wonderful view of the Clyde estuary. Mrs McKenzie, the housekeeper, took my hat and cloak and I was greeted with a warmth that Scotland's climate could never deliver. Eliza, Anne and Little Helen danced around me, pulling me into the drawing room where their mother huddled by the fire with baby Bethia in a cradle at her side. Upon my entering, Mr Edmonstone rose from his chair and shook my hand.

"Greetings, old friend. What a delight to see you."

"Girls! Girls, leave Mr Waterton alone," Mrs Edmonstone chided, "He will be road weary and not wanting to be jumped about." I held out my arms and gathered Eliza, Anne and Little Helen to me.

"Not at all. I am entirely refreshed simply by being here." They scampered away, skipping and laughing. As I lifted Mrs Edmonstone's hand to my lips I felt its frailty. She had been so strong in her native country, but Scotland had turned her into a china doll. Her big, brown eyes had a sunken vacancy, her complexion had surrendered its healthy glow and her black hair was streaked with grey at the temples. A glass of red wine was on the table to her side.

"How do you like Scotland, Mrs Edmonstone?"

She blinked rapidly, as if surprised by the question. "My husband tells me that Dumbartonshire enjoys comparatively mild weather."

"But it is a far cry from Warrow's Place."

She turned to the fire. "It is indeed. I am never warm unless I sit here, and then only one half of me can feel the flames."

"My dear," Mr Edmonstone knelt before her, taking her hands in his, "the summer is not yet upon us, when I shall take you to see Loch Lomond, and the delights of the mountains."

"Will they still be covered in snow?"

"Perhaps so, at the summit." She shivered, and took a sip of wine. "Come, Charles, let us go to my study. I have made some notes regarding the preservation of quadrupeds."

I remained with the family for two weeks, spending many happy hours discussing natural history and its preservation, and playing with Eliza, Anne and Little Helen in the nursery. Mr Edmonstone kindly offered the use of Warrow's Place, should I return to Guiana.

"I am sure I shall return, once this wretched leg gives me some peace." I rubbed my knee. We were in his study, the licking flames of the fire dispensing with the need for candles. "Meanwhile I have many plans for the parkland at Walton. My days are full of devising plans to fox the foxes—and perplex the poachers." He gave a little laugh, and then his expression dropped.

"Charles," he leaned towards me and whispered, "may I confide in you?"

"Of course. What is it?"

"When I die—"

"My good friend," I held up my hand, "you cannot think of—"

"Please, do not interrupt. I must think of it, for the sake of my wife and daughters. My wife is unhappy here. I am sure you have seen it. I have some money, but the sale of my business in Demerara has not provided as much as I had hoped. I may not live to see my daughters wed—"

"May I interrupt you there?" He looked at me with the eyes of hopelessness. "I give you my word that your wife and daughters will always be cared for. My home is their home, as you have always made a home for me."

"You know Eliza and Bethia have weak chests, and Little Helen is not the brightest creature. Maybe Anne will be more robust."

"I would consider it a privilege if you would allow me to act as I have suggested, should the worst happen. You, and your family will always be welcome at Walton Hall."

"Thank-you, Charles. You cannot know what that means to me."

My younger sister, Isabella married John Phillip Steele at St Helen's Church, Sandal on 4th September 1817. He also owned plantations, and frequently travelled back and forth between his home in Park Place, Liverpool, and Guiana.

The following spring, Mother went to live in Liverpool with Isabella and her husband in, as she described it, 'their most comfortable and commodious house,' meaning I was able to continue with my taxidermy, unfettered by her nagging about the smell and what she described as 'all the mess'. Her letters flurried to Walton Hall, all on the theme of my need for an heir. I was thirty-six years of age, and in no great hurry to find a wife. Isabella seemed happy to have Mother with her, and my sister, Helen, was content to oversee my household. I visited Mother whenever I could. She died suddenly on the 11th of January 1819 and was buried in Liverpool.

I spent my time improving the lot of the birds, building boxes for nesting, planting more ivy, holly, laurel and yew, and continuing my war against the Hanoverians. By banning the gun at all times, and the fishing line in the winter months, fowl and fish flourished as never before. Elsewhere, the opposite predominated. My neighbour, Sir William Pilkington, boasted he had shot the last raven in Yorkshire. The scoundrel! When I chanced upon him in Wakefield, I told him he was no better than his father.

The greater part of Haw Park Wood was under my ownership, the remaining acreage belonged to the Earl of Westmoreland. He took no interest in this ancient woodland, and so I approached him regarding its purchase. We quickly agreed a price of £4,600, and my sanctuary was extended to include an even greater variety of habitat. During the legal process of this purchase, and being in acquisition mode, I contacted the navigation company, asking if they would sell the triangle of land which bordered Shay Lane. The reply came that it was not for sale. I asked them repeatedly over the years, but always received the same answer.

A letter from Sir Joseph Banks prompted a visit to London. He was by then living at Spring Grove in Isleworth, and in failing health. I knew that the likelihood of my seeing him again was slim. I gave him two hummingbirds, preserved as if hovering in search of nectar.

"They are perfectly displayed, Charles. Do you say they are not stuffed?"

"You tease me, Sir Joseph." I shook my head, "you know my specimens are never stuffed."

"Not even the heads?"

"No, Sir." He showed great interest. Coming from a man who had seen hummingbirds in their natural habitat, such praise was praise indeed.

"Do you intend to share your method?"

"I already have," I replied, "I gave a short lecture to the Society of Arts and Sciences some time ago."

"And did they show interest? Were they impressed?"

"I think so, but I came away with the distinct impression that their applause was laced with jealousy. I felt as if I had trodden on their toes." Sir Joseph looked shocked. He opened his mouth to reply but shut it again without uttering a word. His face and neck coloured red. "Being chemists," I continued, "I believe they thought *they* ought to have made the discovery of using a solution of alcohol and bichloride of mercury. I wrote everything down in detail. I understand they passed everything to Mr Bullock, the trading director of museums."

"Mr Bullock, you say? He is good at his job, but unlikely to realise the importance of—"

"Quite so. But I cannot entirely take the credit for the discovery. I was first shown its potential by a good and dear friend, and we made a few experiments together. I have no contact with the Society of Arts and Sciences, having broken off with them. I am not one for speaking to those who do not wish to listen."

"I understand, Charles. It is their loss, and that of science."

CHAPTER SEVENTEEN.

How to Catch a Cayman.

Mr Edmonstone's offer of the house at Warrow's Place drummed in the back of my mind. My desire to travel was as great as ever, not least because there were several gaps in my collection. I sailed from Glasgow on February 3rd, 1820, having spent the previous week in the bosom of the Edmonstone family.

"Do call upon my nephew, Archibald." Mr Edmonstone implored me. "He now has a house on Hobabu creek. It is about half way between Georgetown and Warrow's Place."

"I shall do that, with pleasure. I remember him as a most interesting fellow."

"When you arrive at Warrow's Place, you will find Daddy Quashi. He was a slave of mine. When we left, I freed them all. Daddy Quashi said he would like to stay in the slaves' hut. He is very knowledgeable. Treat him well, and he will serve you well."

Mr Edmonstone insisted on accompanying me to the quayside. Eliza, Anne and Little Helen came along to wave me off. Unlike their mother, his daughters had acclimatised well to Scotland, and their brown eyes shone from perfect complexions. Anne gripped my hand. Her sisters skipped around us as final preparations for the voyage bustled around the *Glenbervie.*

Mr Edmonstone shook my free hand, and I felt his weakness of limb. "Farewell, Charles. I..." His voice wavered. I detected tears.

"Do not concern yourself for me, my friend, the forest shall not take me."

I picked up the girls in turn and twirled them around. Their laughter lightened the moment, bringing a smile to their father's lips. I can still picture them, all waving madly as the *Glenbervie* took me from their sight.

Provisions for forest travel were procured in Georgetown as quickly as possible. Yellow fever still had the place in its grips, and corpses were being carried to the cemetery in procession, the likes of which I had not seen since Malaga. I would have been able to leave the so-called civilisation a day earlier, had the priest not been at the gambling tables when he should have been celebrating Mass. With no possibility of practising my faith for some months, I was keen to do so. The finest Catholic priest Georgetown had to offer did not rise until the following afternoon.

The population of slaves and white men alike had been much reduced by yellow fever. Georgetown was not what it had been, and I left with a sense of relief. The moonless night made the dark creeks even darker. The gaps in the overhanging trees gave dim respite in the starlight and I found myself to be entirely disorientated. Only the skill and knowledge of my oarsmen secured a safe passage to Hobabu Creek. I retained one Indian of the team, by the name of Yan. He was a strong young man and could speak some English. Archibald greeted me warmly, despite the late hour.

The next morning at break-fast my host showed me a snake-pole which he had fashioned from an old bayonet. As he was doing so, a slave approached, and told us that a snake had taken a tame old Muscovy duck from the water's edge. Eager to try out the pole, I asked him to show me the snake. He took me to the swamp. Archibald and two of his slaves stayed on the perimeter as I ventured forward. The snake was not far away, only about ten yards in. I recognised him as an anaconda. I made aim with the pole, but thrust badly. The wound was slight, but sufficient to provoke my quarry. He sprang with the speed of lightening and as I turned in retreat, he locked his fangs in the left buttock of my linen trousers. Then, before I could grasp him, he had his tail coiled around my forearm. He was a big fellow, and the pole proved to be nowhere near long enough. I ran to the edge of the swamp, snake in tow, and instructed one of the slaves to cut away my trousers to release me, and the other to kill the snake by inserting my knife beneath his head, so as to not damage the skin in any way.

I thought the episode bode well for my third wandering, and spent the day cleaning the anaconda. The Muscovy, however, was too damaged by its unpleasant death to be worthy of my time. Mr Anaconda is now in my drawing room. I cannot help but smile each time I see him, as I recall the ruination of my trousers.

It can be a mistake to return to a place of happiness. Warrow's Place had been unoccupied for almost four years, and I should not have been surprised at the dilapidations. With the roof partly caved in, and the house occupied by bats, frogs, snakes and owls, the once bustling home had become a sorry sight. As Mr Edmonstone had said, Daddy Quashi was living in the hut which had been the house slaves' quarters. The room where the Edmonstones had entertained many, including Old Hercules, had a melancholy air. I instructed Daddy Quashi to repair the roof, but Warrow's Place was no longer a family home. The forest encroached from all directions, save that of the creek. Upon my arrival, the owls quickly relocated to a hollow tree. Daddy Quashi removed the frogs while I did the same with the snakes. Only the bats remained as my companions.

Warrow's Place became my base. Had the Edmonstones been there, I would not have been able to take in a sloth, and observe his habits for three weeks, before releasing him to his forest home, nor would it have been possible for me to use the main room for my taxidermy.

Archibald had been kind enough to lend me a mulatto by the name of James. He was an intelligent man, who learned my method of taxidermy quickly. He picked up the principals of preservation, and under my instruction became a fine taxidermist. He and Daddy Quashi remained with me during the whole of my stay, as constant companions and knowledgeable guides.

Whilst pursuing a red headed woodpecker, not far from Warrow's Place, I suffered an injury. A shard of wood from a tree stump, disguised by creeping foliage, pierced the arch of my right foot, causing a deep laceration. It bled profusely, but I feared that some rotting wood may have been pushed deeply into the flesh. James helped me back to the house, where I washed it thoroughly before probing the wound with a knife. James, Yan and Daddy Quashi watched with interest.

"All of you, gather some grass and leaves, and boil them up." I told my audience. "I shall need a poultice. In fact, I shall need many poultices, if I am not to lose my foot."

Fortunately, James was acquainted with a couple by the name of Backer, who kept a few cows nearby. He returned with a sack-full of cow dung.

"Here, Boss. This do job better than grass." Boiled and applied three times a day, along with the usual ministrations of the lancet and purgatives, my foot healed within three weeks.

James, Daddy Quashi, Yan and I, made several forays upriver and into the forests. The Guianan trees reach a great height, rising gradually from the river. The leaves range in colour from bright purple to the deepest green, and the scarlet blossom of the Caracara drapes as if the branches are hung with garlands. Each evening, I made preliminary preservations, and made notes of all I had seen and collected. The ague trailed me with its dark shadow, never more than a few feet behind, awaiting an opportunity to overtake. When more severely felt, I would remain a few days at Warrow's Place for rest and recuperation. Having recently recovered from a particularly unpleasant bout, I ventured out into some swampy water. That night I failed to recognise the onset of yellow fever. There had been heavy rain that day, with the most spectacular display of lightening turning night into day. Humidity hung around like a shroud. An early symptom of yellow fever is yawning, and at this point I should have administered purgatives, and all would have been averted. However, I did not, assuming the yawning to be tiredness. I fell into a deep sleep, and then woke suddenly, with the feeling that I was falling down a deep, black hole. Pain seared through my back and head. As I opened my eyes, I saw the bats coming in and knew that dawn could not be far away. Recognising my plight, I dosed myself with calomel and jalap, and called for Daddy Quashi to brew up copious amounts of weak tea. The purgatives did their duty, but the fever and headache kept hold all day, with the back pain easing only a little.

Thankfully, the wake of the storm provided a breeze and the room became cool and airy. The tea eventually quenched my thirst, but by late afternoon, my head was fit to burst with pain and I could not bear to move my eyes to left or right. My pulse raced at one hundred and fifty beats a minute. I cured this by opening a vein, and quickly let sixteen ounces. James bound up my arm and brought a bowl of warm water for me to bathe my feet. The headache began to lessen, and I counted my pulse to be a settled to a satisfactory ninety beats. Thinking the worst to be over, I climbed into my hammock. A restless night ensued, my pulse raced back to one hundred and twenty, and the headache punched hard from behind my eye sockets. By morning the fever had returned. Daddy Quashi sat beside me, pressing wet handkerchiefs to my temples. On my instructions, he brought further doses of calomel and jalap, and by two in the afternoon, the fever had abated, giving way to profuse cold sweating. A better night's sleep followed, and by the following morning I was much brighter. A good dose of castor oil and two weeks of cinchona bark had me to back to rights.

Sir Joseph Banks was correct in his observation of the European constitution. We do not fare well in the tropics. Having survived the plague in Malaga, and many attacks of the ague, I believe I am better constructed than most Europeans. Once again, I noted my succumbing to illness after having been in a swamp.

During the days of my recovery, I gave thought to the best method to capture a cayman. I had seen them killed with multiple arrow shots and had eaten their flesh, which tastes similar to venison, but if I were to preserve such a beast without damaged skin, I had to capture a live one. A shark hook would be needed, and a strong rope. I sent James to Georgetown to acquire these, along with other supplies. While he was away, I instructed Daddy Quashi to find a large piece of solid wood. My plan was to insert the hook securely within a fish, tie the whole on top of the wood, and take the wood into the river by boat, with the rope attached, where it would be anchored by a stone. Once the shark hook and fish were stuck within the jaws of a cayman, we would pull it ashore for the kill.

My strength returned, and Daddy Quashi, James, Yan and two hired Indians packed a canoe. I do not know why I packed my shoes and stockings, but I did. A fair breeze pushed us along, with the sail in full blow as we headed upriver. The bottom of the canoe had been tarred, and the relentless sun made it very sticky, so I put on my shoes. As I had been barefoot for months, I saw no need to cover my legs, and did not put on my stockings. This proved to be a bad mistake. I discovered by experience that sitting motionless in a boat is not the same as walking about when it comes to the effects of the sun on a white man's skin. I feared the blisters would burst, and turn to sores. After we had eaten, I climbed into my hammock, but the pain was terrible, preventing any respite by way of slumber. Even the sweet sounds of the jungle could not lull me to sleep.

Dawn broke, and I tried to climb out of my hammock, but the slightest movement of my legs was so painful, I was unable to do so.

"Daddy Quashi, James, Yan," I called, "help me out of my hammock."

"Why, Boss? You not well again?" James asked. I pointed to my ankles, and he lifted me out. I held on to a tree, but could not bear to walk. For the next two days and nights, Daddy Quashi or James carried me everywhere. Each morning, James took the sheet from over my hammock and rigged it in the canoe to create shade for my burnt legs. On the third morning, I regained my independence with a hobbling gait.

I had it in mind to travel beyond the Great Falls, where I would have a better chance of catching a cayman. All went well, and our little party had plenty of fish and fowl on the menu each night. My ankles recovered, and the beating sun turned my skin so dark I could have been mistaken for a native, had it not been for my clothing.

We reached the Essequibo and climbed the Falls. There is no sight lovelier than that of the forests to each side of this noble river, but being immersed in my quest, I concentrated on the water. Like their cousins, the alligator and crocodile, caymans are stealthy hunters, and masters of disguise. To all but the experienced eye they are a drifting log, or a rock in the shallows. I recalled the story told to me by Don Felipe Ynciarte when a large cayman had rushed from the Orinoco and seized a man, and my thoughts reminded me to respect my quarry. A curve in the river with a gentle sandbank seemed the ideal spot. We cleared a small area of brushwood and set up camp, slinging our hammocks and collecting wood for a fire. One of the Indians found a tortoise and this, along with plenty of fish, provided a splendid supper.

The following day we set up the board with the baited shark hook. The anchor stone was bound with string, the other end being attached to the board. I tied the rope to a tree, and James rowed about forty yards out into the river, where he dropped the stone. Not a breath of wind rippled the surface of the river, giving an excellent view of the board. We watched and waited all day. As the sun set, the air was filled with the sounds of frogs, owls, nightjars and jaguars. A bright moon, almost full, turned the river to polished silver, and the curious sighing of a cayman reached us across the water. It is a dreadful noise, like the mourning of a hundred deaths.

"Look, Boss." Daddy Quashi said, "cayman."

Our quarry circled the board for half an hour or more, before making his move. The fearful jaws opened, and he clamped down. To my dismay, he released the board the moment we tugged on the rope, retreating to a few yards from the bait, where he remained, quite motionless. We ate our supper, whilst at the same time keeping an eye on the board and the cayman. About an hour later, the cayman once again took the board between his jaws but made no attempt to swallow it. I am convinced that he knew he was being tricked, and that I had underestimated his cunning. He let go once again and repeated his efforts an hour or a so later, with the same result. We watched until three in the morning, before making for our hammocks. The next morning, the board was still there, complete with its rope, shark hook and anchor, but the bait was gone.

The following two nights were no more successful than the first. We certainly had the interest of the cayman, but he was far too clever to be foiled by my contraption. I spent my days observing the wildlife, and with the breeding season in full progress, there was plenty to see. Freshwater turtles came in their hundreds to lay their eggs in the sandy banks. Large stingrays moved gracefully about the river bottom. The turtles, their eggs, and the stingrays made for fine suppers. On the fourth day I decided to try a different tactic, and with the assistance of my crew, constructed a platform on the riverbank. From here, I intended to shoot a cayman with an arrow attached to a string, which was tied to rope. We would then take to the canoe and pursue him in the river until he tired sufficiently for me to finish him off with a knife. The arrow would have to pierce his flank where the flesh is soft and elastic. I thought we ought to have been successful, but spent the fourth night in unproductive vigilance. Not a single cayman came within sight and I could only conclude that there was something very wrong with my methods. It struck me that maybe a native Indian, one who was very familiar with the river and the habits of caymans, might be able to help. I asked Yan if he knew of any settlements hereabouts.

"Nearest one is day and half away." We packed the canoe and set off.

To the stranger, the creeks of the forest are a mystery, insomuch as they are all but invisible. I would not have seen the entrance due to the thick bushes, but Yan took us straight to it. The creek was longer and more winding than any I had previously encountered. As luck would have it, we met a group of Indians before we reached their settlement. They were on their way for a few days' fishing. Yan explained our intentions. When offered gunpowder, shot, and fishing hooks in exchange for their assistance, they immediately consented to join us. They invited us to their home, where we dined upon red monkey and ant-bear. The former was delicious, and fit for any table in Paris or London, but the ant-bear had been dead for too long. Putrefaction comes quickly in the tropics, as I was well aware from the need to preserve my specimens quickly. Fortunately, we suffered no ill effects. We stayed a few days and rested. I showed them my piece of wood with the shark hook and they laughed, shaking their heads at my invention.

"When I was a boy," their leader said, "my father once caught a cayman. Tomorrow, I will show you how."

As dawn broke, we packed a store of fresh cassava bread and with three members of the little tribe, set forth to catch the illusive cayman. Their leader pointed to a stretch of water that was particularly deep and still, each side of which had a broad sandbank, the whole being about two miles in length. We made camp where the sandbank met the edge of the forest. I set up my sheet and hammock before trying my luck once more with the shark hook and board, with the familiar result of a cayman taking the bait without swallowing the hook. This was not a useless exercise, for I now knew the deep, still water was home to least one cayman. As I lay in my hammock that night, I considered my failure to capture my quarry. Despite my education and sophisticated equipment, I was about to learn from an uneducated man. I concluded that his method would certainly be as logical as it was simple and looked forward to my lesson.

He whittled four sticks of hardwood, creating a barb at both ends. Each stick was about a foot long and as thick as a man's little finger. He then bound them tightly, so that the rope was pushed up to one end of the sticks, forcing the other end to splay out. He baited the hook with the flesh and entrails of an accouri. If a cayman were to take the bait, the harder he pulled on the rope, the deeper the hooks would dig into his throat.

We followed the Indians upriver to a point where the sandbank was quite steep, and the river particularly deep and still. The one who had made the hook drove a thick stake into the sand, a couple of yards from the river. Then, at the water's edge he pushed in a second stick at an angle, twisting the rope nearest to the bait around this stick before lowering the bait over the water. He then tied the middle of the rope around the stake, and the furthest end to a tree. With the bait thus set, we retired to our hammocks to await the morning. There were plenty of caymans to be heard, their miserable keening punctuated by the roaring of the jaguars. Anticipating success, I slept little. At daybreak I watched the Indian leave our camp, walking in the direction of his handiwork. A few moments later, a great whoop of joy woke the others, and we all set off running. They were all there before me, as I had the inconvenience of pulling on my trousers.

A cayman had taken the bait and was stuck fast on the end of the rope. Daddy Quashi, James, Yan, the three from the settlement and I, all pulled on the rope, but our prey was not about to give up easily. He thrashed about, digging his forelegs into the sand. I estimated him to be over ten feet long. The Indians wanted to spear him. When Yan explained the need to preserve the skin intact, they sat back on their haunches.

"They say," Yan told me, "that they won't help, and that the cayman would have us before we had him."

I could not force them to help and knew from experience that they would simply walk off if they didn't fancy the task in hand, regardless of any reward.

I had travelled over three hundred miles upriver to catch a cayman uninjured and was not about to be defeated when I had one on the end of a rope. Daddy Quashi, James and Yan knew me well enough, and knew the importance of a perfect skin. However, on this occasion, downcast eyes and shaking heads told me they thought I was being somewhat ambitious. The attitude of the Indians told me they thought me to be a madman.

I paced up and down the sandbank, trying to think of a solution. Logic eventually won through and I ordered Yan to fetch the canoe from our camp. I took down the mast, which was about eight feet long, and wrapped the sail around one end. I then explained my intention to thrust the mast down the cayman's throat so he could not bite us, and we could then pull him out of the water without risk. Thankfully, they agreed to this with the proviso that I remained between them and the cayman. I instructed them to slacken the rope if the cayman plunged below the surface.

"Audax omnia perpeti – be bold, and endure everything," I muttered as I went down on one knee, pointing the mast as a soldier would point his gun. The cayman, understandably being in a very bad temper, lunged at the mast. I admit to being somewhat uncomfortable about the situation, and my heart beat a little faster than usual as the strength of his jaws jarred the mast into my shoulder. My crew pulled on the rope, and he came to the surface briefly before plunging back into the depths. On my command my crew pulled again and out he came, thrashing with all his might and digging his forelegs into the sand. I could see instantly that the situation was hopeless. With no more man power to call upon, my only option was to disable his purchase on the sand. I dropped the mast, which remained stuck in his throat, and in one movement leapt onto his back, twisting around in mid-air to face the bank. Pressing my knees to

his flanks, I leaned forward and pulled his forelegs towards me, crossing them back over his shoulders, like reins. Thus mounted, I was hauled ashore as my steed thrashed his tail and twisted his body in all directions. Whilst I retained my seat, he was unable to harm me, my being too far forward for him to turn and bite, or for his tail to whip me. I endured an uncomfortable ride, with only linen trousers between my bony backside and his rough skin.

Over the years I have often been asked how I managed to remain seated, and have replied, 'I hunted with Lord Darlington!'

My crew shouted in triumph, dancing and whooping at our victory. I was left astride and feared the rope, which was still attached to the tree, might give way. Fortunately, my instructions to pull me further up the shore were heard, and the cayman eventually became sufficiently exhausted for me to dismount, pull out the mast, and tie up his jaws. After a while he regained a little energy and thrashed again but by then Daddy Quashi, James and Yan were convinced he could do us no harm and pressed down upon his head whilst I threw myself upon his tail until he surrendered. Thus fatigued, we carried him to the canoe and took him to our camp where I cut his throat. I commenced dissection after we had break-fasted.

A day and a half later the body was gutted and cleaned. James assisted me and the skin was sufficiently soaked in rectified spirit until such time as I could complete the task of preservation.

Having accomplished my goal, it was time to return to Warrow's Place.

Travelling up a waterfall is far easier than a descent. This may sound nonsensical, but it is true. While the upward journey may be laborious, it is far less dangerous. If I had had my way, we would have secured our possessions in the canoe, and travelled down piecemeal, rock by rock, with the canoe lowered by rope. However, the Indian who had made the contraption that caught the cayman, insisted we would be perfectly safe to ride down. I gave in to what I thought to be superior expertise, casting common sense to the wind. I took the helm. Every crew member had an oar, but our vessel was soon half filled with water and we could only surrender ourselves to the force. A wave caught us broadside. Miraculously, no-one was swept overboard and we made it to the foot of the falls where we paddled to the bank. Fortunately, it was a hot day without the humidity that can soak as effectively as a downpour. Had it been the wet season, everything would have been lost, but I am not one to dwell upon what might have been. We unloaded the canoe and the sun soon did its work, enabling us to repack and continue. The Indians from the settlement were duly paid, and Yan, Daddy Quashi, James and I travelled on uneventfully to the coast.

Nothing can be taken for granted, and the River Demerara has plenty of tricks to play upon those who sail her waters. Twice were we beached on the mud flats of the estuary, and the blazing sun had no sympathy for exposed skin. Yan's naturally mahogany coloured skin turned quite black.

"My people will not know me," he laughed.

Eventually we reached Georgetown. I paid Yan and procured supplies before returning to Warrow's Place. James returned to Archibald but visited me as often as he could. I had been in the forests for many months and was content to return to base.

Improvement of my method often pre-occupied my mind, and as I lay in my hammock one night the solution for preserving quadrupeds hit me like a bolt of lightning. Dawn could not come quickly enough, such was my excitement. I needed a fresh specimen, and before noon I was at my table, dissecting a monkey. Firstly, I removed the entire skeleton, alimentary tract and all and organs, as I did with all specimens. Then, with the smallest of my knives, I cut away the gristle from the nose and ears. The most delicate part of the operation followed as I removed the inner part of the lips, taking away the dermis to leave only the epidermis. The whole was then soaked in a solution of spirit and bichloride of mercury.

Timing is everything. At first the skin is too soft, but if left too long it becomes hard and not sufficiently malleable. When I was satisfied that the preservation of the skin was complete and the level of moisture just right, I set about moulding the monkey back into shape in the usual manner of stuffing with sawdust. The challenge of the ears, nose and lips merely required patience. With a piece of wood, the size and shape of a knitting needle, I worked the ears through the nostrils, and the lips and nose through the mouth.

The rainy season set in. Contrary to popular opinion in Europe, Guianan nights can be cold and misty. The humidity hangs like a sodden blanket, with incessant thunder and lightning. Mibiri Creek rose in fury, almost reaching the house. I used the time to observe the birds, taking copious notes of their haunts and habits. By the time I was ready to return to England, I had many rare insects, two hundred and thirty birds, two tortoises, five armadillos, two large snakes, a sloth, an ant bear,[8] my cayman and several perfectly preserved quadrupeds. As you can imagine, there was much careful packing to be done before I boarded the *Dee* . With ten securely locked and stowed boxes, and two live Malay fowls, I was a passenger under the command of Captain Grey. The passage was a most pleasant one, and we sailed up the River Mersey in fine trim, landing at Liverpool in the March of 1821. Naturally, I was anxious to see my specimens safely unloaded onto the dockside. I had landed in Liverpool on two previous occasions and had no reason for concern regarding the import of my cargo, it being common knowledge that I had no financial motivation for my collecting and that none of my specimens were ever to be bought or sold. As such, it was not possible to put a value on my shipment, and I expected to agree a modest sum with the Customs Officer, Mr Kettle, as I had on the two previous occasions. I was looking forward to my onward journey, and to giving lectures at the Royal Society. During the voyage I had started to pen my method of preservation for the extremities of quadrupeds, that it might be copied by others.

8   *aardvark

CHAPTER EIGHTEEN

The Taxing of Taxidermy.

The boxes were unloaded with the utmost care and taken to the depot. A group of gentlemen had gathered, invited by Mr Kettle, to take a look at their contents. Another gentleman whom I had not met before also came for a look. He tapped his cane on the floor, commanding attention.

"What have we here, gentlemen?"

"See for yourself, Mr Lushington." Mr Kettle said, "Mr Waterton has brought another fine collection from South America." I stepped forward and introduced myself, extending my hand. I straight away did not like the man. His arrogant posture and polished shoes spoke volumes of self-importance. When I saw he did not intend to shake me by the hand, I knew he would cause mischief.

"Mr Kettle has already made you aware of my name. What he failed to do was to inform you that I am the Chief Customs Officer. Furthermore, not one of these boxes should have been opened without my permission." He turned on his heel, banging his stick to the floor with unnecessary force.

In the Customs House office, Mr Kettle asked for a modest amount, which I willingly paid. I forget the precise amount.

The boxes were locked and were being loaded onto a cart when Mr Lushington reappeared. I shrank from him as he touched my arm to take me aside.

"I assure you, Mr Waterton, that I have the greatest interest and respect for all sciences and art, but am here to perform a duty for His Majesty. My conscience will not allow me to defer one iota. I can say, sir, that I wish I had been fifty miles from Liverpool today, and that this matter had never been brought to my attention. However, it is I, and not Mr Kettle, who will decide the value and appropriate import duty for the contents of your boxes, and I regret that I cannot agree with his valuation, and must therefore detain your collection."

If he had looked me in the eye for one second, or had a note of sincerity in his voice, I may have given him credit for his devotion to duty, but there was none.

"Mr Lushington," said I, "if, as you say, you respect the sciences, you will appreciate that anything which will further man's understanding has infinite value, while at the same time, if it is never to be sold, there is none."

"Nevertheless, Mr Kettle is too weak. There has been theft and chicanery in these docks, and I am here to stamp it out. Kettle makes exceptions where there should be none." He again banged his wretched stick to the floor. "That is my final word on the subject."

One of the boxes contained birds' eggs, carefully preserved by myself in Gum Arabic, and packed in charcoal. It had been my intention to put them under a broody hen, in the hope of introducing the breeds to England. All such hope was now quite lost, and I returned to Walton Hall with only the Malay fowl for company.

It is the habit of the absentee to imagine that nothing changes in his absence, and I was no exception. Thomas was working as a priest in Rouen, and William as a Master at Stonyhurst. Edward, the baby of the family, was on his way to Australia and New Zealand to study the botanical delights of those far distant countries. He had been inspired by the writings and illustrations of my late friend, Sir Joseph Banks, who had sailed with Captain James Cook to those very parts. My sister, Helen, was now married to Mr Robert Carr, and living in Westgate, Wakefield. I called to see her the day after my return to Yorkshire.

"I did write, Charles. We were married on the 4th of December at St Helen's Church, in Sandal. As you know, Robert is a Protestant."

"I expect your letter lies on a shelf in the mail office of Georgetown. I must have sailed right past it in the Atlantic Ocean."

Other news was not so good, the household being entirely changed. Mrs Bennett had died soon after I had left, having caught a cold which went to her chest. Monsieur Raquedal had been found dead in his room one morning. Harris, the butler, had retired, and lived in the village, his rheumatism and deafness having conspired to make his position untenable.

"I saw no reason to employ a butler." Helen said, "I was quite capable of running things in your absence, with the help of Mrs Hutchinson. She is the new housekeeper."

"I am sure you have done an excellent job, sister dear. How many servants are there?"

"Within the house, you have Mrs Oldroyd, she is the cook, and two others in the kitchen. Then there are two maids and a parlour maid. On the estate, there are three grooms, a stable lad, a footman, a gardener, and your gamekeeper, of course."

"Goodness. So many to look after one bachelor. Why do we have a footman? If my memory serves me well, Mother took the carriage and four when she went to live with Isabella. I shall have to ask some of these people to seek alternative employment."

My sister looked shocked. "But Charles, how will you manage?"

"My needs are few. I simply cannot be bothered with more than the simple life."

"But you need a cook, and at least two others. Surely you agree? Who would see to your clothes? Who would tend the fires?"

She was right, of course. The staffing was for the house and estate, not its lonely occupant. I had neither time nor inclination to bother myself with housekeeping. In the event I kept the cook and two housemaids. Mother would have been appalled. On the estate, I retained the two grooms, and the gardener. John Coe, my gamekeeper, had been so lazy that not only the parkland, but the house itself was teeming with rats. Foxes had bred in their scores. I had no intention of paying anyone who was not earning his wage, and so Coe was dismissed from my employ.

I tramped barefoot around the park, observed the lake and climbed the tallest trees, dismayed at the state of things. Between the poachers and the foxes, my birds had had a hard time of it. There was much to be done.

Another change which had taken place in my absence was the building of a small soap factory on a small patch of land between the New Inn and the navigation. I paid a visit to the owner, William Thornhill Hodgson. I liked the man. His smile creased the corners of his eyes, showing a kindness. He was just a few months older than myself, and hailed from Barnsley. Our conversation remains crystal clear in my mind.

"I had a bleach works at Hoyle Mill but sold out to my partner." We stood at the side of the navigation and watched as a barge lowered in the lock, and went on its way to the next. "Would you care to look around my little factory? The licence cost four pounds. Everything is above board."

"I would indeed, and I am sure everything about your factory is legal, Mr Hodgson." I replied. "How many do you employ?"

"Just two. A man with a family to feed, and then there's the lad." He tipped his head towards a young man who had been following us. Hodgson proudly explained the different processes in the manufacture of his products.

"I will be honest with you, Mr Hodgson, I am concerned regarding the fumes, that they will poison the air and cause damage to the birds and trees." The lad sniggered.

"What is it, Edward?" Mr Hodgson asked. "Why are you not about your work?" The lad shrugged his shoulders and left us. "Take no notice of him, Squire. He worked for me at Hoyle Mill. Like me, he has no family and I treat him like a son. Edward takes great interest in every aspect of the work, but is suspicious of strangers."

I thought nothing of it at the time, nor did I have reason to. "Will you make your own acids?" I asked.

"As you can see for yourself, Squire, there is no room to expand my factory."

I left it at that and lived to regret it.

As letters flurried back and forth between Liverpool Excise Office, Walton Hall, and London, my specimens languished in the depot. I wrote to the Royal Society, explaining my dilemma, and telling that I had hoped to lecture on my method regarding quadrupeds, that it might be taken up by others, and rid the museums once and for all of the poor looking things currently on display. My friends at the Society pleaded my case, and influence was showered upon the government. The matter was to be settled at the highest level of HM Treasury and Customs. The axe fell six weeks later.

With regard to your application for the delivery, duty free, of birds, quadrupeds, reptiles and insects collected by yourself in Guiana, and recently imported from Demerara, the Lords Commissioners of HM Treasury have made their decision.

Any articles of your collection which you intend to give to public institutions will be free of duty, but any which are for your private collection can only be released on the payment of 20% of their value. The officers in Liverpool have been duly informed.

Your Obedient Servant,
J. R. Lushington.

That I had risked life and limb in order to present the fantastical world of nature to all who showed interest, and done so entirely at my own expense, was of no interest to those who ruled. That my specimens would never be sold, and therefore had no value, was an argument for which I had lost my enthusiasm. It would have been like trying to convince a deaf man that he should listen more carefully. Stung with the venom of stupidity, I lost all desire to share my knowledge. I travelled to Liverpool and paid up, valuation having been calculated by some ignoramus. Upon my return, the grooms helped me to unload my priceless cargo. Once inside, I unpacked the cayman, the armadillos, tortoises, sloth and ant bear. They are displayed in the hallway and upon the stairs. My birds and insects remained in their box until the following winter, when, during inclement weather, I set about making cabinets for their protection and proper display.

I will now relate a series of incidents which took place during the following years, and which I hope will be of interest and amusement.

I employed a keeper, Warwick, but despite his efforts, poachers and rats reigned supreme. Even Wouralia was forced to share her shelter with rats. One morning, I saw her gallop in front of the drawing room window. This was most unlike her, and when I made inspection of her little home, I found a nest of new born Hanoverians. I flung the whole lot in the lake and called Billy, the stable lad, to muck out, mend the leaking roof and generally make her home fit for one who had contributed so much, not only to the world of science but also to the enrichment of the soil. She stood, shaking, by the water-gate, but was happy enough to let me put a halter over her head and scratch her ears.

"Come, dear friend," I soothed her, "let us walk together." I took her over the bridge, to the stables, housing her there until her island home was made fit for habitation. Whilst there I noticed the dilapidations of the roof. Everywhere I looked, there was work to be done. The entire estate had been neglected for too long.

I trapped three Hanoverians in the house, and dipped their hindquarters in tar. This method had the desired effect, and rats ran from the house by the score. The cats caught several dozen. Of those who escaped the bite of my feline assistants, some swam for their lives, while others came back inside when the coast was clear. Greater cunning on my part was required if I were to put my enemy to rout. The extermination of vermin from within the walls of Walton Hall, and upon the island, became my goal.

Mrs Oldroyd huffed and puffed around me. "That's my preserving pan, Squire. How am I to make jam if you use it for that stuff?" She was referring to the ingredients for rat poison, laid out on the kitchen table, and as shown to me by Joe Bowren. His recipe had worked wonders at Stonyhurst, and I had not forgotten it. Water, oatmeal, brown sugar, chopped garlic and arsenic boiled up together and then left to set in half ounce portions.

"Do you have another? An old pan, perhaps?" She rummaged about on the shelves, and presented me with an old brass pan, pitted beyond use. "That will do admirably, thank-you, Mrs Oldroyd. I will be no more than an hour in your kitchen, and then you will know more be troubled by the rats in your pantry. Surely that is a price worth paying?"

"You are right, Squire, of course you are, but I think you are also wrong. It will take more than a pot of poison to shift them. You need to brew a pot of magic."

I made my poison biscuits and left them to set. The following morning, thus armed, I set about the house, placing them in crevasses in every room.

The stretch of the navigation which runs alongside the southern edge of the park continued to cause great annoyance. Having had no choice but to accept my father's pragmatism on the matter, the poaching continued unchecked. The bargees sat atop their vessels, guns at the ready, and shot at anything that moved in the trees or on the ground. They did so in broad daylight as if it were a God given right. Warwick and I discussed the problem as we watched a bargee throw a rope to his companion at the lock-side.

"I can't be everywhere, Squire. Even if I did nought else but watch for these fellows, the navigation runs for a good mile alongside the parkland."

"What do you suggest? Man traps?"

"With respect, Squire, we both know they are illegal." We walked the length of the towpath as it bordered the parkland. Approximately half of this distance ran alongside the deep cutting between the navvy's old cottages and Haw Park Wood, making it impossible for the bargees to gain access. We crossed the bridge and walked back along the other side of the navigation.

"I believe I have the answer." Warwick stared at me expectantly. "I shall build a wall."

"A wall, Squire?"

"Yes. A wall that is too high for a fox to jump over. It will, if you forgive my choice of words, kill two birds with one stone. Three even!" We laughed heartily. He slapped his thighs, laughing until tears fell down his weather-beaten face. He wiped them away with his cuffs, leaving streaks of grime on his cheeks.

"Three birds, Squire? How so? I am counting two. The poachers and the foxes."

"The rats. It will also keep them out."

"But the rats and the foxes will enter another way," he said, his tone now serious, "and poachers come from all over the county, not just the navigation."

"You misunderstand me. The wall will eventually go all the way around the parkland. I will create my own world. It will be a sanctuary for nature." His jaw dropped and he stared at me as if I were quite mad. "I shall start here, where my parkland borders the navigation on the level. That should deter them, if naught else."

I had a new lease of life. Gone was the melancholy I had suffered at the hands of Mr Lushington, entirely dispelled as my head was filled with the proposed route of my wall. I ordered the first delivery of stone. The wall would be a masterpiece. The more I thought about it, the more enthusiastic I became. The project would have the added bonus of providing work for local stonemasons, both at the quarry and at Walton. I ordered five hundred pounds worth of stone. Had I not taken Father Clifford's advice, I would have spent far more money on wine than it would cost to build my wall. I laid down fallen branches along the proposed route. In all I estimated it would be about three miles in length. Arches would be constructed where the stream entered and egressed my haven, plus two gateways serving the carriageways to Walton in the west and Nostell in the north. Otherwise, my wall would achieve my aforementioned ambition of foxing the foxes and perplexing the poachers, and vary in height from a minimum of nine feet.

My observation of the habits and habitat of birds both in Demerara and in Europe had served me well, and shown me all I needed to know to entice my feathered friends within my park. The ivy planted three years earlier had taken well, and had it not been for this, there would have been even less wild-life within my acres. Hedgehogs, pheasants and partridges enjoyed the shelter it provided on the ground. Higher, where the ivy had grown up the trees, many species of small birds had chosen to make their home.

Despite this, however, the game birds both on land and in the water had declined in number, reinforcing my belief that by ridding the parkland of predators, it would become a refuge like no other. Having decided to construct my wall piecemeal, as and when I could afford five hundred pounds of expenditure, it would take time to complete. The stretch that paralleled the navigation, but not protected by the cutting, was the priority, and its building accomplished by the end of the summer of 1821. When all the stone had been used up, I laid off the masons until I had another five hundred pounds in my box. It is true to say that had I been prepared to leave myself short of cash, or put my money in the hands of the bank to gain interest, the wall would have been completed more quickly, and quite possibly at less expense. However, that is not my way of doing things. Having witnessed the corruption of the Dutch bankers of Georgetown, and suffered losses myself at two banks in Wakefield, it is my preference to keep my money in a locked box.

Five years later, and eighteen times five hundred pounds, the wall was finally complete. Foxes and hares took off, the area within being too small to sustain them. Some rabbits remained, but they did little harm.

I have never been one for formal entertaining. As the inheritor of an estate, the expectation to do so was of no concern to me. I received invitations and accepted them on the understanding that I would not reciprocate. That is not to say I do not encourage visitors. All who show an interest in my collection and parkland are welcome, but I have no appetite for the fashionable dinner party. The dining table was more usually employed as a workplace for my taxidermy, being in a room of five windows and a good morning light. It became my habit to work on several specimens at a time. The amount of time each piece occupied varied considerably, whether I was cleaning out the internals, or adjusting the pose. One specimen might need a five-minute repositioning, another an hour. That summer I recall a peacock and a weasel, a snake and a hedgehog all sharing the dining table.

I had fallen out with Lord Pilkington over his propensity for shooting birds of prey, but another neighbour, Charles Winn, who had recently inherited the estate of Nostell Hall, was, and still is, often my host. His brother, John, who had shot the last buzzard in these parts, had died in Rome.

I do so enjoy Charles' company and can only deduce that he enjoys mine. During one of our many conversations it came to light that despite his being of the Protestant faith, we share our most famous ancestor, Thomas More.

The way from Walton Hall to Nostell makes for a pleasant walk through farmland. I recall a conversation Charles and I had one summer's evening, as we strolled through his estate sometime during the summer of 1821.

"I had entered the church before John died. I did not expect to inherit. My brother's death changed the course of things for me."

"My responsibilities seem few when compared to yours." We were standing part way down the broad, mile-long avenue, looking back towards the great house. "I see you are making a few changes."

"I am a married man, Charles. Priscilla tells me the kitchen is an impractical distance from the dining room, and it is being demolished. I concede the new kitchen within the house is a great improvement and our food much hotter on the plate. Some other rooms are to be re-decorated. I have employed a London firm."

"Ah, yes. I see."

"Do you, my friend? You are older than I but have no wife. Part of the duty of the inheritor is to create his successor."

"You are right." I sighed. Tell me, did you marry for love, or simply out of duty?" He rocked back and forth from heel to toe, clasping his hands behind his back.

"Priscilla is my cousin. As I said, my brother's death changed the course of my life, and I have done my duty. She has borne me a son, Rowland, and there is another child on the way. But to answer your question—yes, I do love her, but I did not marry for love."

I pondered this enigmatic reply as we walked back to the house. As we approached the doorway he said, "I am thinking of changing the name from Nostell Hall to Nostell Priory. There was a large priory here until fifteen—"

"Don't tell me! Until Old Harry said otherwise."

"Quite so—yes. What do you think?"

"I think Nostell Priory is the rightful name."

Fenton, the butler, approached, telling of dinner being served in the little dining room.

Later that evening, as I walked home, I reflected upon my good fortune, having enjoyed the company of Charles and Priscilla. As the incumbent of Walton Hall, my home and parkland were not so large as to be a millstone around my neck and yet I had all I needed and more, but the question of a successor began to niggle at the back of my mind.

By the end of the summer I had taken on more staff. Thomas White and William Guest were employed as gamekeepers to assist Warwick. The kitchen garden, orchard and flower garden at the grotto were proving too much for one man, and so George Hanby was added to the wage list. He was a simple lad from the village, but a worker, and I never regretted taking him on.

One other person was employed. Joseph Totty was a young man back then, but I saw in his eye a love of the land and animals. He is still my farm manager. I am no good at such things, a matter which he made plain to me over the question of drainage. I admit I was dead set against putting drains in the land, despite Totty being all for it. My conviction was that this new-fangled idea would render the ground too dry but was persuaded to give it a try. To my mind, the long grass in the swampy ground near the creek was a good thing, but Joseph Totty pointed out that while my herons enjoyed it, it was too coarse for cattle. It is a pompous oaf who cannot admit to being wrong and am content to admit that in the matter of the drainage, I was entirely wrong. Pasture which had been shunned by the cattle is now rich and lush and there is swamp enough for the herons. In my defence, I will say the matter proved me right to employ a farm manager.

With the estate thus organised, I was free to indulge in my favourite pursuits. I took twigs of ivy from tree trunks, and replanted it elsewhere in the woodland, where it flourished both on the ground and in the trees. A poor substitute for the ropes of vine in the Guianan forests, but it suffices. Closer to the house, I planted yew, laurel and holly, providing year-round hospitality, Yorkshire style, in lieu of the hayawa and olu trees of the tropics.

The summer of 1822 saw the building of the new Public Rooms in Leeds, and I was invited to a fancy-dress ball on the opening night. I am not usually one for attending social occasions, but as I had the Warrow's passie and other native clothing from Guiana, I decided to go. I can give the precise date as Friday 13th September, because I have the newspaper report.

Charles Waterton, Esq., of Walton Hall, Yorkshire, was attired as Montezuma, a South American Prince. This was certainly one of the most effective dresses present. It was comprised of feathers and ornaments obtained during his travels and research in the interior of America, and had a very striking and interesting appearance. This gentleman delighted the company by repeating several times the dance peculiar to the South American Indians, which he performed in a very surprising and correct manner.

It still amuses me to wonder how the reporter knew my dance to be correct. Reading of it motivated me to locate the headdress and try it on, much to the entertainment of the household.

Over the years my observations led me to believe that if I were to calculate correctly the wingspan, weight and length of the larger species of bird, it would be possible to work out the wingspan required for a man to fly. I set about constructing some wings, and collected flight feathers during the moulting season of the Canada geese. I used light, well-seasoned pine for the framework of my contraption.

I took the completed wings to the uppermost part of the stables roof where I strapped them to my arms. All was set for my maiden flight, gamekeepers and other outdoor staff having gathered to witness the phenomenon. I was about to leap from the roof, when I heard the clatter of hooves behind me. My brother-in-law, Robert Carr, had called by.

"Charles! Charles! Whatever are you doing up there?"

"Can you not see? I am going to fly."

"Come down, man. You are not a bird. I insist! Come down at once." he shouted.

"Why don't you come up here?" From my lofty position I saw true concern written upon his face.

"I have no intention of climbing on a roof, Charles. What will I tell my wife if you are injured, or worse?"

I was entirely convinced that my wings would enable me to fly with ease, but to appease Robert, I agreed to launch myself from a lower roof. It took a while to re-organise myself and in the meantime, Robert ordered the farm labourers to pile up a quantity of dung to break what he described as 'my inevitable fall.' When all was set, I inched my way to the eaves and leapt as high as the weight of my wings would allow, which was not very high at all. Without a doubt this was the only time that my long legs were a hindrance to me. My feet caught the gutter and rather than soar into the sky, I dropped off the edge, landing heavily with my head stuck in the dung. Robert and my audience dashed forward.

"Are you hurt?"

"Only my pride, Robert, thank-you." I flexed my neck this way and that as my keepers helped me from my wings. "Perhaps there will be a stiff neck for me tomorrow."

"It's a wonder nothing is broken."

"I fear my wings are damaged beyond repair."

"I don't mean the wretched wings, man. I'm talking about your neck. It's a good job I had the dung put there."

I stood up and picked the rotting straw from my clothes. "You are right. I am fortunate indeed that you called by, and freely admit I was out of my element. You can tell Helen that in future I shall leave flight to the birds."

I had been home for almost three years before I was finally persuaded to give a lecture. Mr Atkinson of the Leeds Philosophical and Literary Society had written to me several times, asking me to disclose my method for the preservation of quadrupeds. Time had diffused my anger, and Mr Atkinson assured me of his members' genuine interest. Some two years previously, I had donated some preserved birds of South America to their museum, and so my work was already known to the audience. In truth, I was more persuaded by the memory of my conversation with Sir Joseph Banks, when he had advocated a lecture should I ever solved the problem of the lips.

I took several birds to the New Assembly Rooms in Leeds, including a toucan, along with a monkey, some fishes, my cayman, an armadillo, a land turtle and a tarantula spider.

"Imagine, gentlemen, bringing all these specimens tonight, had they been stuffed. Imagine the weight. All the specimens you see here tonight are hollow and are not supported either internally or externally by anything other than their own skin. There are no wires, no stuffing, and they will not succumb to the moths.

I have sought to perfect the preservation of creatures great and small. When I first began, I trialled a range of chemicals and other substances such as soap, arsenic, and turpentine. The latter is known to kill the moth and other insects, but does not kill their eggs. Soap and arsenic preserve the skin only. It is no secret to this company that my preferred preservatives are bichloride of mercury and rectified spirit. They are colourless, and so do not spoil any part of the specimen. Rectified spirit diffuses the bichloride of mercury rapidly through the skin. It is the deadliest poison to insects, and so there is nothing left on which other insects could feed and the specimen becomes entirely soaked through with preservative.

It is vital for preparation to commence soon after death. Decomposition and putrefaction, especially in the climate of the tropics, is rapid. Legs will shrivel and the parts of a bird most thickly covered with feathers will dry disproportionately to others."

At this point I held two examples of a hummingbird bird, one in each hand.

"This bird (I held up one) I preserved in 1812, and this one (I held up the other) in 1820. I showed the first one to Sir Joseph Banks, and he declared it to be the best skinned bird in Europe. Alas, he has not lived to see the second example, which I think you will agree cannot be compared, for sympathy and expression, with the older one. Every bone, including the skull, has been taken out, right to the extremities of the beak.

You see my toucan, gentlemen, with his perfect plumage and brilliantly coloured beak. Those who stuff this spectacular species are forever disappointed that the colours of his beak soon fade away. By using a little knife to scrape away everything from within the beak, the colours are retained. It takes a deal of time and patience.

Take note, gentlemen, of the shape and expression of all which you see before you. It is no accident that I have captured them in a lifelike manner. This is because I have observed them in life, and not simply had a corpse delivered to my door. He who has not seen an animal in his natural habitat cannot know his pose. The quadrupeds are entire and of perfect shape, due to the meticulous application of internal sculpture, which I then corrected by external sculpture. They are, each and every one of them, elastic, hollow, and without wires or other support."

I spoke for four hours, giving detailed information of my work and received great applause. It seemed no-one wanted to leave. A newspaper article in the Yorkshire Gazette was full of praise, saying

'So lively was the interest excited, that the company, which was numerous and of the first respectability, would cheerfully have remained for hours longer.'

One gentleman presented me with a book, entitled 'Wilson's Ornithology of America.'

"Sadly, his work is incomplete, Mr Waterton. The author has passed away." I thanked the man profusely. Had it not been such a dark night, I would have started to read it on my journey home.

Two days later a matter of an entirely different nature put my name in a newspaper.

It is pertinent to say at this point that my usual hours of sleep are between 9.15 p.m. and 3.30 a.m. Had it not been for my fascination with Mr Alexander Wilson's book, I would have been fast asleep. I was in my bed, reading by candlelight, when the unmistakable sound of a gun being discharged came from the woodland. During the preceding weeks, estates from Bretton to Nostell had been cleared of a vast quantity of game and so I was in no doubt as to what this was all about. I leapt from my bed, dressed quickly and ran to the stable block to rouse my keepers. I found Warwick, White, and Guest already dressed, and each carrying a gun.

"I know you say, 'no guns' Squire," Warwick brushed cobwebs from his weapon as he spoke, "but I reckon we need them tonight."

"I reckon you're right," I said, "and we must be quick, if we are to catch them red-handed."

I took the gun from White. Four men with three guns between them would surely frighten off our intruders, or so I thought.

"Mine isn't loaded, Squire." I turned to see White's face to be as pale as his name.

"They are none of them reliable," Warwick said, "on account of lack of use. Likely none of them will fire."

"They don't know that," I replied," and in the dark, they won't see the rust."

I had not handled a gun on the estate since my unfortunate accident when I shot myself in the hand, and the lack of maintenance of our arms was testimony to the intervening years. We were not long in the woods before we heard several shots, and made our way in that direction with caution. We soon encountered a group of men and within seconds they were lined up before us, each aiming their weapons directly. I counted nine guns shouldered at me and my little army. One poacher took a pace forward.

"I will fire on the first person to approach," he growled.

"And I shall do likewise." I countered, raising my gun. Guest and White followed my example.

The leader laughed. "We will give you battle if you so choose, Squire. But a blind man could tell you your guns are no match for ours. We outnumber you and outmatch your force in every way. If you wish to see the dawn, stand back and lower your weapons, if weapons we can call them."

He was right. I had underestimated both their numbers and their ability to see in the dark. I lowered my gun and stepped backwards, indicating to my brave keepers that they do the same.

"Warwick—White—Guest." I whispered, "Run to the village and rouse some men. Bring them quickly. These must be the villains who have been robbing me and my neighbours these past weeks. Quickly now!"

They returned within the half hour with a dozen men, but the poachers were gone. With hindsight I was able to say it turned out to be a good night's work, for this particular band never returned. Nor did the estates of Sir William Pilkington of Chevet, Mrs Beaumont of Bretton, or Godfrey Wentworth of Woolley ever suffer so heavily again. Mrs Beaumont took the trouble to write to me, expressing her sincere thanks.

CHAPTER NINETEEN

The United States of America and Canada.

My reading 'Wilson's Ornithology of America', fanned the expiring flame of wanderlust. My lecture in Leeds had raised much interest and I can only assume that news of my intention to travel reached the press. At the time there was much speculation regarding the linking of the Atlantic and Pacific Oceans between North and South America. One proposal was to build a canal across the Isthmus of the Darien. To my amusement, a newspaper reported that I was on my way to supervise its formation! Whilst I remain convinced that such a waterway will be built, I am equally convinced that such a feat of engineering will be nothing to do with me. I might be able to preserve a quadruped, but engineering on such a scale is entirely beyond my sphere.

On the 11th April, 1824, I sailed from Liverpool aboard the *John Wells,* bound for New York, under the command of Captain Isaac Harris, but before I boarded, I met with a journalist from the Liverpool Mercury, and was able to put the record straight regarding any involvement in the proposed Darien Canal.

The passage was long and cold, but elegant accommodation and the polite attention of Captain Harris and his crew more than made up for the discomfort of the waves. I cannot say the same for all passengers, for the *John Wells* carried many poor emigrants, and their accommodation was less commodious. To their credit, however, and that of the crew, they were well treated and my admiration for these people, who would never see their homeland again, was boundless.

I had no intention of collecting specimens on my travels, simply intending to observe with the aid of Alexander Wilson's book. However, I took with me a preserved head of a domestic cat, which I had mounted on a small plinth, and a red cotinga, in the event of there being an opportunity to exhibit my work.

We arrived in New York on 16th May. The hôtels were of the highest quality, and the service beyond compare. With all charges included, I never paid above two dollars a day, which is little enough when considering the capital accommodations and abundance of food.

There are those who will tell you that the American people are too forward, too inquisitive, too enquiring of one's business, but these critics mistake genuine interest for prying. The American is interested in you and is very willing to tell you about himself and his country. Considering the recent history between our two countries, I was pleasantly surprised at the lack of malice towards an erstwhile colonist. Since independence, the population has increased from three million to ten million, and a fine navy has been built.

The appropriately named Broadway came as a magnificent sight after five weeks of nothing but a wild North Atlantic Ocean. At three and a half miles long, I know of no other street anywhere in the world that is so attractive. The fine houses give a stately atmosphere, while the high and luxuriant trees relieve the lines of architecture. With no jostling or persons rushing about, no fear of pickpockets and no steam engines filling the place with soot and smoke, I happily spent many an hour watching the ladies as they took their walk in the early afternoon. Fashion in America is altogether more practical. I especially noticed the tasteful style of headwear. Perhaps nowadays, with the steamships so safe, some of our milliners would do well to travel west for inspiration rather than copy the impractical designs of Paris.

I tarried for some weeks and could happily have stayed longer in the company of such warm and hospitable people, but on a fine morning in July, I boarded a steamship, prepared to encounter the bugs, bears, buffalo and brutes for which the endless wilds of America are reputed. The eighty-mile journey up the Hudson to Albany was made a thousand times more interesting by my fellow passenger, Mr Gregory Feltham. An educated man, he had travelled in France and England, and we passed many an hour in conversation whilst sitting on deck.

"It appears to me," I said, "that the scenery has been much changed by the hand of man."

"It has indeed," he replied, "the axe has felled thousands of trees to make way for the plough, and to build the farmer's homestead."

"And to breed cattle."

"America is vast, Mr Waterton, and the more people who come to live here, the more the land will be tamed." I was pondering the future of the land around us, when my friend pointed to the horizon. "See, the Catskill mountains. Slide Mountain is the highest in the range. It is an area rich in wildlife, and from what you have told me, just your sort of thing."

"If the birds of the river are anything to go by, I am sure you are right." We fell into a comfortable silence for a while and then he shifted in his chair a little, half turning towards me.

"Trees were felled by the soldiers of our two countries, to build their warships."

"This river was at the forefront of the war, was it not?"

"You are right again. I can show you some landmarks, if you wish."

He named the regiments and their captains, pointing to where the English fired their broadsides and where the Americans, sometimes no more than ill equipped farmers, rushed to battle. He pointed out an ancient oak which had escaped the axe, and a tract of woodland which gave indication of how rich the land had been before the days of the pioneers. Oh, that I could have seen it before the white man began his destructive invasion.

We parted company at Albany, after taking tea and shaking hands in the most civilised manner, never to meet again. I like to think he enjoyed my company as much as I enjoyed his, his open ways and friendliness being so typical of the American.

The foresight of Governor DeWitt Clinton meant my onward journey was largely by steamboat. Engineers were in the final stages of completing three hundred and sixty-three miles of the canal which the governor had envisaged some years earlier. More than eighty locks raise the water by five hundred and sixty-four feet, through the state of New York and all the way to Lake Erie. The journey to Schenectady is enchanting, and Mr Wilson's book enabled me to identify many species which I had not previously encountered, along with more familiar feathered friends.

How I wish I had met the author. Fertile fields and wooded mountains delight the eye of the traveller all the way to Utica. Here I disembarked and stayed in the delightfully situated town for two days. The people of Utica struck me as most polite and friendly. From there I took the stage coach and thus my journey continued, overland or afloat, by stage and steamboat. At no point did I feel unsafe and began to wonder if I had come to the wrong place. I had seen nothing of the bugs, bears, beasts and buffalo of which I had been warned.

At Lake Oneida, well-dressed ladies took to the steamboats simply for pleasure, taking in the delights of the surrounding landscape and the deep, clear lake. The spacious inns, excellent food and attention of the innkeepers all contributed to making this a popular destination for visitors.

Such accessibility, alas, comes at a price and I could not but mourn the loss of ancient landscape. Trees lay prostrate, as meadows, cornfields and pastures burst into the traveller's view. Having said that, I must add that the whole of the country between Utica and Buffalo is a delight to the eye of the beholder, with its lakes and mountains, meadows and villages and, of course, the birds.

Shortly before my arrival at Buffalo, I stepped from the stage onto some rocky ground and sprained my foot. It swelled to a great size within half an hour and was very painful. Once again, the attentions of my American hosts knew no bounds, but their hospitality could not abate my discomfort. I had had a similar, but less severe experience some years previously, when I had been given the excellent advice to let cold water from a house pump flow over the offended joint, thereby reducing the swelling. The innkeeper showed me to the pump, and I doused my foot three times a day, resting between times in his fine inn, until I was able to put my foot to the ground and limp my way around. Taking the stage once again, I passed into Canada and travelled the twenty miles to Niagara. The force is so great it can be heard more than three miles away and the mists can be seen rising to mingle with passing clouds. Here I saw two white headed eagles, or bald eagles as they are known in America, soaring in the mists. These birds are decreasing in number, due to the baffling propensity for shooting them. If I were an American, given that this noble bird is their emblem, I should think I had committed some sort of sacrilege by killing one of their number. As the ancient Egyptians held sacred the ibis, the Dutch protect the stork, and the vulture sits unmolested on the roofs of Angustura, and even as the robin is revered by the English, so the American should revere and protect this magnificent symbol of their country. Time will tell if light dawns before it is too late.

I stayed at one of the two large inns on the Canadian side of the falls. It is from here that the best views can be seen. I hobbled about the wooded and rocky environs of Niagara, passing the time in the unaffected company of fellow travellers. In the evening I attended a dance, where to my chagrin, I could only watch from a sofa with my foot elevated after a day's roaming. The true elegance of the ladies was a delight to behold, and one young lady particularly caught my eye. Her air and grace struck me as equal to any I had ever seen. I enquired of her to a gentleman.

"The young lady is from Albany, sir."

I pointed to my swollen, stockinged foot. "How I wish I could ask her for a dance, but my unlucky foot renders it impossible."

"Is it the gout?" he asked.

"No, not gout!" Such was my mortification at the suggestion, I spoke too loudly, and heads turned to me and my foot. "I have never suffered in that way, and hope I never do. My foot is sprained." Seeing that I had worried him, I sought to amend, beckoning him closer that I might whisper. "But for my injury, I would ask to marry her." He stepped back and saw my smile, and all was well between us. Nevertheless, I recall my comment evoked within the thought of my friend, Charles Winn, his home, wife and son, and wondered if such bliss would ever be mine. Having reached the age of forty, the matter of an heir was now more often in my thoughts, especially when I was in the company of the American ladies. I found their frankness, dignity and good humour quite delightful.

Fearing I might be remembered by my fellow guests as a gouty man, and in order that the record be forever set straight, I penned the following in the visitor's book.

C. Waterton, of Walton Hall, in the county of York, England, arrived at the falls of Niagara in July, 1824, and begs leave to pen down the following dreadful accident:

-

He sprained his foot, and hurt his toe,
On the rough road near Buffalo.
It quite distresses him to stagger
Along the sharp rocks of famed Niagara.
So thus, he's doomed to drink the measure
Of pain, in lieu of that of pleasure.
On Hope's delusive pinions borne
He came for wool, and goes back shorn.
Here he alludes to nothing but
The adventure of his toe and foot.
Save this, he sees all that which can
Delight and charm the soul of man,
But feels it not, because his toe
And foot together plague him so.

Following my disappointment at not being able to dance with the fair young lady from Albany, I decided that such a desperate situation demanded desperate solution. If to hold my foot under the cool water of a water pump was beneficial, I considered the likelihood of a miracle if I were to hold it beneath a fall which, I was reliably informed, discharged six hundred and seventy-two thousand, two hundred and fifty-five tons of water per minute. I descended the winding staircase with some difficulty and tentatively held my leg forward. The truth is, the magnitude of the mighty roar was overwhelming, and I stepped back, fearing the force would take away the pain in my ankle by taking away my foot!

I remained in Niagara until the pain and swelling had lessened to the point where my limp was barely noticeable. Rather than retrace my steps, I decided to sail Lake Ontario and thence to Montreal and the city of Quebec. To my immense good fortune, a family from New York,

Mr and Mrs Jardine and their three daughters, were embarking upon the same route. Mr Jardine invited me to join them each evening. The young ladies sang delightfully and this highly accomplished family, like so many others whom I had had the good fortune to meet, were only too pleased to tell an Englishman of the history of the landscape.

"Over there," Mr Jardine pointed across the lake, "General Wolfe breathed his last, and Montcalm was mortally wounded in the battle of the Plains of Abraham."

"Over there, fell Brock." One of his daughters said.

"And here," a sister pointed to the nearby lakeside, speaking with pride, "General Sheaffe captured all the invaders."

In the harbour, British vessels of the war could still be seen in various stages of death. Most had already sunk to a watery grave, but some masts were visible upon shattered decks, awaiting their inevitable destiny. After a day or two we had seen all we wished to see of the city and boarded the steamer, *Columbus,* for our journey back to Montreal. This enormous vessel had over five hundred Irish emigrants on board, all huddled together, with no clue as to their future and only memories of Ireland. No man with a heart could fail to feel their desperation. The sight has never left me, and my abiding hope is that they fared better in their new home than they had in their old one.

Whilst in Montreal I had the good fortune to meet with a college professor of the town. He was interested in my taxidermy and travels. I told him I had taken many notes of my observations, and of my annoyance at the all-too-often preposterous conclusions of the closet naturalists.

"What I find most irritating is the way their word is taken as fact, without question."

"But what of Canada, Mr Waterton? How do you find the words of Mr Wilson?"

"My experience of your country and that of New York State has been greatly enlivened by Mr Wilson's work." I said.

"A work sadly unfinished, but happily being continued."

"I am pleased to hear it. By whom?"

"Charles Bonaparte, aided by some of the most scientific men of Pennsylvania."

"A relative of Napoleon?"

"Indeed, yes. His nephew. You should follow his example, Mr Waterton."

"In what way, Professor?"

"Publish, sir. Publish your notes for the benefit of others. You have much to tell, especially of South America, where few will ever travel. You have knowledge that no other man possesses. Do not keep it to yourself."

"I never have wanted to keep it to myself, but it has been my experience that few will listen."

"If only one man ever follows in your footsteps, it will have been worth your while to publish. You cannot speak directly with everyone but once your work is in print it is there for the world, and forever."

I left Montreal with regret, feeling both refreshed and inspired as I journeyed on through the lakes Champlain and George, and thence to Saratoga. I parted company with the Jardines and took the stage to Albany, and from there, back to New York City.

New York City welcomes all who enter her harbour. Luxury of every sort is there for the traveller, along with a welcome for those who would make this city, or her wide environs, their permanent home. Fortunately for the Englishman, the Americans do not bear a grudge, although I dare say they would prefer us to quit the West Indies!

By comparison to New York City, I found the nearby Philadelphia to be much more quiet, the attractiveness of the white marble buildings contributing in no small way to the pleasant atmosphere. Mature and healthy trees were everywhere, breaking the monotony of the rigid order of the streets.

I had been recommended to visit a certain museum and I am forever glad that I did so. Not only did I see for myself a magnificent skeleton of a mammoth, but also met the man who had, through his own endeavours and expense, extricated the enormous bones from a morass on farmland in New York State. Charles Willson Peale's museum displayed many specimens of nature, taxidermy and art, all by his own hand. His taxidermy was all stuffed of course, but his skill, both with stuffing and with the paintbrush, was admirable. I told him of my red cotinga and the cat's head and he asked me to bring them along the following day. When he saw my work, he went into raptures at their lifelike appearance.

"I must commit them to canvas, Mr Waterton. Please, hold up your right hand." He took the cotinga and placed it on my forefinger as if it were a pet canary. "It will look as if you have a live bird on your finger."

I doubt I should ever have had my portrait painted, had I not met Charles Willson Peale. I was forty-two years of age at the time of my visit to Philadelphia, and not likely to become more handsome. In my opinion, I knew what I looked like, and did not need a painting to remind me, but the artist was an interesting man with many strings to his bow, and so I relented.

"I am duly flattered, but cannot sit still for long."

"No matter, no matter," he took up a sketch pad. "I only need an outline, and then you can go about your business."

The outline took longer than I expected, and I can say with impunity that I have never, before or since, sat so still for so long unless incapacitated by some malady.

"Please do not be offended, Mr Peale, if I decline the finished object," I said, "but it is bad enough to look in a mirror for the purpose of shaving."

"Then I shall hang it in my museum."

We discussed the excellent work of Alexander Wilson whose book had prompted my journey.

"I hear that Charles Bonaparte, nephew of the great Napoleon, is to complete the work. Do you think he will he do it justice?" I asked.

"I doubt it, but he will do his best, and no man can do more than that."

Charles Willson Peale introduced me to Mr George Ord, a naturalist and ornithologist with whom I have corresponded ever since.

I have only two negative experiences of the United States, which I feel obliged to recount, in the interests of fairness.

Firstly, the climate is erratic. Tropical heat at midday can be followed by a chilly night. An immigrant who disembarked in the noonday heat may think his old coat to be superfluous, but by the evening he will be glad he did not pawn it, if indeed he did not!

Secondly, the American man is very fond of smoking. This habit makes for foul breath, and a foul place where the smoker stands. Those who are caught downwind have his habit forced upon them.

My greatest fault, and I am sure there are those who will tell of other imperfections, is that I do not always predict the consequences of my actions. I spent some hours on the streets of New York, watching the people as they went about their business. I sauntered here and there and stood for a while on a street corner, observing my fellow men (and women). Only when it began to rain did I realise how cold I had become. My bones shivered from head to toe, and I marched to my quarters as quickly as I could. To remedy my condition (and upon the insistence of Mr Fervent, the aptly named hôtel owner) I took a hot bath. His recommendation was a pleasant experience, and with my bones warmed through once more I felt thoroughly restored and made the mistake of going out again. I caught a cold, and no ordinary cold at that. Mr Fervent, on seeing my shivers, sent for Doctor Hossack. Over the next six weeks I was bled eight times, and lived on white bread and weak tea. When autumn, or fall as it is known in the United States, arrived, I still coughed.

"Doctor Hossack," I wheezed, "what do you think are my chances of surviving the Atlantic? I am thinking of going home."

He paced the floor in deep contemplation before giving his reply. "I think if a fair wind were guaranteed you would survive, but I suggest you think of the winter ahead. England can be as cold as New York and with this in mind, it is my recommendation that you go south, to a warmer clime."

Until then, I had not thought to return to Demerara, but once Doctor Hossack had put the idea in my head I was drawn to the tropics as if by a magnet. I hied me off aboard the first ship bound for the West Indies and am forever convinced that Doctor Hossack's advice saved me from death by consumption.

The passage to Antigua took thirty days, due to a head wind. At the time it seemed tedious, but upon arrival the crew and all passengers were thankful for this act of providence. The wind had pushed us away from a hurricane which had uprooted trees and demolished houses. I spent a dull week in Antigua, all was misery and downcast, and this was not entirely due to the weather. Those houses which had not been destroyed were desperately in need of a coat of paint. The pavements were uneven, and everything had an impoverished depression about it.

Guadeloupe was no better, nor Martinique or St Lucia. Even Bridgetown had lost its cheer since I last visited. All the British islands had a gloomy air. The reason for all this was slavery, or rather its continuing demise. The inevitable abolition cannot be argued against, but it brought its own brand of misery. Had the consequences of this foul trade been known at the time of Queen Elizabeth, she would surely not have sent her ships to rob the coast of Africa of its sons. Her love of sugar rotted her teeth and created a hell on earth.

Georgetown was like an injured beast in its death throes, thrashing about in an effort to stand tall one more time, but with no hope of doing so. Ignorance and corruption were the base of it all. The town had its foundations built on greed. Light was fading when I arrived, and so I was forced to stay one night in the town before hastily gathering some supplies and making (what turned out to be) my final journey to Warrow's Place. Here, the quiet dignity and spirituality of the natives brought into sharp focus all that was wrong with western society. These people lived with the land, not seeking to tame it. I found them to be happier by far, and more content than the richest of men.

Once again, I spent some time with a sloth for company. Details of my observations can be found in my little book, so I will not repeat them here. Being the dry season, I was able to enjoy the interior regions and follow my whims in relative comfort. Since my previous visit, when I solved the problem of preserving the extremities of quadrupeds, I had adjusted the process to make it less time consuming, but equally effective. I could preserve the smallest detail of dimples, warts and wrinkles. I could, in fact, make a specimen into anything I wanted. This being the case, I decided to have a little fun with a howler monkey.

Firstly, I preserved his head and shoulders faithfully to his appearance. Then I quite literally turned him upside down and preserved his hind quarters, but not as nature intended. I set myself the challenge of making his rear end look like a human face. I did it purely for my own amusement, and it has given me much of that. I write here not of the smile which its countenance brings to my lips each time I pass him at the foot of the stairs, but of the reaction it provoked. I never intended it to be a likeness of any individual, all such comparisons are in the eye of the beholder. The people of Georgetown accepted it as a good joke. I called it 'The Nondescript,' and used a sketch of it in the frontispiece of my little book, hoping that its appearance would stimulate to investigation those who are interested in museums and not be mistaken for a portrait of the author. I had no wish whatsoever that it should pass for any other thing than that which the observer should wish it to pass for. I have never considered myself obliged to tell its story, leaving it to others to decide what it is, and what it is not. Rumour abounded that I had shot a human being and mounted his head and part of his bust and was said to have bribed a Customs Official to secure the safe transition of the piece. There were those who said The Nondescript bore a resemblance to Mr Lushington, others said there was a likeness to a member of the House of Lords. All is in the eye of the beholder.

The Nondescript resides on his little plinth at the foot of the staircase at Walton Hall. He has become an old friend, oblivious of his fame and the amusement he has given. My cayman lives on the first landing, alongside the wooden hook with which he was caught, and a giant crab.

I left Georgetown in January 1825 with the Nondescript amongst my specimens. All went well until we reached English waters, where the weather was dismally bleak and cold in the Channel, precipitating a return of the ague. Despite this frequent reminder of the unwholesome climate of the tropics, part of my heart is forever wandering the forests of Guiana.

PART THREE

CHAPTER TWENTY

A Bachelor's Home.

Doctor Gilbey of Wakefield, our family physician at the time, became a frequent visitor at Walton Hall. For six months he grappled with my poor lungs and an irritation of the heart. By August of that year I was able to walk a hundred yards, but not without discomfort. The good Doctor's remedies, combined with my own, took a further three months to take full effect, by which time winter had arrived. Roaring fires and fresh air sustained my recovery. Whenever the ague threatened its shadow, I increased my daily dose of sulphate of quinine, derived from the quinoa bark of Guiana, and the shadow retreated after a few weeks.

During this inconvenience, I did not waste my time. My perimeter wall was at last complete and things generally went along pretty well. I put my enforced captivity to further use by setting about the publication of my notes. Most of the work was written in the depths of the forests, and so there was not a great amount of work to do. My good friend, Charles Winn, encouraged me to write a few words about myself, as a preface. I have since been assured that these words have been of interest to some, and this, along with the entreaties of my sisters-in-law, has encouraged me in writing these memoirs.

'Wanderings in South America, the North-West of the United States, and the Antilles', was published on the 1st September, priced £1.11s.6d. Over the years my words have been torn apart by the closet naturalists who still believe, amongst other fanciful notions, that a vulture will kill to eat. These criticisms, from men who have never observed this magnificent bird other than as a badly stuffed specimen in a museum, rankle me more than I can say. I have more respect for the Hanoverian rat. These are the same men who blame the scolytus beetle and the woodpecker for killing healthy trees. Nonsense! The scolytus only goes for rotting, diseased wood. I have proved this by taking the lower bark from healthy tree. Only then, when the bark is damaged, will a beetle enter, bore in and lay eggs. When hatched, the woodpecker hammers into the tree and eats his dinner. Without the scavengers, nature could not keep a balance. On the other hand, the parasitic mistletoe is praised for its ability to cure epilepsy and while I am happy to graft mistletoe to an apple tree, it is my belief that it is more likely to kill its host than cure an epileptic. If the sufferer has faith in a so-called remedy, then it will bring him hope, and it is not for me or any other to deny him his optimism.

During my absence, the keepers had done a tolerable job. There was a matter, however which constantly tumbled about in the back of my head, and there was but one man of whom I felt I could ask advice. I wrote to Charles Winn, asking if I might visit. His wife had produced another son, Edmund John. His reply came by return.

Dear Charles,
You know you are always welcome here at Nostell Priory. Priscilla and I look forward to your company. Would Friday week be convenient? We dine at seven.

Yours sincere friend,
Charles Winn.

Due to my poor state of health, walking to Nostell was out of the question and I was forced to travel by carriage. Fenton led me to the drawing room.

"My dear fellow," Charles shook me by the hand. "How are you? You have lost a deal of weight." I gave a short bow to Priscilla and kissed her hand.

I was wearing my blue swallowtail coat, and it hung loosely from my shoulders. "Then it is as well I did not visit earlier," I laughed, "for I believe I have gained a few pounds."

"Truly? Goodness me! You must have been no more than a skeleton. Let us hope you put on a little more before the night is out."

I turned to Priscilla. "How are your sons? In good health I trust?"

"Rowland and Edmund are both strong boys, thank-you, and a joy to us. I could not be happier."

"I am pleased to hear it."

"After dinner," my host said, "I would like to show you some additions to my collection of paintings. I have been to the salerooms recently."

The evening passed pleasantly. Charles and I shared many likes and dislikes, including an aversion to smoking and drinking. He was not opposed to a glass of wine, but neither did he withdraw after dinner to drink copious amounts of spirits. After showing me the paintings, we played a game of billiards. During our game I broached the subject which was so much on my mind.

"I have to think about marriage, you know."

"You do indeed, and what are your thoughts?" Charles took a shot and potted a ball. He moved around the table to line up another.

"I think the entire matter to be difficult. I do not have a suitable cousin, as was your good fortune, and cannot bear the prospect of entering formal society. I have not the courage for it. Where would I start?"

He looked up from the table. A smile played around the lips of my serious friend.

"Then you must look somewhere between the two. Surely you have friends with daughters?"

"I do, but they are all too young, and not of the Catholic Faith."

"They cannot be too young, Charles. Only too old."

I fell into the habit of carrying grains of corn in my pocket, thereby always ready to provide a meal for any bird which chose my company. Wouralia quickly learned this and she would trot towards me with great excitement whenever I emerged from the house, and would be waiting for me at the gate when I crossed the bridge on my return. When I scratched her ears, she nuzzled my pocket for more, and then nodded her head in thanks.

By working with my keepers and continuing to ban all fishing between Michaelmas and May Day, the numbers and variety of fish and all wildlife increased beyond all expectations.

That is not to say I eradicated the poachers, the foxes or the rats. One night, when I was going my rounds in Haw Park Wood, I came across two poachers. Upon seeing me, one of them fled, but the other stood his ground. By quick thinking, I took his knife out of his hand and struck him a punch to his gut. In a flash, he grabbed at me and my hat fell off. We tussled, falling to the ground together, he atop and I beneath. In the struggle he managed to get his hand down the side of my cravat. The fellow was clearly more experienced in combat than I. He twisted the cloth, and just as I thought I had gasped my last, instinct to survive pulled up my knees, and I thrust him off. He had had enough and ran away, taking my hat with him and leaving his own, no doubt in error. More significantly, he also left his knife and twenty snares. Despite the intervening years I find my hand at my throat as I write of the narrow escape, rubbing the flesh as if it were still sore.

Another incident which took place at night almost lost me a servant. Warwick had been despatched to Stonyhurst a few days earlier to collect a pair of swans which the Fathers had given to me. The night was as black as it was quiet, with no moon, and heavy cloud. Only the occasional screech of an owl broke the silence. I heard the cart approach, telling of the keeper's return. I stood beneath the portico, looking out but unable to see anything, when I heard a loud splash. I ran from the house in the direction of a man's voice, shouting as he thrashed about in the water, some few feet to the left of the footbridge. I knew the lake to be about eight feet deep at that point, but could see nothing, only hear his struggle.

"Come here, man. Come to my voice. Push your hands and feet against the water. Swim!" Eventually he made it to the wall, and I hauled out Albert Norris, a man whose duties included ferrying coal to the island. By this time, Ogden, who was employed as my mason in those days, had run across the bridge to assist. I took off my jacket and wrapped it around a shivering body.

"Th-thank-you, Squire," he shivered, "Y-your voice saved me. I-I was to drown for sure, I cannot swim."

"What on this earth were you doing out here, man?"

"I-I heard the cart, Squire, and r-ran out to help with the swans. I m-missed the bridge in the dark and ran s-s-straight into the lake."

"Warwick and Ogden will see to the swans. You must come with me." I led him back to the house. "Mrs Hutchinson! Bank up the kitchen fire." I shouted. Norris was frozen to the bone, but ultimately none the worse for his adventure. The incident caused me to consider planting a hedge around the edge of the island, but I never did as I countered it would impede the landings of waterfowl.

The winter was another harsh one, and I had every sympathy for the poor. But sympathy does not fill bellies. I could not sit at my table knowing that there were families in the village who felt the pangs of hunger. To alleviate the matter, I gave the sum of one hundred pounds to be distributed amongst the needy and apportioned a plot of ground to each poor family, that they might grow potatoes.

The following summer, and to my great delight, my old friend Edwin Jones came to stay for three months. We were school boys once again, climbing trees and seeking nests without the fear of punishment.

He brought with him a most unusual gift. Edwin Jones knew my humour like no other and had designed a pair of brass door knockers for Walton Hall. Each bears a likeness to myself, one has a smiling face, the other is wincing. The hammer of each is placed in the centre of my forehead, but the likeness with the smiling face has a fixed knocker, and can do me no harm.

Edwin was a talented artist who never had the opportunity to pursue his gift as a career, but his imagination knew no bounds. He was very complimentary of my taxidermy and roared with laughter when he saw The Nondescript. He had seen the printed sketch in my little book.

"Too comical for words, Charles. Have you any other pieces like this?" he asked.

"No." I replied, "but we could have some fun, if you like."

He sketched out a weird beast, challenging me to turn it into reality. While Edwin amused himself with his painting, I constructed 'The Nightmare' from various parts of various creatures. Like The Nondescript, it stands on a small plinth. The humanoid face is but three inches across and has a hideous grin. He has Satan's horns, and tusks in the shape of those of a wild boar. His ears are shaped like those of an elephant. The tiny human-like hands of a mole stick out at each side. He has one cloven hoof, and an eagle's foot with widely expanded talons, and the tail of serpent.

A small plaque with the words, 'Assidens procordis pavore somnos auferam,' is attached to the plinth. 'Sitting in the region of the heart, I take sleep by fear.'

The piece gathers dust on the fanlight shelf above the front door.

I had no idea what Edwin was up to with his palette and easel. On the evening before his departure, and to my astonishment, he presented me with three paintings. His boundless imagination had created literally fantastic works, which remain amongst my most prized possessions. My favourite is the one where the subject (a likeness of myself) sits astride a cayman, as a second image (of myself) helps the native Indians and Daddy Quashi to haul me and the cayman out of the river. The background shows many of my ornithological specimens, and the trees of Guiana. The other two paintings are of The Nondescript, and of a monkey feeding a cat.

After Edwin's departure I began to take particular note of the rooks, and counted one hundred and sixty nests. Some cared for their young right through until the second week in October. On the 12th of March, they once again set about the business of nesting. They took daily flight to Nostell. I ran across the fields to the sound of their cawing, too many to count, they were still arriving as I stood in the wide avenue before the house. Some days I would make sure I was there before them. I knew the precise time they set off, and with the aid of Captain Lauwens excellent watch was able to time them with great accuracy.

In the February of 1827, I estimated there to be between two and three thousand birds upon my lake. A moorhen came onto the island each morning, waiting patiently below the dining room window for some grains of corn.

Due to inclement weather and a further recurrence of the ague, it was late summer before I could travel to Dumbartonshire. With so many years having passed by, Charles and Robert had left home and were in business in Glasgow. Mrs McKenzie was still the housekeeper, and I recall her fussing around Mrs Edmonstone like an old hen, making sure her mistress was, if anything, rather too close to the fire. When Mr Edmonstone and I were at last alone in his study. I came straight out with my pre-occupation.

"I would like to ask for Anne's hand in marriage, when she is old enough." Mr Edmonstone leaned back in his chair, his eyes closed. Tears seeped through his eyelashes, glistening in the firelight. "Have I offended you?"

He shook his head. "No, Charles. You have made me much happier." He opened his eyes and dabbed away the tears with a handkerchief. "I know it could not be Eliza, her back and chest are weak, and she suffers from headaches. My dear Little Helen and Bethia are happy children, but too young, and you have a pressing need. While Anne is not robust, I am sure she will not disappoint you."

"I must attach a condition, which I hope you understand. If I am to marry—"

"She must convert to the Catholic Faith."

I was relieved by his pre-emption. "There is a convent in Bruges. Eliza could go with her, Little Helen too, if you so wish."

"Tell me, Charles, have you been thinking of this for some time, or did you ask me on impulse?"

With my fingers steepled, I tapped them together at their tips, I tried to recall when I first felt an attachment to Anne. "I do believe I fell in love with Anne when she first held my hand at Warrow's Place—or maybe—maybe when I first saw her as a babe in arms."

"Definitely not an impulse," he smiled, "I wondered if you had suddenly seen a solution to my worries, and that you might live to regret it. I always thought you to be a confirmed bachelor, despite the pressure to produce the next generation of Watertons."

Anyone who looked at him would discern he was not in the best of health.

"I shall always do all I can to ensure your family are comfortable." My friend closed his eyes again. Silence held the air. After a minute or so I said, "You are agreeable to my proposal?"

"I am," he nodded, his composure quite recovered. "But Little Helen is too young for Bruges, in both years and intellect." I nodded back and by the time I left all was convivial. Upon my return to Walton Hall I wrote to the Mother Superior of the Convent des Anglais, Rue Carmes, Bruges, and everything was soon arranged. Eliza and Anne were to be instructed over the following two years, under the care of Mother Nyren. Meanwhile, Anne and I were officially engaged.

To my great sadness, Charles Edmonstone never became my father-in-law. He died early the following year, leaving his wife and younger daughters at the mercy of Mrs McKenzie. Eliza and Anne were comforted by the good sisters of the Convent, and by the knowledge and understanding of their father being in a better place. Naturally I wrote a letter of condolence to Mrs Edmonstone, imploring her to come to live at Walton Hall with Little Helen and Bethia, but she refused my offer.

With the completion of my wall, the problem of foxes taking both waterfowl and game birds disappeared overnight. The acres within were too few to sustain a lair, but the fox is a wily creature and his cunning worthy of respect. Given the opportunity to visit and steal, he will take it. I once came across a young fox while setting rat poison traps close by the northern gate. His ears were alert to me, his eyes fixed and unblinking as if he asked, 'What are you doing here?' I was puzzled as to how he had gained entry, knowing one of my keepers would have informed me had there been a breach of the wall. In quest of the answer, I went through the gate and into the adjoining pasture where I saw exactly how the young fellow had accessed my sanctuary. I had asked White to replace a rotting gate in a field boundary, and he had leaned the old one against the wall, thus creating a convenient ladder. I thought, perhaps, I might prop it up on the other side but instead I left the gate open to make it easier for Mr Fox to return to his family and take his chances against the scarlet jackets.

Many years later a similar offence was committed, this time forcing the use of a gun. I had two very beautiful Egyptian ganders, and the death of one of them was due to the negligence of one of my farming tenants. He had placed a sheep rack close to my wall, providing easy access for a fox. Anyone who is familiar with the Egyptian breed will know they are a feisty bird. My fellow would have put up a fight, but one he was bound to lose against a hungry fox. The evidence was irrefutable. Pawprints in the snow showed where he had jumped down, run parallel to my wall for fifty yards or so, and then down to the lakeside. His success would motivate a return, and I had no intention of giving up my remaining Egyptian. With the assistance of Ogden, I set up an old spring gun with a wire attached to the trigger. We thought our trickery had a poor chance, but next morning the thief was lying dead as mutton. The whole of the charge had passed through his liver and heart, so he had not suffered.

"Perhaps," I said, "I should have had you remove the sheep rack and left it at that."

Ogden looked surprised. "But Squire, he had tasted goose, and would have been forever trying for more." He was right of course, and even the foxhunters who could have had a day's sport told me I did right in blowing the thief to atoms.

I have refrained from mentioning anything to do with politics, beyond the restrictions all English Catholics have endured since the time of the Old Goat's marriage to the Boleyn woman. The politicians had slowly been forced to slacken the rules against us, and public Mass became legal. Prior to 1828, I rode the twelve miles to Leeds once a week for Mass, but in the above-mentioned year, my journey to Leeds became unnecessary as St Austin's Church opened its doors in Wakefield. Although inauspicious from the outside, the brickwork is handsome in its own way, and the presence of God within is entirely unmistakable. I darken the doors of the Protestant church in Sandal when there is no alternative. Perhaps I should explain. Catholics still cannot have their own cemetery, but we

Watertons have our crypt at St Helen's, which dates back to the time when all churches were Catholic.

In the April of the following year, with the Duke of Wellington as Prime Minister and Sir Robert Peel as Home Secretary, the so-called Catholic Relief Act passed through the Houses of Parliament. Peel had opposed any form of emancipation for years, but with Daniel O'Donnell's election, he was forced to concede civil strife in Ireland to be a greater danger than the presence of a Catholic in Parliament.

The entire Act was a sham. Rather than improve the Irish lot, it made it worse. By increasing the voting threshold of wealth five-fold, thousands lost the vote. The word 'relief' is an imposter. There is nothing in the act to relieve the starving and half naked poor of Ireland. I don't believe for one moment that Sir Robert Peel cared one fig as to whether the soul of a Catholic went up to the King of Brightness or descended to the King of Brimstone. His intention was to bind the church to the state for financial reasons. War is expensive. Clauses and provisos abound in the Act. To my dismay, many Catholics signed Peel's Oath, happily swearing,

'I do hereby disclaim, disavow, and solemnly abjure any intention to subvert the present Church establishment within this realm...'

I shall never sign it, not because *I* wish to subvert anything, but because *it* seeks to subvert the Catholic Church, once and for all. It is the opposite of that which it pretends to be. The clause which particularly offends me forbids Jesuits and other religious orders from accepting novices, in the hope, no doubt, of their eventual extinction. Jesuits are particularly singled out! How, in all of Christendom, could I sign that? I quote part thirty-four.

'And it be further enacted that in case any person shall after the commencement of this Act, within any part of the United Kingdom, be admitted or become a Jesuit, or brother or a member of any such religious order, community or society aforesaid, such person shall be deemed and taken to be guilty of a misdemeanour, and being thereof lawfully convicted, shall be sentenced and ordered to be banished from the United Kingdom for the term of his natural life.'

CHAPTER TWENTY-ONE

From Utopia to Hedes.

Let us move on to the happier times. In the May of 1829, I travelled to the Convent des Anglais, Rue des Carmes, Bruges. On Monday, the eleventh day of that month, at five-thirty in the morning, I became the happiest man alive when I married Anne. My wife was seventeen years of age, delicate as the petal of a rose, and with the grace and beauty of the gentlest soul. Blonde curls framed the prettiest face I have ever seen.

Eliza returned to England, taking gifts from Anne to her sisters. On her way to Dumbartonshire, Eliza stayed at Walton Hall for a week or so. She and my sister, Helen, attended to the changes necessary for the presence of a lady of the house. Mary Ann Day was employed as my wife's personal maid, and one of the larger bedrooms on the first floor was decorated and furnished in a feminine manner. New bedlinen and curtains were purchased. Meanwhile, Anne and I visited Antwerp, Paris and Ghent. Oh, how I enjoyed walking with her at my side, her arm through mine, absorbing the admiring glances of fellow promenaders. I suspect some pondered as to whether she was my wife or my daughter, or perhaps my niece, but I cared not one fig of what others thought. I bought many little trinkets for her along the way, as mementoes of the places we visited. Our tour lasted three months, terminating where we had started, in Bruges.

Naturally, we called at the Convent, where we were warmly received by Mother Nyren. A letter had arrived for Anne. I watched her pretty smile as she gazed at her name, 'Mrs Charles Waterton.'

"It is from Eliza, Charles. I know her hand." She opened it slowly, as if savouring the moment. Tucked inside, she found a second letter, from Little Helen. As she read, I deduced from her countenance that all was not well, and after reading both letters, she handed them to me. They were dated June 23rd, and so were over a month old. The first was from Eliza, and I copy them here with the permission of my sisters-in-law.

Cardross House, Dumbartonshire.

My Dearest Anne,

Forgive my not writing sooner, as promised, but matters regarding the household of Cardross House have prevented my doing so. On arrival, I found our poor dear mother in a most pitiful state. She is reduced to a mere skeleton, unable to move without assistance. Mrs McKenzie has behaved in a most shameful manner towards her and the whole family. It has been quite clearly proved that she mixed a considerable quantity of laudanum in the wine mother drank, and that she stole jewels from her.

Cousin Archy was useless. At first, he took Mrs McKenzie's side, but was forced to see the error of his ways when confronted with the evidence. The whole town seems to know our shame. The people stare at me most dreadfully, and I sometimes feel inclined to knock them down.

Little Helen was summoned to appear as a witness in the Sheriff's Office. Thankfully, her examination was short, for she is far from well. The poor thing has come through a great deal. Mother's maid tells me that before our dear father's death he became so fond of Little Helen that she had to sleep in his room with him.

She is now quite determined to become a Catholic and would give anything to get to Bruges right away but knows she must wait for the new intake in September. She is already well instructed and since my return does nothing but read my books.

I am sure everything will become right in the fullness of time.

When I visited Walton Hall, I found it to be quite beyond description, especially the lake. Lay aside any fears, dear Anne, Mrs Carr spoke in the kindest manner, and said she longed very much for your arrival in England.

Please give my kindest remembrances to your husband and thank him for the kindness he has always shown to me.

Yours, with greatest affection,

Eliza.

The letter from Little Helen.

My Dear Anne,

Allow me to return to you my best thanks for the beautiful neckband which you were so kind to send for me. I shall wear it with the greatest pleasure. Bethia has asked me to thank-you for the purse which you sent her. Dear little creature she is so proud of it. She asked me to tell you she will write when her cough ceases to pursue her.

I congratulate you most sincerely on your marriage, and trust that you may be long spared to enjoy the happy prospects that are now open to you.

I send kind love to you, and everything that is kind to Mr Waterton. I am, my dear Anne,

Your attached sister,
Helen Edmonstone.

As I read them now, Little Helen's short note speaks volumes from that which it does not say. Had it not been accompanied by Eliza's letter, I might have wondered at its brevity. Little Helen is a dear soul. I have never known a word of complaint to leave her lips.

Naturally, the letters unsettled my wife, and I admit to being glad they had not found us earlier and spoiled our honeymoon. We had travelled by train through Holland and France, and had Anne not been struck with sickness, we would have travelled further. She brightened every afternoon, and I should have realised the cause, but as my only other experience of a woman with child had been my mother, who produced children as easily as shelling peas, I failed to connect Anne's sickness with her happy condition.

Once back at Walton Hall, our new family physician, Doctor Houseman, quickly diagnosed her pregnancy, and I do believe Anne was truly shocked. The doctor assured her the sickness would soon pass, but it did not. My poor, frail wife suffered right up until two weeks before her confinement. Being such a delightful soul, she busied herself by making lace bonnets and gowns for the baby, without a word of complaint.

Eliza had repaired to Dumbartonshire to care for her mother, Little Helen and Bethia, while all the time suffering a dreadful cough, exacerbated by the cold, damp air of Scotland.

Given all that dear Little Helen had been through, it came as a relief to us all when the time came for her to go to Bruges. Eliza arranged for her to be escorted there by Mr Gordon, the trusted family friend who had been appointed her guardian after her father's death.

My wife wrote to her frequently, her letters are treasured.

Walton Hall,
November 16th, 1829

My Dearest Little Helen,
Mr Gordon paid us a short visit on his return from Bruges and informed us of your safe arrival at the ever-dear Convent. Charles has travelled to Scotland with him because Eliza had written and told us her chest was as bad as it had ever been. We are so very worried. My husband is to try to persuade her to come and stay with us. I think a change of air will be more beneficial than anything a doctor may prescribe. I miss Charles most dreadfully. If you write to her, please do your utmost to convince her to come to Walton Hall.
I suppose you are beginning to get used to the confinement, change of diet, and the rules.
I haven't mentioned religion, because I sincerely hope that you have now seen and heard enough to convince you that the Catholic religion is the only true one. I know it is difficult at first, but I would cheerfully and willingly submit to it all again, knowing the peace of mind and consolation that follows the struggle.
Ask the good nuns to pray for me, they are always dear to my heart for their kindness to me while under their care.
Your attached sister,
Anne Mary Waterton.

Shortly after this letter was written, I had a visit from my solicitor. I recall it was a bitterly cold day. I was about to put on my coat, and check Wouralia had enough straw to keep her warm, when I saw Mr Nettleton walking across the bridge. He had such haste and purpose in his footsteps that I knew I would not like whatever business had brought him to Walton Hall.

"Whatever is the matter?" I asked.

"We need to speak in private." He had a quiet, clipped tone which worried me far more than if he had shouted at me. I led the way to the drawing room where he perched on the edge of his seat, as I leaned back in mine.

"Have you come to inform me of a death?" I asked.

"No, nothing like that."

"Then what can it be, this bad news of yours? Am I mysteriously bankrupt? If it is not death, it can be righted, whatever it may be." I remember smiling, but my smile was not returned.

"I understand, Mr Waterton, that your wife is with child."

I nodded. "That is true, and a reason for happiness, is it not?"

"Indeed, yes, but…"

"But what? Spit it out, man."

"You were married abroad, were you not, in a Catholic ceremony. Your child will, therefore, be regarded as a bastard under English law, unless you marry again, here, before the birth."

Disbelief shuddered through me. Numbed by the shock, it took a while for me to find my voice, and then it was no more than a whisper. "How, in God's name, can I tell Anne? How can I ask her to travel to a Protestant church?"

"I'm afraid I cannot help you there, sir. I am but a lawyer, but I advise you to do so as soon as possible. There will be bans to be read and so forth. I am sure the vicar at Sandal will be sympathetic to a quiet ceremony." We sat for a while in silence, watching the flames lick the coals.

"So, this is what our government calls 'Catholic Emancipation,' is it?" I stood up and paced the length of the room.

"I am not saying I agree with the law, Mr Waterton, but I feel it is my duty to inform you of the matter. I knew it would displease you⬚"

"Displease?" I am ashamed to say I shouted, "is that what you call it? My wife, I repeat, my *wife,* is to go to a Protestant church as if she were a common whore, caught out, and marrying to please an irate father, with a gun at the head of her lover. The humiliation of it beggars all belief." I sank back into the chair, head in hands.

"I sympathise, but—"

"Go, please, Mr Nettleton I do not mean to rant at you." I heard the door open and close, and leant back, tears of frustration burned behind closed eyes. I berated myself for such stupidity because I should have remembered this to be the case. In my joy I had forgotten this thorn in the side of all Catholics. My elation had swept away the malevolence of the Protestant state. Anne and I were married, but our child would be a bastard. Leaden legs carried me up the stairs. Anne lifted her head from the pillow as I entered the room.

"Whatever is wrong, Charles? You look worried." I sat on the bedside, my rough, calloused hand holding her dainty fingers as I related the solicitor's news.

"Such is the stupidity of the law, my dearest." I had no idea how she would react, or if I had any expectation of tears, but she smiled her sweet smile, and sat up to kiss my cheek.

"God has witnessed our marriage, Charles, and blessed us in the True Faith. Nothing can change that. If this ceremony could be arranged as soon as possible, and in the afternoon, when the sickness passes, I would be grateful to you."

Our second wedding took place on 20th December, 1829. My good friend Edwin Jones travelled to Yorkshire to be a witness, the other being Joseph Wood, a Catholic with whom I was acquainted and who lived in Sandal. Edwin drove us to St Helen's Church. Neither Anne nor I desired any fuss. To add further insult, the certificate named Anne as 'Anne Mary Edmonstone of this parish, a spinster alias his wife, known as Mrs Waterton.' We returned to Walton Hall, and never spoke of the day's events, settling back into our quiet routine as if it had never taken place. It would be a further seven years before Catholics were permitted to hold marriage ceremonies and keep a register, and twenty years before a Catholic Diocese could be established.

Doctor Houseman attended frequently, assuring us that all was well. Anne wrote to her sisters, and passed the time at her needlework. The following letter demonstrates Anne's gentle character in a way far better than I could ever describe.

Walton Hall
February 18th, 1830.

My Dearest Helen,
Your letter of the 7th of January, informing us of your reception into the Catholic Church gave us infinite pleasure and now I hasten to offer you our sincere congratulations on an event of such great importance to your future happiness.
I have been, and still am, very much troubled with severe pain in my back, which is made worse by the slightest exertion. Doctor Houseman has ordered me to keep as quiet as possible.
Eliza wrote to me about six weeks ago. Charles was unable to persuade her to come to Walton Hall and so she remains in Cardross with Mother and Bethia. Charles feels that as Mother will not leave the house at all, our brothers should take responsibility, but it seems that Eliza has a different opinion.
Please give my kindest love to the nuns,
Accept my kind love, and pray for,

Your attached sister,
Anne Mary Waterton.

No-one could fail to love Anne. Mrs Hutchinson and Mary Ann attended her every need as if she were a daughter, whilst keeping their professional distance. My own emotions were a mixture of excitement, love, and fear. How I wished I could have endured her back pain for her. Both Doctor Houseman and Mrs Beresford, the village midwife, recommended she rest.

In the latter weeks of her pregnancy, rather than risk disturbing Anne's sleep, I returned to my childhood bedroom. Each morning, Cook prepared a light break-fast, and I took it to her on a tray, but Anne would just shake her head.

"I cannot, Charles. I will eat later in the day, but not now."

"Nothing at all, my dear?" She would shake her head again. True to her word, Anne would have a bowl of soup in the afternoon.

Mrs Beresford tried to persuade her to take more sustenance, but to no avail.

"Your wife should eat more, Squire, just a little at a time but at frequent intervals." Mrs Beresford clamped her hat firmly on her head. "I shall call again in a few days, that is unless you call me."

"I cannot force her, Mrs Beresford."

"No, and no more can I, but she will need her strength soon."

"Why does she have such pain now?" I asked, thinking it a reasonable question. Mrs Beresford looked at me as if I were a fool.

"The baby has turned, ready for the birth, but is in such a position as to press into her spine."

"Why will she not eat?"

"I believe the baby is a big one. Your wife is tiny and non too robust. She has no room left inside for a full stomach, that is why I say she should eat a little and often."

The matter-of-fact logic of the experienced midwife took a few moments to sink into my dull, male brain. I took a deep breath to speak, but no words came. I exhaled with a sigh. I called after her as she bustled down the path.

"Thank-you, Mrs Beresford."

On the morning of the 5th of April, Mrs Hutchinson approached me as I made my way to the kitchen.

"She'll not want to eat this morning, Squire," the housekeeper said, "the baby is on its way." I was rooted to the spot, entirely speechless. "I have sent for Mrs Beresford." I turned and ran, two stairs at a time, to Anne's bedside. Mary Ann was with her.

"Do not worry, Charles," she whispered, "all will be over soon, and we shall be parents."

"Dearest Anne, I am helpless."

"No, Charles. You are the best husband I could wish for. Go now, go and pray for our unborn child, that he or she will soon be safely here. Mary Ann will care for me until Mrs Beresford arrives."

I cannot remember in any detail the events between that moment and the birth of our son. I know Cook did her best to tempt me to eat, but I could not swallow a crumb, and nor could I sleep while my dear wife struggled so. I went for a walk, but was not away for long, fearing something may happen whilst I was out of earshot. The sun crept slowly across the sky that day with every minute turning into an hour. As the night approached, I sat on the straw in Wouralia's shelter with her beside me, forelegs tucked under her body as she nuzzled my pocket for corn.

Dawn broke, and Anne laboured on. I tried, without success, to work at my taxidermy. I walked to the stables, and chatted with the groom and the gardener, but cannot recall a word of our conversation. I dare not go so far as the grotto. Had I known it would be a further twenty hours before our son was born, I might have done so.

Edmund came into this world, a fine big healthy boy, shortly before dawn on the 7th of April, in the year 1830. My face ached with smiling as I held him in my arms and he grasped my little finger. The joy of his touch reached the very wingtips of my delight.

My dear Anne was exhausted. Doctor Houseman recommended a light diet, and plenty of rest. A wet nurse came from the village, and all was set for a happy family life.

What happened over the following twenty days is no news to anyone who knows me. Anne took a fever, as is not uncommon after childbirth. My sister, Helen, and her husband came to stay. Robert kept me company while Helen lavished every care upon my poor, dear Anne. When it became clear that she would not recover, Robert sent for Father Norris from St Austin's Church.

With the lightest touch, Anne pressed her fingers in my hand. "Do not grieve for me, Charles. I am content in God's will." Her whispered words have echoed in my head from that day to this.

During the last week of her life, neither Father Norris from St Austin's nor Doctor Houseman left Walton Hall. I held her hand as the priest administered the last rites and sacraments. She passed from this earthly life on 27th April, shortly after midnight. She lies in the centre of the Waterton crypt in St Helen's Church. There was no ceremony, our prayers for her soul having been said in the Chapel of Catherine of Alexandria. Only myself, my sister Helen and her husband, and Doctor Houseman were in attendance.

From the day of Anne's death, I have not slept in a bed. This was not a conscious decision at the time, but a habit which evolved from those dark days when I wished away the dawning of the sun. Its gaudy cheerfulness slighted my grief. I could no more lie in a bed than I could turn back the clock, such physical comfort being disparate with my spirits and a bed the embodiment of my loss. Even the softness of a pillow was too much to bear. Instead, I took a block of firewood from the basket at the side of the fireplace in my attic room and rested my grieving head upon it. These days I have a beechwood block for a pillow. I fashioned it from a root about two feet long by nine or ten inches wide, and eight inches deep, creating a slight hollow on one side where my cheek rests in as much comfort as I need. Years of use have given it a polished appearance. When travelling I use my portmanteau as a pillow.

Little Helen was informed by Mr Gordon. She has shown me his letter.

1st May, 1830.
My Dear Child,
It falls to my lot to communicate a piece of news which will harrow your soul with grief. If it were not for your religion, I know it would be worse. Your dearest Anne, pride of the Convent in which you presently reside, and object of the love of her husband, your sister, and

yourself, is no more. She has begun that life of happiness which will last for eternity, and in which there will be no sorrow. She suffered terribly in her final week, when every possible attention was given to her by her husband, her physician, and her priest. Father Norris has written to Eliza, and she has shown me the letter, in which he says that he has never witnessed so much faith, resignation, and devotion in a dying person. He wrote of her praying constantly that the will of God be done. You may well imagine the extent of her husband's grief, and that of Eliza. Religion whispers its thousand consolations to her, as it will to you.

Your little nephew, Edmund, is well and thriving, unaware of the terrible loss that he has sustained. Eliza says she will write to you next week. Your brothers are well, and Bethia's cough has subsided.

Your affectionate guardian,
John Gordon.

A wet nurse and two nursery maids were employed, and in the knowledge that my son was well cared for, I left Walton Hall and its sorrow to visit the only man I knew who could guide me to the future.

"Charles! How delightful to see you..." Father Clifford's voice trailed off as he waved me into his room. This most wise of men perceived that all was not well. "What has happened? Why the sadness?"

I sat on the rug as I had as a pupil, and he in his chair. Nothing had changed other than the ages of the occupants of the little room. He knew that I had married, for I had written to him with the joyous news. When I told of my being a widower with a baby son he nodded slowly in silent understanding. We knelt before the crucifix and statue, praying for Anne's soul. I cannot remember his words, only that they gave the first crumb of comfort.

We dined in the happy company of the pupils and the other priests and Masters. How I wished I were one of them. Later, when Father Clifford and I were once again in his room, I broached the subject of the future.

"It is my intention, Father, to take Holy Orders. I can see no other way to —"

Father Clifford held up his hands. "Charles, before you go any further, please consider that the life of a priest is not an escape. It cannot change the past." His words shocked me to silence. "God has other work for you."

"I had not thought of escape, Father, but of penance."

His eyes widened. "Penance? How so?"

"If I had not permitted myself to be bound by society's pressure to produce an heir, Anne would still be alive. I killed her, don't you see? I wish a thousand times a day that I had not married her, that I had been as an elder brother and cared for her and her sisters without allowing myself to be persuaded of the importance of lineage. How else can I atone for my sin, if not by giving my life to God? The penance must fit the sin, is that not so?"

"Charles, you are an intelligent man, but grief is clouding your thoughts. Stay with us for a while, and then return to your son. It will be bad enough for him to grow up motherless without being abandoned by his father. He will need you far more than God needs another priest. These walls will help your wounds to heal, but they are not your future. Spend time with your brother, William will be a willing audience."

He was right of course. Of all my siblings, William had the most quiet and natural character, and a life in the sanctuary of Stonyhurst suited him well. Scattered to the corners of the world, we brothers communicated by letter, but infrequently. Thomas had sent a letter of condolence, but Edward would as yet have been unaware of Anne's death.

William listened to my outpourings of grief as we wandered the hills and fells, and I slowly began to accept God's will. My conversations with my brother provided much food for thought, and threw my thoughts back to the simplicity of the lives of the indigenous people of South America.

By the time I returned to Walton Hall, and to my relief, Eliza was in residence. While I had been unable to persuade her to come for her own health, she had done so for the sake of her nephew. Edmund was a contented child, I do not remember ever hearing him cry, although I suspect he must have. He had the sweetest face. To look at him was to look at his mother, such a bitter sweet feeling to touch his blonde curls, his smooth cheek, his long, delicate fingers. Only his pale blue eyes, I concede, are as my own.

Eliza had received a letter from her sister.

The Convent des Anglais

Carmes,

Bruges.

15th June 1830.

My Dearest Eliza,

I fully expected to have received a letter from you before now, and by your silence I begin to fear you are unwell, or that something is wrong. Sister Alicia has asked me to write a few lines. She wishes to know when you are coming for me and whether she should buy a bonnet and a frock, or will you bring them. I hope, upon reception of this, you will reply without delay.

I have lately been troubled with pains in my back and head. I have a strengthening plaster on my back and today have had another applied to the back of my neck for my headaches. I think it will do me some good, at least for the present.

Have you heard from our brothers, or Bethia? Is there any news of Mother? Dear Anne's death will indeed be a great shock to her. I am afraid she will be unwell.

Give my kindest regards to Mr Waterton and kiss dear Edmund for me. I do not expect your answer next week, but I shall be greatly disappointed if I don't get it the week following.

Adieu, dearest Eliza,

Your affectionate sister,

Helen Edmonstone.

Eliza showed me the letter.

"You must reply, Eliza."

"I shall, Charles, and I shall write to Mother Nyren also. Little Helen may be too much trouble for them."

"Arrangements must be made for her to come here. Tell Mother Nyren we shall bring her home as soon as possible, and next month at the latest."

There was no doubt other than Little Helen would come to live at Walton Hall, and the sooner the better. She had been right to fear for her mother, who died within the twelvemonth. Bethia remained in Scotland under the guardianship of her brothers and Mr Gordon.

Eliza soon received a reply from Mother Nyren.

The Convent des Anglais,
Bruges.

Dearest Eliza,

I shall not miss one post in replying to you. Your concern for your sister is both touchingly affectionate and unnecessary. Do you not know the hearts of your Bruges friends to be most sincerely and tenderly attached to you and to all yours? Set your dear heart at ease. Little Helen does not, and never has given us any trouble. Dear Mr Waterton and yourself may be quite certain that we shall consider ourselves happy to have her here for as long as she is allowed to remain with us.

I add one thought, which is that you must not expect her to make much progress in the scholastic way. She is often unable to apply herself to learning, and we will never force her in any way, for we know she does her best despite her aches and pains. When free of suffering she takes up her lessons, but when unable to do so she advances in the knowledge of religion and piety. She is a dear, good girl. I think she is perfectly happy and will leave us with regret. At this moment she is not in the best of health, but I do not consider her too ill to permit her to stay here longer.

I long to see you, dear Eliza. Poor Mr Waterton, how my heart bleeds when I think of him. I pray every day that God may comfort him.

It is good that you are with him, for I know that you will soothe his grief with your sisterly and affectionate conduct. We are delighted at the thought of your visit. Little Edmund is, I suppose, too young to be of the party.

Little Helen sends her very best love to you, and to Mr Waterton. She says she longs to see you and will write very soon.

God bless you and all yours in the earnest prayers of

Your affectionate friend,
Marian Nyren.

I purchased a carriage, large enough for four people and their luggage to be comfortably conveyed, and we travelled to the Victoria Hôtel. Our party consisted of myself, Eliza, Mr Gordon, his manservant and Mary Ann. The manservant rode atop. Our driver was one of the grooms. The following morning, he drove us to the quayside before returning to Walton Hall.

We enjoyed a calm crossing, and many tears were shed upon our arrival at the Convent, Eliza and Little Helen had not seen one another since the loss of their sister, and their grief was yet to run its course. Dear Little Helen looked smaller than ever, as if she had shrunk inside her novice's habit. Dark rings beneath hollowed eyes stared with an emptiness. To see her and Eliza clinging together was to know their deep sorrow. Only the knowledge of Anne's having gone to a better place gave them comfort.

Eliza and Mary Ann stayed at the Convent, while Mr Gordon, his manservant, and I took rooms at the Hôtel du Commerce. At that time, the people of Bruges complained bitterly of living under the Dutch flag and the Protestant rule of William. Trouble was brewing, and I sympathised with their cause. Suppression, poverty and unemployment fuel revolution, and there was plenty of all three. For all this, I perceived no direct threat to our safety, and Mr Gordon and I walked out with the ladies each afternoon. Little Helen seemed a little overwhelmed when she first stepped into the street, but with Eliza on one arm and Mary Ann on the other, she was soon looking around at life outside the Convent. I recall a conversation as we took tea one afternoon.

"Mother Nyren says you can stay at the Convent, if you wish, sister dear." Eliza said.

"Oh no! I mean—I love the Convent, and the nuns, but I want to see Edmund, and to play with him." Little Helen melted hearts wherever she went. Her innocent honesty and childlike manner never failed to make those around her smile. When the time came for us to leave it was all fuss and love from the nuns. If Mother Nyren told us once that we were all welcome to stay longer, she said it a hundred times, insisting that we bring Edmund on our next visit.

In the weeks since Anne's death I had had little time to myself, and so I decided to remain in Europe for a short while. My sisters-in-law would be safely escorted, giving no need for me to cross the North Sea just to turn around and cross it back again.

With no particular destination in mind, I took the stage-coach to Liège, and then travelled on to Cologne and Frankfurt, taking every opportunity to visit churches and museums along my way. From there I went to Bavaria, and the little town of Würzburg, where I obtained permission to view a collection of fine paintings belonging to an elderly gentleman by the name of Herr Berwind. His heavily accented English was perfectly grammatical.

"I have collected the paintings over many years, my first purchase being in 1798, when war—war—war was all we knew. It came to my notice that the price of art is downwardly affected by revolution, and began to buy in earnest. They are all for sale."

The collection was varied, with artists as diverse as their subjects. I stopped in my tracks and turned to face him.

"But why, Herr Berwind? Why sell when it has taken so long to—"

"I am eighty-two years of age, Mr Waterton, and dying." Leaning heavily on his walking stick, he peered at me with the concentration of the partially blind. "I can barely see them, moreover, when I am gone my family will have to pay heavy taxes on their value. If they are sold, I can give them the money before I leave this world."

As we walked from room to room, Herr Berwind's stick tap-tap-tapped the polished floor. I admired his calm acceptance of death, and this somehow brought into focus my own need to accept widower-hood. I thought it would be a shame if his collection were split up. I expect my opinion was, in some part, a consequence of my treatment at the hands of Mr Lushington. There was no-one more likely than I to be sympathetic concerning the unfair demand for taxes.

"How many are there?"

"One hundred and forty-eight."

"Do you think, Herr Berwind, that we could come to an agreeable price if I were to buy them all?"

"I am sure that is possible—but tell me, Mr Waterton, do you intend to sell them for a profit?"

"No, sir. That had not crossed my mind. Truly, it had not. They would hang in my home."

He pulled a bell cord and a manservant appeared. My command of the German language is sufficiently good for me to understand he had ordered coffee to be served in the drawing room. I am not a lover of coffee but drank it on this occasion, not wanting to offend my host. We agreed a price, and I promised to return in the afternoon. The bank in Würzburg was most accommodating, and by four o'clock the money had been transferred from my account to that of Herr Berwind. All that remained was for me to arrange for the paintings to be properly packed and transported.

I wrote to Eliza, notifying her of my purchases and asking her to have them displayed wherever she and Little Helen thought fit. With such thoughts of home, I headed back to Bruges. My European tour had been as pleasant as it had been uneventful, but I was not yet home. As previously mentioned, the people of Flanders were unhappy with the rule of Dutch William. They grumbled as they went about their work, as they ate their food, as they drank in the beer houses, wanting no more to do with his idea of a United Kingdom of the Netherlands. These were a people prepared to fight for real liberty in religious matters, a principle with which I empathised as only an English Catholic could.

I alighted from the stage-coach in the large square in the centre of Bruges. When I had arranged my accommodation for the night at the Hôtel du Commerce, I headed back towards the square, my destination being the grille in the wall of the Convent in order to pass a message to Mother Nyren that I was in Bruges and would call on the morrow. The air hung heavy in its stillness, bristling with inevitability akin to the compressed air in the advent of a thunderstorm. Darting shadows, their footsteps like the first drops of rain, persuaded me that danger was not far away and that I should seek shelter. I spotted a partially open door but before I could reach its threshold, musket balls whistled past me on all sides and as the storm of revolution broke free I was, quite literally, caught in the crossfire. As I put my foot on the doorstep, a fat old dame shut the door full in my face, leaving me to take my chances with the musket balls.

"Thank-you, old lady," I shouted at the peeling paintwork, "it must make you happy to put a foreigner in danger." Having had the chance of safety slammed in my face, there was nothing for it but to make a run for my Hôtel. The owner was peering through a window as I entered the courtyard. When he saw me, he ran outside and opened the gate, shutting it quickly behind me, before turning the key and drawing a bolt.

"Thank God you are safe, Mr Waterton. All my guests are here now. I fear it will be a long night."

"I think you are right," I replied, "I thank you for your concern."

"My other guests are in the dining room, sir. Will you join us for a glass of wine?"

"I thank you again, but no. It is time for me to retire to my room." With my hand on the rail of the wide, spiralling staircase I climbed to my room, wearied by relief. I was safe enough, but as a precaution I lay on the floor to the side of the bed furthest from the window, falling asleep to the sound of shattering glass as shops were looted by hungry revolutionaries.

By the end of that summer, Dutch William had been ousted, and the Belgium we know today began to enjoy religious freedom.

CHAPTER TWENTY-TWO

Fatherhood, and a New Routine.

I begin a new chapter here, as my life moved into a different era. Edmund, Nanny and the nursery maids were accommodated on the first floor of Walton Hall, as were Eliza and Little Helen. My sisters-in-law also had their own sitting room overlooking the rear of the island and the southern side of the lake. By the age of eight months, my son was able to sit unaided, and when I made faces at him, he rewarded me with a smile. Little Helen amused him with her natural playfulness. My concern over Edmund being deprived of maternal love faded a little each day as I witnessed the affection showered upon him by Eliza and Little Helen. Nanny informed me he slept through the night and was a child of the most delightful disposition. I cannot disagree with her opinion, not simply as a besotted father, but because not once did my son disturb my sleep. No longer a retreat for a crusty old bachelor, Walton Hall became a family home once more. My sister, Helen Carr, helped Eliza in those early days, setting on more staff, explaining the domestic arrangements and showing her the system of transporting coal and other goods to the island. The fires are lit summer and winter for I cannot bear to be cold. Should the weather be hot (which does occasionally happen in Yorkshire), the windows are opened. Around this time John Warrener came into my employ as butler, and William Ireland as my manservant. They are still here. Warrener has a young lad to help him now. Mrs Hutchinson reigned over three housemaids. Mary Ann became a personal maid to Eliza and Little Helen. Mrs Jenkins, the new cook, and her assistant, Tilly, were joined by two scullery maids. Three gardeners attended the kitchen garden and orchard, as well as keeping the island and the grotto in good order. Two grooms attended the horses, and the farm runs as smoothly today as it did then, under the management of Joseph Totty, who oversees both the permanent and seasonal labour.

I settled into a routine which has served me well ever since and is sufficient for my needs. Each evening, when I return to my room, I carry wood and coal up the stairs to set the fire ready for next morning. My Italian cloak provides warmth in the night, but in frosty weather, I also make use of a napless blanket. I light the fire, banking it to keep alight until I wake.

My everyday clothes are pegged on a rope which stretches across the room. The rope provides a place to sling my cloak and blanket during the day, and also the apron which I wear when about my taxidermy. It has a pocket in front for my knives and other tools. I have three shelves, one of which is my library of favourite books, all of which I have read many times. Don Quixote, Dryden's Chevy Chase, Dyer's Grongar Hill, Tristram Shandy, The Sentimental Journey, Goldsmith and White's Natural History of Selbourne, The Spanish Life of Francis Xavier, Ovid and Washington Irving are all well-thumbed. The other two shelves house the necessities for taxidermy, i.e., oil, varnish, spirits, pigments, powders, wire, pins, nails, beeswax and pieces of cork. I have an old pine table and cherry wood chair where I divest my specimens of all innards prior to preservation. Over the door hangs a painting of a lobster with some peaches and a pineapple. Like so many others in the house, it was part of Herr Berwind's collection. Eliza did not like it, so it was banished aloft. A map of the world, upon which I have marked the routes of my travels, and those of the Jesuit Missionaries, is pinned on the wall to the right. I put it where it receives no direct sunlight, in order to minimise its fading. A bowl, some soap, and a razor reside on a small table and my towel is on a roller behind the door.

I rise each morning at half past three o'clock to the calling of my Cochin-China cockerel. He is a huge fellow. My day begins a little later in the winter months, but never later than ten minutes after four. Old More keeps me to a timetable. I attend to the fire and sweep the hearth before lying down for another half hour, luxuriating as the flames lick their way to warmth. I then shave and dress before praying for an hour in the Chapel of Catherine of Alexandria. At five o'clock I return to my room where I read a chapter or two from my little library before writing letters and attending to my taxidermy. As Old More strikes eight, I go downstairs, where pigeon pie awaits.

Eliza sits at the opposite end of the table to myself, rightly taking the position of the lady of the house. Once replete (unless during Lent) I don an old jacket or coat, depending upon the weather conditions, and leave the house to attend to estate matters, with visits to tenants, discussions with Joseph Totty and patrolling with my keepers, returning to the house at noon, when, unless some domestic matter needs my attention, I read until dinner is served at half past one. Eliza likes to have the meals served at the same time each day, and I do not object. She tells me she became aware of the advantages of habitual punctuality during her time at the Convent. That being the case, I most certainly cannot grumble. Unlike those who follow fashion even in the household timetable, we continue to have our dinner served as the midday meal, after which I return to the outdoors until shortly before six o'clock, when tea is served. My sisters-in-law and I then retire to the drawing room where we sit before the fire until between eight and ten o'clock, when I take myself to my bed-less bedroom.

From the day of her arrival here, Little Helen has shown great interest in the birds, and often joins me on fine mornings as I take a stroll around the island. Her delight when a bird lands on the water is a joy to behold. She laughs and claps as if she has never before seen such a thing. Having adopted my habit of giving them a few crumbs, she has become especially popular with the wild ducks which follow her around like bridesmaids.

I have never known a bird to desert the nest as a result of my visiting to count the eggs. Once, I witnessed a young heron fall from its nursery, and was quickly on the scene. It appeared to be uninjured, so I secured it within my coat, climbed up, and replaced it in the nest. The anxious parents were back before I had reached the ground and, I am pleased to say, successfully reared the chick.

During Lent, I fast. The discipline lifts my faith, not only in religious matters, but in my physical condition. Bread, water, and weak tea with no cream, milk, or sugar are all that is needed to sustain my mind and body, and after the first few days, my stomach accepts its lot, and does not grumble too much. There are those who try to tempt me to a piece of gingerbread, knowing this to be my weakness. Sometimes I think Mrs Oldroyd and Eliza are in cahoots, although I am sure they mean well.

"Surely, Charles," Eliza might say, "a little sugar is good for you."

"Eliza," I say, "the Pope's padlock has been on my grinders since Ash Wednesday, and shall remain there until Easter Day." She will then tut-tut and bustle away, shaking her head.

My difficulties truly start when I break my fast and gorge on too much meat. Mrs Oldroyd (who does not usually leave the kitchen) comes to the dining room and triumphantly places a large meat pie before me with a flourish. After consuming more than my share, the ensuing gripes force me to the sofa, where I declare I shall be wiser the following year.

As much for Little Helen's pleasure as my own, I bought a telescope. It is a very good one, and cost twenty-six guineas, but as I told myself at the time, a telescope is something that is either excellent or useless and cannot be bought on the cheap. Mounted on a stand with castors, the observer is comfortably accommodated in an armchair which also has castors, enabling her or him to move from window to window of the drawing room and have a conversation, whilst all the time their eye is on the world outside, no matter what the weather.

When George Ord, my correspondent with whom I first became acquainted in Philadelphia, came to visit, he was fascinated by the differences between the birds of America and their English cousins. Such joy to converse with one whose principles and interests match one's own. We walked and talked in daylight and darkness of everything from politics to partridges, and never a word of disagreement. George and I could debate, rather than argue. We observed the crows, water birds and herons, the starlings, and the nightjars. He took interest in the pea fowl and hens, and their laying, and the swallows and swifts which nested in the farm buildings. As is the way of the American, he had no ceremony about him, and was a great favourite with the fishermen. From the comfort of the drawing room, and with the aid of my telescope, we watched a pair of white owls making preparation for a brood on the island, their chosen site being a sycamore stump.

All this is not to say I reneged on my social duties. We visited my friends at Nostell Priory and Mrs Beaumont at Bretton Hall where he was awestruck by the grand scale of the houses and their estates. Shortly after his return to the United States, I wrote to him with a mixture of news, good and bad.

The day after his departure, I spotted the golden headed wren, and two kingfishers. I wrote of the success of the white owls, with two chicks hatched in the stump, and that I had ordered the fishing cease, lest the activity disturbed the wildfowl which were due from the Arctic.

He had thought Mrs Beaumont to be a very grand old lady, despite her inability to hold a sensible conversation, and I knew he would be saddened to read of her death. It was reported she had awoken at about one o'clock in the morning and, in her confusion, told her maid that it was time to get up. The maid realised her mistress's mind was wandering and went to make her a cup of beef tea, but on her return, the old lady had already breathed her last. The future of the estate echoed that of Stonyhurst, insomuch as there was no heir to take residence. Sad to say, this has happened in many cases, and the big houses are boarded up. Forty servants were discharged from Bretton, and all the horses and carriages sold off.

An invitation arrived, requesting my presence at a meeting of naturalists and philosophers in York. Had George still been my guest I would have attended, but knowing it would be the usual round of foolish belief and intractable opinion, and without my American friend to back up my first-hand knowledge, I couldn't be bothered. Rather than spend my time with stuffed heads who would not listen to knowledge borne of experience, I made it my business to become more acquainted with the village of Walton and its residents. Being away from the turnpike roads, it is a quiet place, devoid of industry excepting what was, at that time, William Hodgson's Soapworks. Jack Ogden informed me that Mr Hodgson was having some difficulty with the Customs and Excise.

Naturally, I was interested, and made a point of visiting. I was ignorant, prior to my visit, of the complexities of taxation on soap manufacturers. I arrived at dinner time, and the men were sitting by the navigation eating their bread. I went to Mr Hodgson's office.

"I wish I had never become a soap maker, Squire, and that's the truth of it." He sat at his desk, head in hands. "I should have stayed at Hoyle Mill in my bleachworks."

"Whatever has happened?" I asked. "Can you not pay—is that your trouble?" He looked up, staring at me as if I had taken leave of my senses.

"I *have* paid, Squire. I pay every penny at every turn, and there are many of those in this business. Each stage of manufacture is inspected."

"What do the excise men want?"

"It's like this, Squire. Soap is taxed at threepence a pound. My soap was weighed after the fats had been boiled with the alkali and salt. I gave notice to the Excise within the time permitted, filled out the form, and paid the tax. Later in the process, water is added, and it was after this that the excise men weighed again, and declared I had lied about the weight."

"Can you not pay the difference?"

"I said I would not pay threepence a pound for water."

I could see his point, but his despair seemed excessive. "What are they doing about it, these bullying men?"

"They have seized the soap, and taken it away."

"How much was there?"

"Almost a hundredweight. They have inspected everything. They have searched my home, they have even searched my closet." I think I must have looked rather blank, being rather shocked at the thought of one's closet being searched. "Perhaps I should expand," he said. He spread his hands on the desk. "A pound of soap must not exceed twenty-five cubic inches when hot, and twenty-seven when cold. If the specific gravity increases within forty-eight hours of the soap being cut into lengths, the rate of duty is increased to fourpence ha'penny a pound. Stock can be seized on a whim."

I could only agree. I felt sorry for him, but sympathy is no cure, and I left him in a state of melancholy.

Edmund passed his second birthday, and was the centre of our lives. He ran everywhere, earning himself the nickname, 'Trotts.'

I took my family to the coastal town of Bridlington, known for its bracing air and variety of sea birds. We stayed for a week, and Eliza's cough cleared quickly. Ireland, Mary Ann and one nursery maid came with us. Little Helen and Trotts raced on the sands, each falling into fits of giggles as they ran from the waves. I demonstrated how to skim a flat stone to bounce through the water. Eliza enjoyed the shops, and bought lace and other fabrics for the house. For my part, I was more interested in the seabirds, and in order to view them better, I hired a boat and boatman to take me to the foot of the nearby cliffs. In places, the white rocks are almost three hundred feet high. The boatman clearly did not understand my desire to take a closer look at the nests without shooting the birds.

Kittiwakes, herring gulls, and gannets flew about, landing on their chosen nesting sites in noisy dispute over their claimed territory. The great black backed gulls soared to their cliff top nesting ground. When I had seen everything I wished to see from the boat, I asked the boatman to take me back to the harbour where I purchased some rope at the chandlers. After some experimentation, I created a sort of bosun's cradle. While the ladies and Trotts enjoyed the delights of Bridlington town, the boatman and I set off for the cliff tops. After securing a loop of rope around a large boulder, we agreed a system of signals. One tug meant I wished to be lowered further, two tugs to stop, and three to be raised. With everything safely arranged, the boatman lowered me down the cliffs. The grandeur and beauty of the scene beggared all description, entirely worth the unpleasant moments when the rope jerked unexpectedly or the wind blew me against the rocks. The sea roared at the base of the stupendous cliffs, with tens of thousands of seabirds on the wing. Oh, lucky, lucky birds to have such a wonderful home, but I cannot say they were happy to have me amongst them. There are men who shoot hundreds of the cliff inhabitants, just for fun, and while I have killed many in my time, it has always been in the interests of science and not for gratuitous pleasure. The herring gulls were particularly inhospitable. Kittiwakes and jackdaws rose in circular flight while the guillemots, razorbills and puffins left the ledges in a straight, downward line until they plunged into the sea on their quest for a fish. I obtained kittiwake, herring gull and gannet eggs for my collection before signalling to the boatman to raise me up.

Over the previous winter, Eliza's cough had returned with a vengeance. This, along with frequent and fervent requests from Mother Nyren that we visit Bruges, made our minds up that a short tour of Europe should be undertaken. Yorkshire had shown no signs of a warm summer, and it was hoped that the continent would offer something better.

Eliza, Little Helen, Trotts and I left Walton Hall on Monday, 8th July, 1833, travelling by stage to London. We were accompanied by Mary Ann and Ireland, staying in the capital for a week, visiting the National Gallery and the Zoological Gardens in Surrey. Trotts squealed with delight when he saw the monkeys. Their antics amused him so much we had difficulty in persuading him to leave. Hitherto, he had only seen my preserved specimens, and could not have known they had once been alive.

We left England's shores from Dover aboard a steamboat. The sea was kind to us, and we remained on deck for the passage. Mary Ann had never been on a boat of any description before, and was convinced we would all drown as soon as we left the harbour. I told her that the passage was a short one, and that as I had crossed the Atlantic eight times without shipwreck, my presence was a good omen. I don't think for one moment that I reassured her, for it was only when Eliza told her to be quiet lest she upset Trotts, that she bit her lip and remained silent until we docked in Ostend.

A carriage and four took us to the Hôtel du Commerce. As we were driven through the town square, I recalled my previous visit when the uprising had been in its early days. All was now settled, and the Belgian people free of religious prejudice. An altogether calmer atmosphere prevailed. Had it been otherwise I could not have taken my family there.

Next morning, my sisters-in-law and I were up with the lark and away to High Mass at St Saviour's, while Ireland and Mary Ann remained at the hôtel with Trotts. By the time we returned, all was set for break-fast, and the talk was all of our impending visit to the Convent.

Mother Nyren and the nuns greeted us as if we had been given up for dead, and our presence nothing less than a miracle. Trotts, despite his blue eyes, was declared the image of his mother. His laughter and quick footsteps echoed through the cloisters to the delight of the nuns and novices alike.

"I do declare," Mother Nyren said, "that Anne's boy has brought a new joy to these walls."

We visited many of the churches, celebrating Mass each day and watching the nuns and priests going about their blessed lives. We took Trotts to see the archers of St Sebastian's Guild on the Rue des Carmages. One of their number told us that King Charles II had been a member during his years of exile, and proudly showed us his portrait which hung in the hallway.

Our next destination was the town of Ghent where we attended High Mass at St Michael's and visited many of the fine churches. We travelled by barge. Little Helen had to be persuaded to come inside when cold showers brought on the shivers. She took great interest in everything around her, good and bad, absorbing every detail. The weather remained cold and showery, and not at all beneficial to Eliza's cough. Happily, our onward journey saw blue skies and warm sunshine. At Alost, we saw acres of hops in the fields. Little Helen craned her neck out of the window for a better view. Eliza tapped her on the shoulder.

"You will have a headache."

"It will be worth it, sister dear."

In Brussels we visited the Palace of the Prince of Orange, where, much to Little Helen's amusement, we were obliged to put on slippers before being allowed to enter the rooms, lest we damage the wooden floors. Trotts giggled helplessly as we all slipped and slid our way around. I am sure he thought it was all a game. Eliza was not amused.

Our tour took us to Genappe, Namur, Huy and Liège. We visited galleries and churches at every opportunity, with the frequency of our devotions lifting our souls. On then, to Cologne, by way of Vervier and

Aix-la-Chapelle[9] where we took the healing waters every day for a week. I was at the pump at five o'clock each morning, avoiding the crowds before attending Mass. We stayed at the Hôtel du Dragon d'Or, where the cooking skills of the aptly named widow Van Gulpen made sure we were never hungry. On subsequent visits to this fine city I have observed the enormous quantities of food consumed by those who come expressly for their health, thereby negating the effects of the waters by over eating. We declined more than a sufficiency from the table. With Eliza much revived, we travelled on to Cologne by coach where we boarded a steamboat on the River Rhine. Overnight stops were made at Bonn, Frankfurt and Würzburg.

"So much more comfortable than the coach." Eliza declared.

Little Helen nodded enthusiastically. "We can see everything, Eliza. Everywhere is so beautiful." In Würzburg it came as no surprise to discover that Herr Berwind had died. Had it been otherwise I would have endeavoured to spend an hour or so with him.

I cannot say the tour was entirely successful. Travelling with a two-year-old was difficult at times. While my sisters-in-law and I had been happy to observe at all that passed by, little Trotts was unimpressed with his imprisonment. Too young by many a year to appreciate the talent of Reubens and Van Gogh, Mary Ann had had her work cut out to amuse him in the galleries and churches. His fidgeting in the coach became irritating, and Eliza and I took the decision to turn for home. We had travelled as far as Huttenheim. Little Helen's face told of her disappointment.

"We shall come back, and go to Rome," I said, and she clapped her hands in joy, her equilibrium entirely restored.

Back in Cologne, we were forced to take shelter from the sun. I had not enjoyed such heat since I had been in South America, but Trotts' young skin and the ladies' tight clothing were not designed for the ferocity of the rays. We varied our homeward route to encompass Bergheim with the weather remaining warm and dry, but all changed

---

9 Aachen

overnight, and the remainder of our journey was a battle to keep warm and dry. We were so cold in Brussels that we asked for fires to be lit in our hôtel rooms. Ireland and Mary Ann were dispatched to buy gloves for everyone, and a warmer coat for Trotts. Such is the unreliability of the European climate. The primary reason for our tour had been to improve Eliza's health, and I feared that all the benefits thus far achieved would be negated by the dampness of the lowlands. Naturally, we could not leave for England without visiting the Convent. The nuns wanted to hear all about our travels, especially the churches. To their delight, Little Helen gave lengthy and precise descriptions of all she had seen.

Despite the cold, damp weather endured during the latter part of our tour, Eliza's cough had all but disappeared. We sailed from Rotterdam to Hull on a rolling sea. Mary Ann and Ireland had been of invaluable assistance. Mary Ann had organised my sisters-in-law's wardrobe and attended to all Trotts' little needs. Ireland had dealt with hôtel staff and made sure we always had the best rooms.

Sad news awaited us. Father Clifford, who had retired to Palermo for a warmer climate, had died. I could never place too high a value on the advice and understanding I had known from this wise man, nor could I imagine how my life might have been different had he not taken me under his wing. Adding to our sadness, a letter to Eliza and Little Helen from Robert Edmonstone told of their mother's death. Her ending had been slow, but, Robert wrote, 'peaceful at the end.' My sisters-in-law sat side by side on a little sofa, the letter held between them.

"He says," Eliza read,

"Mother had not been in her right mind, and for the last three weeks did not recognise anyone, not even Charles and me, but kept asking for Father, and shouting for the servants to search for snakes. She thought she was at Warrow's Place."

"Then you must be glad she is no longer in such torment."

"I feel I should have been there." Eliza said.

"You could not have helped, Eliza, and with the best will in the world, the damp air of Dumbartonshire—"

"I could have gone," Little Helen interrupted "I could have looked after Mother."

Eliza put the letter on a little table to her right, put one arm around her sister's shoulders, and squeezed her hand. Tears flowed. As I took my handkerchief from my pocket, bird food scattered over the carpet. I recall the handkerchief was gratefully received, despite being rather crumpled and full of crumbs, causing them to smile through their tears.

CHAPTER TWENTY-THREE

Storm and slavery. Death and Deliverance.

A light breeze whispered through the evergreens on New Year's Day, 1834. The winter had been mild, with few frosts, making for an easy life for the birds, and indeed for all creatures, including *homo sapiens*. Coming from the north west, the wind had no barrier as it rustled through the leaves in my little valley. By dusk the bare branches of the deciduous trees were thrashed about by the invisible force, and the holly, yew and laurel tossed around, this way and that, like the skirts of a dancing maiden. In the house, curtains billowed and windows rattled as the wind increased to hurricane force. The long staircase window bellied in and out in an alarming manner, but held fast. Smoke blew down the chimneys causing us all to cough. Little did I know that before the night was out, Mother Nature would provide me with enough work to keep me busy for the whole of that year. Trotts was in his bed before the worst of it, sleeping soundly with a nursery nurse sitting at his side, lest he woke and was afraid.

The wind lessened shortly before dawn and I set out to inspect the damage. To my relief, Wouralia and her stable-hut were unaffected. She nuzzled into my pocket as if nothing untoward had happened. The sycamores had stood firm and done their job of protecting the house from the worst of the blast. As I crossed the bridge, making my way to the stables and farmyard, I held on to the rail and scanned the parkland. The horizon had changed in places and I could see from my vantage point that many mature trees had been lost, but the Lombardy poplar had withstood the test.

Considering some parts of the stables and farm buildings were over four hundred years old, matters could have been worse. The buildings form a rectangle with a central courtyard. I would not have been surprised if the whole lot had blown down, despite their sheltered position. They had been built, added to and repaired by generations of Watertons, and had been in a poor state before the hurricane. While the walls had remained largely intact, a large oak tree had fallen onto the western block, demolishing part of the stables and the coach house. The roof, which had been a mixture of stone tiles and thatch, was in a bad way. The thatch had endured better than the tiles, which were scattered around like playing cards, but the beams had been no match for the weight of an oak tree. Two farm labourers had started to stack the tiles up against a wall. Joseph Totty stood in the centre of the courtyard, scratching his head. Warwick and Ogden were also there.

"It's a bad do, Squire, that it is." Totty shouted above the wind.

"Is anyone hurt, do you know?"

"No-one as I knows of, and I expect someone would have told me by now if there was. That's the miracle of it, and no animals hurt neither. Them two stables was empty. I reckon you'll be needing a new carriage though, Squire."

We stepped over the roof tiles towards the fallen tree. Thatch blew around in all directions, as hens, turkeys and pea fowl foraged for insects amongst the debris.

Joseph Totty had not been exaggerating. The old roof timbers, riddled with worm and dry rot, had offered little resistance. I picked up a short length of wood, axe marks giving evidence of its age. My grip reduced it to dust. Both the little carriage and the one I had bought shortly after Edmund's birth were shattered to matchwood. I climbed onto their remains for a better view.

"Shall I set more men on, Squire? To mend the roof, I mean?"

"Keep the men salvaging what they can and do only what is necessary to prevent further dilapidations. I need to see this as an opportunity." He gave me a strange look, and I was about to explain when Kaye, the gate-keeper, came into the yard. He gave a long, low whistle as he surveyed the mayhem.

"I thought the damage to the gatehouses was bad, but it's nothing compared to this, Squire."

"You haven't lost the roofs, then?"

"No, Squire, but two windows have blown in and some guttering is down, and there's a tree across the avenue. That will have to be shifted."

"Come with me, Warwick," I beckoned. "We must inspect the parkland. I fear there will be many homeless birds."

We walked in silence, save for the sound of the wind, and the breaking of twigs beneath our shoes. By the time we reached the heronry, the wind was no more than a breeze. The lofty nests had been all but totally destroyed, with not one remaining intact. The woodland looked as if it had been trampled by an army of giants. As we approached the top of the hill on the eastern side, it became evident that my wall had been a victim of the storm. A beech and an ash lay at an angle, having crashed through the stonework. Further along, we found a good forty yards to have been blown flat to the ground.

"Always a breeze up here, Squire."

"This section takes the worst of it. I shall have it rebuilt with buttresses. There will be plenty of work for the jobbing men."

"I expect there is damage all over the village."

To my shame, I had not thought of others, not even my tenants. We descended the hill and walked along the lakeside path towards the stables and farmyard. "After break-fast I shall have my horse saddled and take a ride around the village. What day is it?"

"Friday, Squire."

"I need Ogden up here right away. I shall also need a carpenter and a glazier." As we made our way along, my woodman, Morley, fell into step with us.

"There's a fair bit of work for me, I'm thinking, Squire. What shall I do first?"

"Go to the village and find someone to work with you. First task will be to clear the avenue."

"Right you are, Squire." He let out a long sigh and doffed his cap before quickening his pace, leaving Warwick and I to survey the little island. The willow trees had all been uprooted, their branches lay prostrate, half submerged. A group of moorhens swam around, exploring the new landscape.

"I see the little island has been punished," I said, "perhaps it will suit the birds, there will be plenty of nesting sites amongst the fallen branches."

The following weeks and months saw many a workman's cart between Walton village and the estate. Morley chopped enough fallen timber to provide firewood for Buckingham Palace, but left even more to slowly rot in the woodland, providing homes for beetles and bugs as nature intended.

My wall was repaired before Easter, and I bought two new carriages to replace the ones that had been smashed. Fasting during Lent was more easily borne due to the distraction of all the building work. I employed an architect, Mr Finch, and gave him instruction to keep as much of the original quadrangle as possible. Its dimensions of forty-five yards long and thirty-six in breadth had served well, and I saw no reason to change things for the sake of it. I had a list of requirements, and asked him to incorporate them in the plans. He cast his eyes down my list.

"You want the horses to be able to converse with one another?"

"Yes. Horses are happier in company. They are a herding animal."

He blinked rapidly. "And you say the dog kennels must have a good view. Do you mean that you must be able to see the kennels from the house?"

"No, no. Not at all. I mean the dogs must be able to see the comings and goings. Otherwise they will be bored."

"Quite." Mr Finch made a strange noise somewhere between a laugh and a cough.

"You may think this all very strange, but I know a thing or two about animals, and—"

"I know you do, Squire, and I think your ideas are excellent. Lucky indeed, are the creatures who can call you their Master. However, I am a little worried at the thought of fireplaces. The risk of fire in the stables—"

"In the stables? I do not mean in the stables, I refer to the saddle and tack rooms, the coach house and accommodations above." He continued to stare at me like a cod fish. "For the cats to keep warm in the winter, and

I dare say my employees will be happy enough to have a fireplace in their quarters." At this last information, his faced relaxed.

"Of course, Squire. I was unaware of the staff being in residence." He went on to advise the entire roof be replaced with stone tiles, rather than patch it up.

The courtyard was an ideal site for a pigeon cote. The old one had been damaged in the storm, but also its position near the avenue rendered it vulnerable to poachers. I relieved Mr Finch of creating the design and set about the task myself. Be it a pigeon cote, a nesting box, or a display cabinet for specimens, all my projects have a function. I have enjoyed construction since my childhood, finding it of great satisfaction to see the products of my labours in use. I could never make anything simply for ornamentation. I well remember, as a young boy, my father told me that the inside of a pigeon cote should be whitewashed every year to keep the nesting alcoves free of fleas and vermin, but that the owner must not paint the outside, lest other people's pigeons might take a fancy to such superior housing!

Foundations were dug at twelve feet square. Of brick and mortar construction, my design had two windows and a doorway at the first-floor level. This I considered the only way to avoid the occupancy of rats. Accessed by fifteen stone steps, the grand accommodation provided six hundred and sixty-six recesses. The room below had two fireplaces on opposite walls. Fires were lit in winter and the warmth from the chimneys as they soared through the cote encouraged the pigeons to breed all year round. Ingress and egress for the birds was via a traditional glover, that is to say an opening in the pyramidical roof, covered by a glazed frame and supported on four short legs and with just enough room left for the occupants to come and go at will. The finished accommodation stands three storeys high and is topped with a cross. Straightaway, I had the old cote shut up and to my delight the new one was occupied that very first night.

The following spring, I had seventy-one dozen birds for the game dealer.

The repairs to the farm buildings, stables and coach house have proved their worth in many ways. The accommodation, with its fireplaces, sound roof, well-fitting doors and windows, is superior by far to any in the area. As a result, my stablemen and other workers tend to stay, and Joseph Totty needs only to find extra labour at harvest time. I do not have to worry when the wind blows, and being in a hollow, lightning will not strike down upon the buildings. Although the Marjay cat was long dead, many felines have enjoyed the hearths, as well as the stablemen. The improvements opened my eyes to other areas of the estate in need of repairs and renewals. Over the following years I had improvements made to the gardens, both at the grotto and on the island.

By banning the gun and providing nesting sites, my parkland had become the sanctuary I had hoped for. After the hurricane, the surviving flora and fauna of the entire estate seemed determined to bounce back with renewed vigour. Just twelve months later, I estimated there were three thousand ducks on the lake. I planted spruce firs and elm trees between the orchard and the grotto, and had the little cottage built near the upper temple. With its large fireplace and an upholstered chair, I can sit up there for hours on the coldest of days with the door wide open. This last winter a cock robin regularly came inside to perch upon my shoe as I fed him with crumbs. His bright eyes and cheerful red breast warmed my soul in a way the fire could not.

The plantations in Demerara had fallen out of cultivation. The slaves had been freed, and my brothers and cousins were entitled to their share of the twenty million pounds of taxpayers' money that Parliament had agreed would be paid to the slave owners by way of compensation for their loss of income. As head of the family, I was tainted by association, and much as I tried to separate myself from the matter, it came to find me. As usual, when politicians take up a task involving money, there are complications. Bearing in mind that many families who owned slaves were also Members of Parliament, there was bound to be argument. Slaves had differing value, so the owners of the more valuable people wanted more money. The whole business still causes bile to rise to my throat. The estate known as Walton Hall had three hundred slaves, and I was paid £16,283:6s:7d for them. La Jalousie and Fellowship had two hundred and ninety-two slaves, and I was recompensed to the sum of £15,482.4s.8d.

I divided the money between my remaining brothers and tried not to think too much about this disgraceful episode in my family's history. It grieves me to know that as I write there are still slaves in the United States of America.

I first became acquainted with Doctor Hobson, a physician from Leeds, when the rebuilding of the stables was in progress. Despite the many years of friendship which ensued, I always addressed him as Doctor Hobson, and he addressed me as Mr Waterton. I write of him in the past tense, not because he is deceased but because we have had a disagreement. Doctor Hobson, I am sure, had none but good intentions when he wrote his little book, but I hope it is never published. Unfortunately, my former friend (for we have now quite fallen out) fell into the trap of many, insomuch as he exaggerates and embroiders, puffing up the anecdotes and placing himself centre stage. He, of all people, should know of my distaste for falsehood and the gilding of the lily. If the story is a good one, there is no need for embroidery, if it is not, it should not be told at all. His work contains far too much fiction purporting to be fact. Nonetheless, I do not permit our disagreement to mar my memories. Doctor Hobson and I have spent many a pleasant hour in one another's company.

He was one of many visitors on the day we first met, tickets having been issued to the Leeds Philosophical Society. The Doctor and I immediately struck up a rapport, not least because his first words to me were in Latin. He stood next to the sundial, looking over the lake.

'Si poema laquens pictura est, pictura tactitum poema esse.' 'If a poem be a speaking picture, a picture ought to be a silent poem.'

After myself and Little Helen, Doctor Hobson has been the most prolific user of my telescope. Many a visitor, especially those less agile than I, has enjoyed it as I have enjoyed their company and delight as they watch the activity upon the lake. During inclement weather I have spent countless hours in the comfort of the drawing room, taking notes as I watched the lake and little island. I cannot recall Doctor Hobson ever coming here and not taking at least half an hour at the telescope. On one such occasion, when the wind and rain battered the windows, we had the following conversation.

"Were you never in fear of your life, Mr Waterton, when in the wilds of South America? Were you not fearful of the natives?"

"The natives?" I exclaimed. "Never! The natives of South America are the most peaceful people I have ever met. A traveller can easily avoid danger if he makes friends with them and respects their knowledge. It is no good pointing a gun at a man and then wondering why he does not trust you and seeks to harm you. To earn respect, one must show it. 'Give, and thou shalt receive.' I quote the Gospel According to St Luke, chapter six, verse thirty-eight. Respect cannot be demanded. I recall feeling threatened by the jaguars as they roared and prowled around our camp at night, but never by the natives."

"But they make the deadliest poison known to man."

"For hunting purposes, so that they can feed their families. Unlike our fellow countrymen, they do not kill for pleasure or go to war. Wourali does not poison the meat."

"But what of the snakes?"

"Well as you know, I captured a few, but to my mind the fools in Georgetown were forever putting themselves in greater danger than I."

He looked up from the telescope and leaned back in the chair, his brow deeply furrowed. "How so?"

"By eating too much, drinking alcohol to excess, and spending each night either at the gambling tables or in a brothel, risking the pox—need I go on?" My friend made no reply and so I continued. "I ate as the natives ate, lived as they lived in harmony with the forests. As for fear, I think it best compared to the soldier who fights in battle. At the time, he is too busy with the fight and does not think of his safety. Only afterwards, assuming he has survived, will he reflect on what might have been."

"But you still suffer from the ague."

"From time to time, yes. I do not suppose I shall ever be completely free of it, but it is kept at bay by a tincture of quinine sulphate. Did I ever tell you that my greatest relief came from quinoa bark? It was a native remedy long before a European set foot in the swamps."

"No," he replied, "but I am not surprised."

"I shall survive as I always have done by fasting, purging, and tapping the claret." My mention of blood-letting provoked the usual response.

"There is no proof that bleeding a patient has any effect. I have told you so before, and know I am wasting my breath."

I laughed, and he returned his attention to the telescope, focussing on a group of wild ducks. "Are you not going to berate me for fasting?" I teased.

"I believe fasting has its uses, especially where there is evidence of a malady in the intestines. Purging cures constipation, but there is no proof that it does anything else."

"Proof! What more proof do you need other than the way my entire household escaped the recent influenza? Old people of Walton have been carried off to the churchyard in numbers. We escaped it entirely by my giving everybody a very strong purge on the first appearance of a symptom. Furthermore, I have no sign of rheumatism." I poked the fire and heaped on more coal. "How many of your ageing patients can say that?" He paused from his observations and turned to look at me, sighed deeply and shook his head.

A piece of surprising news came to me from the village, conveyed by Jack Ogden. William Thornhill Hodgson had entered into partnership with Edward Simpson, the irksome young lad I had first met some thirteen years previously. I made it my business to visit the soap works. As I passed the New Inn, I saw ahead two men carrying a large tray across the road. William Hodgson was in his office, his desk piled high with papers.

"Ah, Squire. I am pleased to see you. I had thought to come to your home, but here you are, saving me the trouble."

"What is happening, Mr Hodgson?"

"Good news, Squire, I—"

"I hear you have entered into partnership."

"Indeed so. Young blood. That is what the business needs. I adopted young Edward a few years ago you know, unofficially of course, there were no lawyers involved and—"

"No, I didn't know. Has he no family?"

"None. None at all, but he is a good lad. Not really a lad now, and he has a good business head on his shoulders. Edward Thornhill Simpson he is now. He took the Thornhill from my family, so I, William Thornhill Hodgson, am now in partnership with Edward Thornhill Simpson. Edward is a married man. He and his wife worship at the Methodist Church, all respectable. What do you make of that, eh?" I was about to say I hoped there would be no expansion of the business when I saw a cloud of sadness pass over his face.

"Is something wrong, Mr Hodgson? Do you regret your decision?"

"No, no. Nothing like that. It is just that they had a child, a daughter. Isabella, they called her. The prettiest child I ever saw, but she died back in February. Just eight months she was." He wiped a tear with the back of his hand.

"But he still has his wife, does he not?"

"Yes, yes. And a new son, George, but they still grieve for Isabella. I am hoping the new baby, and our new business venture, will help Edward to look to the future."

"May I ask, what new venture is this?"

"Hodgson and Simpson, Soap Manufacturers, are expanding. We are on the move. Edward and I have invented a chemical seed manure and it's proving to be very effective."

He rummaged about on his desk and proffered a copy of The *Farmer's Magazine,* pointing to a letter beneath the title, 'Valuable Discovery. Hodgson and Simpson invent Chemical Seed Manure Enabling Wheat and Turnips to Grow on Poor Cold Soils.'

"It is also successful with corn. We need larger premises to keep up with demand."

"Where are you going to? Are you away to Wakefield?" My heart soared with expectation of the stinking processes leaving the village, but my joy was quickly dashed away.

"No. Not at all. Young Edward arranged the purchase of the triangle of land over the way. A good four roods. It belonged to the navigation company, but they had no use for it and we bought it for a song. We are expanding." I was stunned to silence. The memory of riding out with my father, in the far distant days before I went to Stonyhurst as clear in my mind as if it had been the day before. "Is something wrong, Squire?" His question brought me back to the present.

"But that land belonged to my family. I wanted to buy it back. I have asked the navigation company time and again, but they always said it was not for sale."

"I had no idea. What did you want it for?"

His question disarmed me, I thought it impertinent. With hindsight, I realise he saw everything through the eyes of the industrialist, and that land alongside a navigation would be wasted if it were not utilised for production of some sort. "I—I don't know." I stuttered, "I just did. My family owned it before the navigation was built, and I wanted it back."

"I will make good use of it."

Unconvinced that he and I would ever agree on what constituted 'good use,' I changed the subject. "You have settled matters with the Customs, then?"

"Oh yes, yes. All a storm in a teacup really. Edward sorted it out. Young Edward has big plans."

"I'm sure he has."

"The people need employment, Squire."

"Chemical manufacture comes at a price, Mr Hodgson. You make the air foul."

"Beg pardon, Squire but you are a user of chemicals in your work, are you not? My works are small, I have not room to manufacture more than a little soap. Have my assurance that I shall do greater good than harm."

I left with my heart in my boots, knowing that whatever Edward Thornhill Simpson's plans were, I wasn't going to like them.

George Hodgson Simpson, the baby who was supposed to heal the wound of his little sister's demise, died at the age of four months. I could do no other than feel sorry for the Simpsons and wrote a letter of condolence. Only when I enquired of his address did I become aware that he was my tenant. He and his wife, along with two servants, lived in Beechfield House, a property which had been acquired during my father's time.

On the morning of the 15th of April, 1839, I rose to find a bitter frost. After praying in the chapel, I attended to my taxidermy as was my routine. At first light I put on my warmest coat and stepped outside, expecting to see Wouralia waiting for her corn, but she was nowhere to be seen. The grass crunched beneath my footsteps as I made my way to her shelter. The old donkey had died in her sleep. She had contributed more to science than many a puffed-up closet naturalist, and had appeared well enough the night before. She had not suffered, and had enjoyed twenty-five years of unfettered life on the island. I still miss her trotting hooves coming to greet me as I come over the bridge and at the time, I considered buying another donkey, but Eliza convinced me that Wouralia was irreplaceable. Even young Trotts joined in the debate.

"But Papa," he said, "we do not have to be so careful where we step now there is no donkey litter."

I ruffled his curls. "Only the geese and ducks to watch out for, eh?"

The men of science continued to seek uses for wourali. I refer here to the poison, not the donkey. It had been found to cure some cases of lockjaw[10] and there was considerable belief, and hope, that it would be efficacious with hydrophobia.*[11] Both of these dreadful ailments produce spasms, and it was therefore logical that the muscle relaxing quality of wourali could effect a cure.

I had for some time been in correspondence with Doctor Williams of the Faculty of Nottingham and Sir Arnold Knight of Sheffield regarding

10   *tetanus

11   rabies

the use of wourali as a medicine. We had agreed it should be tested in a case of hydrophobia at the first opportunity. For the sufferer, there would be nothing to lose and everything to gain should the administration of wourali prove to be effective. We were all aware, however, of the need to act quickly, for once the symptoms are apparent, death is never far away. Shortly after Wouralia's death, Doctor Williams sent a letter to me by express delivery, asking me to proceed to Nottingham as quickly as possible, and to bring some wourali with me. His letter explained that a policeman, Officer Phelps, had been bitten by a pointer six or seven weeks previously and had appeared to be quite well, but was now showing symptoms of hydrophobia. I travelled by train that same day, and was joined by Sir Arnold who boarded at Sheffield. He had also received an express letter from Doctor Williams which explained the circumstances in more detail. The dog had fallen into a deep hole. The policeman had fetched a ladder and climbed down to the frightened animal to haul it out, but it did not appreciate Officer Phelps' kindness. As he carried the dog up the ladder, it bit him on the face and lips by way of a thank-you. No doubt the owner of the hound was grateful.

Some weeks previously, I had heard of six men being bitten by a rabid dog. They had been sent to a General Infirmary, where the affected flesh had been cut away. I had sent some wourali in case hydrophobia developed, but it did not.

In the case of Officer Phelps, due to the bites being about his face and lips, the option of surgery had been dismissed. In any event, it was not known at the time that the dog was rabid. When he began to feel unwell, the officer returned to the surgery of Mr Davison who had tended the bite wounds in the first instance. Whilst being examined Officer Phelps asked for a drink, but when he saw the running tap, was seized with convulsions. Mr Davison at once realised the gravity of the situation. Knowing of Doctor Williams' interest in such cases, he sent a message to the faculty.

Sadly, Officer Phelps died two hours before Sir Arnold and I arrived. The policeman had been attended by the most eminent men. Doctors Williams and Percy, Mr Attenburrow, Mr Sibson and Mr Davison had been unable to prevent his death. I left a quantity of wourali with them to use in future cases. Whether it will work remains to be proven.

Not all deaths are so mourned. In that same year, the Hanoverians were finally eradicated from Walton Hall, the fowl house and the potato store. They have since tried to return to the latter two, and constant vigilance is needed, but never again have I seen or heard this most despised of vermin in my home or anywhere upon the island. When I am gone to dust, if my ghost should hover over Walton Hall, it will rejoice to hear the incumbents say that in the year 1839, Charles Waterton effectively cleared the mansion of every rat, young and old.

Having passed his ninth birthday, Trotts was old enough for Stonyhurst. A place was secured for him to start his more formal education that autumn. Hitherto, Edmund had been educated at home by a tutor and had taken to all his lessons with more enthusiasm than I had ever shown for the schoolroom. He showed a fascination for all things ecclesiastical and was a favourite of the priest at St Austin's. He never ceases to surprise me, even now. When I broached the subject of his going to Stonyhurst, thinking he may be a little daunted at the prospect of leaving the security of his home and the doting love of his aunts, I was not prepared for his reply. We had just finished break-fast, and were all at the dining table, my specimens being of smaller animals at the time.

"Papa," said he," I am delighted at the prospect. I know from your wearing the swallowtail coat on important occasions, that you wish you were still a pupil. Before I go, however, I would like to visit Bruges. I don't remember very much of my previous visit, but my aunts have told me so much about the Convent that I would like to see it for myself once again."

I could not help but smile. "But you were little more than a baby, Trotts. Are you sure you remember anything at all, and it is not just that you have heard your aunts speak of it?" I looked to my sisters-in-law, who were both smiling affectionately at their nephew.

"They have spoken of the nuns, and the Convent des Anglais, but I remember the big square, and the place where the soldiers practised their archery. My aunts have not told me about that, but I remember it distinctly—it is on the same road as the Convent."

"What do you say, Eliza?"

"What can I say? I have not spoken to him of Saint Sebastian's Guild of Archery. Have you, sister dear?"

Little Helen shook her head vigorously, and then said, "May we all go, Charles?"

I thought it an excellent idea, but before I could reply, Trotts put forward an irrefutable argument.

"If I may add one more thing, Papa, should you still be in need of persuasion, Aunt Eliza's chest has not recovered from last winter."

With the gloom and failures of the past months' trial of wourali, or rather the lack of a trial, and Trotts putting forward such a strong case, such a diversion could not be denied. "I think it a capital idea. Well done, Trotts. We shall make a grand tour of Europe. I should have thought of it myself. I shall write to your Uncle William with the sad news that Stonyhurst will have to wait a little longer before another Waterton becomes a pupil."

CHAPTER TWENTY-FOUR

European Adventures.

I took the train to London and obtained the necessary passport. The novelty of once again travelling for pleasure caused great excitement between Eliza and Little Helen. They had new dresses made in light fabric suitable for sunny Italy, and warm dresses and capes for our journey through Europe and passage over the Alps. Edmund had been taken to the tailors and had more outfits than I. Finances were set in place with the bank, and trunks were crammed with clothing.I packed my little knives and other necessaries for taxidermy. We planned a leisurely route to Italy and intended to spend a year or two on the Mediterranean coast.

Before leaving, I called up my gamekeepers and made them promise, if they valued their position, that they would protect all hawks, crows, jays, herons, kingfishers and magpies in my absence, and that they would not kill any snakes. My sister, Helen Carr, agreed to visit as often as her health would allow and to write to me of any matters which needed my attention. She was forty-eight years of age. Doctor Hobson had assured her that the pains in her back were something from which women of her age occasionally suffered, and that they would pass with time. I helped my two sisters-in-law and Mary Ann into the carriage. My little boy and I sat with our backs to the horses, and our considerable luggage was secured atop. Ireland sat next to the driver. In this order we proceeded to Hull, staying for one night at the Victoria Hôtel. The following morning we embarked upon the steamer, *Seahorse*, and proceeded to Rotterdam where we stayed at the Hôtel des Pays Bas for two nights before proceeding to Bruges. Ireland and I stayed at the Hôtel du Commerce, but the nuns insisted that Eliza, Little Helen, young Trotts and Mary Ann stayed at the Convent. They needed no persuading. We stayed for about a week, and of course we visited St Sebastian's Guild where the archers gave instruction to Trotts on how to aim an arrow vertically, and then run out of the way before its descent. How I laughed at the daring game, although Eliza and Little Helen covered their eyes for fear of witnessing a tragedy.

Leaving Bruges, we took the stage through Flanders to Aix-la-Chapelle where we enjoyed this most delightful of towns and its environs for the whole of August (medicinal qualities of the warm water at the pump being reason enough to tarry). I admit I am not impressed with European scenery, having experienced the magnificence of a Guianan forest, but if there is an exception, it is Aix-la-Chapelle. The town and surrounding countryside have such a calming atmosphere, due in no small measure to the hand of Mother Nature as she warms the waters. I make no attempt to give an analysis of the health restoring qualities. In fact, to tell the truth, I have no real science in me. I merely look at art and nature as I pass along and write down that which gives me delight. The qualities of the waters are almost beyond belief, along with the mild and courteous manners of the majority of the people. We would have stayed longer had these attributes not been so terribly balanced with the gluttony and gambling habits of some residents and other visitors.

Multo plores satieta quam fames perditit. Surfeit has killed many more than hunger.

We still make annual visits, and will continue to do so for as long as I am able.

By the time we packed up, Eliza's cough had quite disappeared. At Cologne, as our servants arranged the riverboat cabins, we were joined by Alexander Fletcher, an old friend of the Edmonstones from Edinburgh. Unbeknownst to me, Eliza had written to him from Walton Hall, telling of our plans. His reply, which he assured her he had sent by return, had not arrived when we left. We were as surprised as could be. A jolly addition to our party, he and his manservant took cabins aboard and we proceeded together along the Rhine. For my part, I was glad of some male conversation. We discussed the politics of the day, the young Queen Victoria and her impending marriage, and Robert Peel's refusal to be her Prime Minister. For a Protestant, Alexander Fletcher was remarkably sympathetic to the plight of British Catholics.

A sharp wind kept the ladies from the deck for the first part of our passage, but after a week, more tranquil waters took us through the valleys all the way to the Swiss border. As we passed along, Little Helen began taking notes of all she saw.

"I am doing as you do, Charles, and writing down the names of all the birds I see. Will you help me? I only know the ones I have seen at Walton Hall."

"It would be my pleasure. Will you sketch them also?"

"I had not thought of it, but will try."

"Perhaps Trotts will help you."

Little Helen frowned. "I don't think he would like that, but I shall ask him."

Summer merged into autumn as we travelled on south by road through Switzerland, crossing the Alps at the Pass of Splügen. We had visited several museums along our route, but I cannot say I enjoyed viewing the taxidermy. I could have made a better job with my left hand. Everything was stuffed into unnatural shapes with the moth having penetrated to a great extent. If only these people would use bichloride of mercury, they would be rewarded by a bird worth looking at forever.

Whenever we stopped, Little Helen and I would alight in search of bird life, but alas, to our everlasting disappointment, there was not a feather to be seen. The earth appeared as one huge barren waste. Not so much as a skinny partridge. For fear of the higher altitude cold (albeit a much drier cold than that of Yorkshire) undoing all that Aix-la-Chapelle had accomplished, we pushed on. Once through the pass all was different with every day bringing a warmer climate and with it a foretaste of the delightful temperatures to be enjoyed in an Italian autumn. Our route took us to Milan, and from there to Florence and Bologna. Our bones warmed, but still we saw very few birds. Some coots, a heron or two, a few blackbirds and a scanty show of hooded crows were all that was on offer.

From a distance the towns appear to be enchanting with their olive and cypress trees interspersed with the houses, but the visitor cannot look up as he walks the streets. A handkerchief soaked in lavender water is essential, and a wary eye for that which may soil his shoes. The town dwelling Italians would do well to dispose more of their waste matter on the fields and less on the streets.

By November we were in Rome, but before we entered the Eternal City, I had a little adventure. I think it barely worth relating, but deem it necessary to do so in order that my friends in Rome do not give me credit for something which deserves no credit at all. A rumour spread that I had reached Rome after walking barefoot from Baccano, a distance of almost twenty miles, and that I had done so in order to show my respect and reverence for the sacred capital of the Christian world. Would that my motive had been so pure! Unfortunately, the idea never entered my mind at the time and I had no motive other than that of easy walking and enjoyment.

We had arrived at Baccano in the evening, and whilst we were at tea, I suggested to Mr Fletcher that we should leave the inn at four the next morning on foot for Rome and secure lodgings for the ladies, who were to follow us in the carriage after break-fast, which was not served until after nine o'clock.

"I shall be delighted to join you, Mr Waterton," he said, and so we agreed to rise at three, and be on our way by four o'clock. I put a shoe and a stocking in each coat pocket, and we left the inn under a starlit sky. The frost glistened by the light of the planet Venus, which shone like a little moon. Having been accustomed to go without shoes for month after month in the rugged forests of Guiana, I took it for granted that I could do the same on the pavement, but fifteen years had gone by, and I failed to consider that the soles of my feet had undergone a considerable alteration.

I lost sensation on the cold stones of the road but went merrily along for several miles without suspecting that anything might be wrong. Only when we paused to admire the splendour of Venus did I notice blood on the pavement. Inspection of the sole of my right foot showed a piece of jagged flesh hanging loose by a string of skin. There was no chance of fixing it back in place, so I twisted it off. The bleeding soon stopped, but within the next mile, as the sun warmed the road and feeling returned, the wound opened further. Mr Fletcher was all worry and sympathy.

"We should hail the next coach or carriage or cart, or anything with wheels, Mr Waterton. You cannot go on like this."

"I thank you for your well-intended suggestion, Mr Fletcher, but inaction will stiffen my foot, and I fear the pain will increase. If St Ignatius could walk over a hundred miles barefoot from Gaeta to Rome, then I must hobble on without complaint."

"Will you put on your shoes?"

"I have suffered far worse and survived. Do not look so alarmed, my friend. I shall put on my shoes and stockings."

I forced my feet into the shoes with some difficulty. My left foot bore two unburst blisters but was in better shape than my right. We reached Rome after what was, for me, a very uncomfortable walk, and it was this unfortunate adventure which gave rise to the story of my walking barefooted to Rome, thus gaining me an underserved reputation for respect and reverence.

We secured comfortable apartments in the Pallazo di Gregorio. Imagine my delight when, a day or two after our arrival, we were visited by Fathers Glover and Esmonde, two of my fellow pupils from my Stonyhurst days. They made a great fuss of Trotts.

Alexander returned to Scotland and its winter chills. I had little choice but to relax as my wound kept me confined to the sofa for some weeks. I hobbled to Mass each morning, and occasionally bought a bird at a market near the Rotunda. With my taxidermy equipment set up, I was reasonably amused, but otherwise had to be content with Eliza, Little Helen and Trotts telling me of the delights of Rome. In turn they listened in disbelief when I told them of my climbing adventures with Captain Jones.

I tried to interest Trotts in my techniques of preservation.

"There are but three requisites. All that is needed is a penknife, a light hand and practice. Observation of the posture of birds, or any creature, will give a natural look. Would you like to try your hand?"

"Thank-you, Papa, but no. I hope you are not offended," he yawned, "but I do not have your interest in such things. I can see your skill, and see your specimens are far superior to any other, but that does not mean I—"

"No, dear boy, I am not offended."

"I would like to go to the Church of the Gesù with my aunts, if I may."

"And would you like to stay there for religious instruction?"

His angelic face lit up. "You mean I could stay all day? That would be wonderful, Papa."

"I shall speak with one of the Fathers as soon as I am able." I ran my hands through his curls, and he skipped away. I should have reckoned on the impatience of youth. Later that very same morning, Father Glover attended our apartments, having been told by the enthusiastic Trotts of my proposal. My son's education commenced the next day. Each morning he accompanied his aunts to Mass and remained there until late afternoon. The Fathers and Lay Brothers called him the 'English Angelino.'

As soon as my foot recovered sufficiently, I made it my habit to attend the early Mass as I had on my former visit to Rome. Whilst waiting with others for the doors to open, I sometimes asked what it was that made the Jesuits such favourites and invariably receive the answer that although other religious orders were good to them, the Jesuits were more attentive, showing greater charity. The Jesuits were the ones who, (I was informed) when cholera struck, were to be seen in the most infected parts of the city performing acts of charity and piety in every way they could.

I wrote to my sister, Helen, and to George Ord, informing them of our address and that we were all in good health. Sadly, the same could not be said of my sister. Of my siblings, Helen had been my closest friend, and her death hit me like a cannon ball in the gut. I no longer have my brother-in-law's letter, and will explain later why this is so, but I recall the wording precisely, for I read it over and over again, as if by doing so, I would better believe it.

Dear Charles,

It is with the utmost sadness that I write of Helen's death. Her health declined rapidly after your departure, and she suffered the most dreadful pain. Doctor Hobson prescribed laudanum, but she was unwilling to take it, saying she preferred to leave matters to God. I confess it came as a relief to me when I no longer had to watch her suffering, perhaps that is selfish of me, I don't know. When I knew she would not recover, I sent a letter to the Convent. When you did not reply it became apparent that you had set out for Rome.
Helen is at rest in the family vault.
All is well at Walton Hall.

Your grieving brother-in-law,
Robert Carr.

Helen was forty-nine years of age when she died, and had been married for twenty years. She had no children.

Next to leave this world was Bethia. Upon receipt of this news, dear Little Helen wept constantly for two days. Her faith eventually gave her comfort as she prayed for her sister's soul, and Eliza persuaded her that Bethia was now with my dear Anne, and no longer troubled by her weak lungs.

For one who detests the noxious habits of my fellow humans when in close proximity to one another, I like Rome more than any other city. I cannot say why, for the gambling, overeating, drunkenness and jealousies are as rife in Rome as in any other city.

I could no more spend a year in Malaga or Georgetown than I could fly like a bird over the dome of the Vatican, the latter scenario being my preferred option. Perhaps the answer to my puzzlement lies within the Vatican City. It has a peace about it like no other. Only one who does not live there can appreciate the effect of being at the centre of the Holy Catholic World. For the Romans it is the everyday.

I became a curiosity in the bird markets when it became known that I was buying birds to preserve them rather than for the table. At first the stallholders seemed wary of me but as we became better acquainted, they put aside any rare specimens which came their way, saving them until I attended the market. They were good Christian men, who could be seen every morning at half past four o'clock at the door of the Church of the Gesù.

Everything that has wings, from a wren to an eagle, is regarded as good food by the Romans. Hawks, owls and crows are plucked ready for the spit, and the legs of fowl are sold for soup. Little wonder we rarely saw anything fly. Jackdaws, buzzards, magpies, alongside hedgehogs, frogs and snails are all sold for the table. The Italians are blessed with stomachs as strong as that of my old friend, Daddy Quashi, who could grow fat on grubs, hornets and stinking fish. Anything that has had a heartbeat is food, with the exception of the Hanoverian rat which I often saw lying dead in the street, trodden underfoot.

Rome is hot in the summer and so, like many Romans, we decided upon a sojourn to Naples. Ireland engaged a driver by the name of Pasquale, and a suitable barouche in which to make our journey south.

I saw more birds on the route from Rome to Naples than I had on the whole of our journey from England to Rome. Kites and buzzards, sparrow hawks and windhovers were ever on the wing in the azure sky.

During our stay in gay but noisy Naples, we visited the beautiful monastery of St Martino, which is situated on a hill near St Elmo's Fort, and had an adventure as absurd as it was unexpected. We were enjoying the drive to this well guarded citadel when Eliza asked,

"What shall we do while you are in the monastery? We will not be allowed in."

"Not just you, Eliza," I replied, "it is forbidden by law for any female to enter any such place."

"But what are we to *do*? You will be hours, I'm sure."

"Perhaps you could spend some time at the fortress. I expect you would find it of interest."

We agreed that they should continue their drive to the gates of the fort, and saunter there until Ireland, Trotts and I returned. Imagine my surprise when, having enjoyed the magnificent views from the monastery, I found my sisters-in-law, Mary Ann and our driver, Pasquale, to be under military arrest! I was quickly informed by the soldier that one of our horses had left a deposit on the carriageway, and that our driver had refused to clear it away.

"This is the rule of the commander of the fort."

"Are you telling me," I said to the soldier, "that the commander's organs of sight and smell are so refined that he cannot tolerate the least impurity on the road that leads to his domain, and that every driver is obliged to remove, without delay, what may drop from the extremities of his horses, or pay a fine to a soldier?"

"That is so, signore."

"I will not pay!" Pasquale shouted furiously at the guard, stepping closer to his adversary.

"You shall pay in full, or I'll keep you all here until morning!"

I stepped between the warring parties, and turned to Pasquale. "What will you do?"

"Signore," he said, "they have falsely accused my horses of uncleanliness, for my horses have not had one single motion this afternoon. The ladies in the carriage can bear witness to this."

The guard stepped around me, staring at Pasquale. "Your horses have committed the offence, for I myself removed what fell, and put it over the wall and I will be paid for my work!"

"Not by me," said Pasquale, his black eyes flashing with fire.

"Friend," I addressed the soldier, "did you actually see the horse commit the offence?"

"No, signore, but I removed what they had dropped while it was still warm, and there has been no other horse on the road to the fort this afternoon."

Now I saw that I had the whip hand, for as I had left the ladies in order to visit the monastery, I had observed an ass going quietly on the road. I pulled myself up to my full height and addressed the soldier in my most stern voice.

"I demand you send for the officer on duty. You can you can keep us under arrest all night if you so wish, but nothing will be paid."

Trotts pulled at my cuff. "Papa, look." He pointed to a young officer walking towards us.

"What is the cause of this uproar?" he asked.

First the soldier and then Pasquale gave account. The officer listened patiently, but as it was a case of the soldier's word against Pasquale's the impasse remained.

"The dispute can be settled in a minute," I said to the officer. "I am confident of our horses' innocence, and if we go to the place where the soldier has deposited the cause of the arrests, I will prove this."

"How so?"

"I saw an ass on the road in front of our barouche, shortly before I went to the monastery. As I am pretty well versed in natural history, it will not be difficult for me to prove, by the size of the nuisance, that our horses have been falsely accused."

The officer saw immediately that his soldier's claim was groundless, and rebuked him accordingly, before bowing to the ladies and requesting that they continue their drive. Pasquale growled like a bear with a scalded head, declaring that this could only happen in Naples.

Shortly after our return to Rome, I was approached by a young man whilst at the marketplace.

"Mr Charles Waterton, I believe. I was told I might find you here."

"I am he, have we met?" I asked, although I knew we had not.

"No, sir. I am William Makepeace Thackeray, and I have read your book. I am merely an admirer of your work. I write a little myself."

"Of what?"

"Simple words of fiction, not yet published." He shuffled from one foot to the other.

"Is there something on your mind, Mr Thackeray? Forgive me, but you give the impression of having something to impart."

"I do. Charles Bonaparte is in the city. It was he who told me I might find you here. He has published again."

"I suppose he has been sitting in his comfortable chair and writing fiction and portraying it as fact."

"His book, 'Fauna Italia', and has a princely price of twenty pounds."

"I fear anyone who parts with their money will not learn anything new. He has not spent enough time in the woods to give us much original and correct information."

"Do you dislike fiction?"

"No, Mr Thackeray, not unless it is being peddled to the uninformed as fact. Let me elucidate. I was entirely unimpressed with his completion of the book started by the learned Mr Wilson, whose sad demise had prevented his finishing 'Wilson's Ornithology of America.'"

William Thackeray's reputation as an author has grown over the years and he has visited me at Walton Hall, but on our first meeting we were simply fellow Englishmen, discussing the written word.

The time came to commence our homeward journey. We boarded the beautiful, two hundred horse power steamship, *Pollux,* at Città Vecchia in the late afternoon of the 17th of June 1841, bound for Genoa, via Leghorn. The sea spread before us like glass. Had the *Pollux* been reliant upon sail, we should not have been able to travel, but thanks to the power of steam, we were scheduled to arrive in Leghorn the following morning. During our eighteen months in Italy I had preserved eighty birds, a porcupine, a badger, three lobsters, and one dozen land tortoises. I packed them carefully and forwarded them by coach to Leghorn, along with several paintings and sculptures which I had bought.

Ropes were cast off with the usual shouting and commotion of a quayside. The sails remained furled as the engines reverberated through the ship, and the great paddles churned the water. The hooter sounded, and we were away. Trotts leaned over the side to watch the foam. His aunts held onto him by his coat. Beyond the harbour walls, the sea remained as flat as a millpond. Mary Ann and Ireland settled our belongings below while Eliza, Little Helen, Trotts and I, along with our fellow passengers, promenaded the deck, passing pleasantries regarding the coastal view and our good fortune of enjoying such a calm sea.

The engineer, Mr Frederick Massey, introduced us to an elderly sea captain from Naples, who was on his way to Leghorn to buy a ship. He wore a coat which would have made excellent clothing on a frosty day in Yorkshire. When I enquired why he did so on such a warm night, he drew me close and whispered,

"My money, in gold coins, is sewn into my belt. I do not want anyone to see its bulk."

"What did he say?" Trotts' eager face looked to me, "Why is he wearing that warm coat?"

"Please, sir..." the captain's face implored me to keep his secret.

"The captain," I said to my son, "likes to keep his coat on. That is all there is to it. Come now, I intend to find a quiet corner of the deck, suitably situated away from the walkway and the smoke from the funnel, and where I shall spend the night."

"Papa." Trotts tugged at my cuff, "may I remain on deck with you?"

"I think it a capital idea. It will be fearfully stuffy down below. What do you ladies wish to do? We could ask for some chairs."

"Shall we, Eliza?" Little Helen asked, "please say yes."

Eliza frowned, making it plain that she was not so enthusiastic, but the eager look on Trotts' face dissolved the crease on her forehead. "I am outnumbered, so I shall capitulate." Trotts jumped up and down with excitement. "Find Mary Ann will you please, Trotts. She too may stay on deck if she so wishes, and Ireland. Ask them to bring some blankets. Despite this heat, it may be chilly before dawn."

We ate tolerably well, but I recall saying something to Eliza about it being a short trip, and that the food would prevent starvation. The ladies and Ireland settled in chairs, whilst Trotts and I lay on the deck with my Italian cloak between our bodies and the boards. A light breeze came as welcome relief as we sailed further from the coast. I spread a blanket over my sleeping son. The sounds of the engine drumming and the swish of the water through the paddles combined with the gentle roll of the *Pollux* like a lullaby.

A tremendous crash woke us. My first thought was that the boiler had burst, but within a second the scene of devastation told a different story.

A ship, which I quickly learned to be the two hundred and forty horse power *Monjibello,* had struck the *Pollux* just above her paddle box, her bow penetrating the very cabin which Trotts and I would have occupied. In all probability she would have cut us in two. Her bowsprit had come into contact with our funnel, which was smashed to pieces and driven overboard. All was chaos. Passengers and crew ran about like demented chickens as it became obvious that our vessel would not remain afloat for many minutes. Women screamed and men shouted, as it was every man for himself to get aboard the *Monjibello* (which had suffered damage but did not appear to be sinking) as best we could. To my eternal disgust, the captain, mate and entire crew of the *Pollux* all scrambled to safety, leaving their passengers to their own devices. Before we were able to make good our transition, the two vessels began to part, taken by the swell. At that moment, I truly thought we were lost. I had sailed across the Atlantic Ocean and back four times, and yet here, within sight of the Italian coast and the island of Elba, on a calm sea, my family and I were to drown. Then a passenger of the *Monjibello* took the helm and steered her close to the sinking *Pollux.*

My son was on his knees, his hands clasped before him in prayer, "Blessed Virgin, take us under your protection."

"Oh, save the poor boy, and never mind me." Eliza cried.

"Calm, Eliza," I said, "keep calm. If we remain cool and temperate, all will be well."

With the *Monjibello* right alongside, Trotts was the first of our party to safety, then Little Helen and Eliza. An ashen faced Mary Ann, her worst fears of the sea confirmed, clung to Ireland as she sobbed her way across. I was amongst the last to leave the *Pollux.* Mr Massey was with me, but no sooner than we were safe, did he turn around and return to the doomed steamer.

"The boiler," he shouted above the din, "I must release the valve, or she will blow and take us all." Before anyone could dissuade him, he disappeared below decks. Last to cross was the old sea captain. I am sorry to say he slipped. A sailor grabbed his hand, but to no effect. The weight of his gold took him to the bottom. His was the only life lost. A triumphant Mr Massey reappeared. He told me later that the water had been up to his knees in the boiler room. Moments later, the *Pollux* sank, stern first, just twenty minutes after being struck.

One might have thought, at this point, that our troubles were behind us, but no. The same gentleman who had taken the helm now set forth in a row boat, his self-appointed mission being to go ashore at Portolongoni on the island of Elba (this being our nearest landfall) and ask permission for the *Monjibello* to dock. As he rowed away, I enquired of Mr Massey the identity of this natural leader.

"You do well to note his leadership, Mr Waterton, for he is Charles Bonaparte, none other than the nephew of Napoleon."

As the saying goes, you could have knocked me down with a feather. In an instant I was forced to revise my opinion of the man. Whilst he was no great ornithologist, in that moment, he immediately and everlastingly commanded my respect. His actions had saved my son's life, and as every parent knows, there can be no greater debt of gratitude.

Most passengers had donned their night attire before the collision, and had been tucked up in their stuffy cabins. They now stood in a variety of undress, awaiting our hero's return. To the disgust of all passengers, it was noted that the captains and first mates of both the *Pollux* and the *Monjibello* were without their breeches, making it obvious that they had been in their cabins when at least one from each ship should have been on duty. Fortunate indeed that my party had chosen to stay on deck, and fully clad. My sisters-in-law had lost their bonnets, and I had lost my hat, but otherwise we were decent, though somewhat dishevelled. An English gentleman challenged our captain.

"I see now why I could not find you when I saw the lights of the approaching ship."

"I saw the lights, also," a young man said, "I told a sailor, but he said I was to mind my own business. I saw Mr Massey run to the bow, shouting in English and in French in the vain hope that a sailor from the *Monjibello* might have been on watch, but there was none."

There was little food on board what was now a very crowded ship. The *Monjibello* had left Leghorn at about the same time as the *Pollux* had left Civita Vecchia, full to capacity for the overnight trip. The captain of the *Monjibello* pleaded for calm and the mood could have turned very nasty indeed had we not seen the row boat. A cheer went up but when it drew near, Bonaparte's gloomy countenance told of bad news.

"Those in authority have seen with their own eyes our shipwreck, but they will not permit us to land because the passengers from the *Pollux* have no passports."

The passengers of the *Monjibello* became especially annoyed. After all, they *did* have their passports. There was nothing else for it but to remain at anchor for the remainder of the night. At dawn, an inspection was made of the *Monjibello,* and with the captain satisfied of her seaworthiness, we sailed on to Leghorn. All aboard were hungry and tired, adding to our ill humour. We anchored up and awaited clearance from the Customs. No difficulty was anticipated, but alas! Officialdom ruled! The harbourmaster of Leghorn, in his infinite wisdom, decided that twenty days' quarantine must be observed because no bill of health could be produced for the *Pollux.*

Once again, Charles Bonaparte set forth to plead our case. This time he stood before the Council of Leghorn, where he remonstrated that the letter of the law need not be their only guidance. After two hours of mitigation, he returned with the necessary paperwork to satisfy the harbourmaster, and we were permitted to disembark. I made it my business to personally thank Mr Bonaparte for his exertions on our behalf but declined to engage in further conversation. We shipwrecked mariners were a bedraggled sight. I saw two priests wearing one shoe each.

"I recommend you cast lots for a shoe," I laughed, "so that one of you might walk in comfort as we tramp the streets of Leghorn."

Our own individual losses were heavy. The costly wardrobe of my sisters-in-law, our books, writings, money, passport, correspondence (including the aforementioned letter from Robert Carr) maps, the ladies' jewellery and our letters of credit all went to the bottom with the foundered steamer. Little Helen lost an ivory crucifix of rare value. It had been sculptured by an excellent artist of the fifteenth century, and could never be replaced. My little boy was deprived of a relic from the catacombs. He had been given a bone by Cardinal Fransoni, which he had intended to place in our chapel.

The dressmakers and tailors of Leghorn profited from our disaster as we replaced our wardrobes with necessities before returning to Città Vecchia in the vessel which had run us down. Upon our arrival the Officers of the Customs, knowing of our shipwreck, let every article of clothing purchased in Leghorn pass duty free of the heavy charges usually made, but I must add that when I went to the English Consul for a new passport, he charged the full price.

I bought a dozen little owls from a vendor in the market at the pantheon, and a large cage for their safe transport. I felt sure that if they survived the journey, they would do well in Yorkshire. We left the Eternal City once again on the 20th of July.

In the town of Novi, I wrote the following in a hôtel guest book.

The Pollux, once so fine,
No longer cleaves the wave,
For now she lies supine,
Deep in her wat'ry grave.

When she received her blow,
The captain and his mate
Were both asleep below,
Snoring in breechless state.
If I the power possess'd

I'd hang them by the neck
As warning to the rest,
How they desert the deck.
Our treasures, and our clothes,

With all we had, were lost.
The shock that caused our woes
Took place on Elba's coast.

We travelled overland, taking a route via Genoa, Mont St Gothard, Lucerne, Basle and Aix-la-Chapelle. The journey was long and wet, and I feared for my little owls. I bathed them in warm water, and took a bath myself. This course of action proved disastrous, as five little owls died that night and I started to feel the rumblings of dysentery. We travelled on to Bruges where Eliza and Little Helen stayed at the Convent, recounting our adventures, good and bad. When not in the closet of the Hôtel du Commerce, I wandered the city, where I purchased two barnacled geese and two ganders, with the hope they might breed on my lake.

We stayed for ten days before recommencing our homeward journey. I had recovered a little. Mary Ann boarded the steamer at Ostend with faltering steps, but all went well, with the exception of the death of one goose, and we were back at Walton Hall by the end of August. Eliza's cough was no more, at least for a while, but the dysentery would not leave me. I wrote to my physician, Doctor Hobson who attended the following day.

"I suppose you have let some blood?"

"I certainly have, and had I not done so I would not be here, and at your mercy."

"It does no good, Mr Waterton. You are weak enough as it is without bleeding yourself." He prodded and poked my guts in all the sore places.

"Doctor Marshall disagrees, and it is thanks to him that I am skilled with the lancet. His instruction has saved my life countless times."

"Then unless we are to fall out, we must continue to agree to disagree, my friend." He left me with a bottle of kaolin and morphine large enough to block the guts of an elephant.

Of my owls, one had a broken thigh, no doubt he took a tumble in the cage, and I was forced to kill it, and another died two weeks later.

Having been absent for nigh on two years, I was anxious to inspect the entire estate and would have done so but for a weakness of the limbs. My heart beat so quickly I could only walk a hundred yards on the flat before being forced to rest.

CHAPTER TWENTY-FIVE

Trickery and Trauma, Success, and Litigation.

During my absence the cats had done their duty in keeping the Hanoverians at bay and White and Guest had taken me at my word, but the same could not be said of Warwick. The pigeon cote had been raided twice, and as a result we had few pigeon pies that year. The growing sport of shooting domestic pigeons meant that game dealers were approaching poachers for supplies, who were in turn approaching gamekeepers. Cotes such as mine were being raided by throwing nets over them during the night. The thieves would then disturb the birds so that they flew from safety straight into a trap. Warwick told me the poachers had been about their business while he had been occupied at the fish trap. According to Ogden, Warwick had spent more time in the Cross Keys than at his game keeping. Before coming into my employ, Ogden had done his share of poaching, so was more wily than most it came to who-was-where and what-they-were-doing. When challenged, the sheepish look on Warwick's face spoke volumes. A few nights later, when he showed cowardice in the face of poachers (one of whom I shot and injured in the leg), there was nothing for it but to dismiss him. I suspected he had been in their pay but had no proof of it, and whether he had or not made no difference to the result.

"But Squire," he pleaded, "you will make me homeless."

I poked him in the chest with my forefinger, "You should have thought of that when you were lining the pockets of the public house landlord."

"I have three children, Squire. Will you see them homeless? How will I tell my wife?"

"Again, Warwick, you should have thought of that before. Your fate is your own doing, not mine." With nothing else to say to the fool, I walked away as he cursed me with every bad word he could lay his tongue to. His absence was no loss to me, and he found no sympathy in the village when he tried to defame me by spreading malicious gossip. While I am not usually one to talk of such things, the villagers know who pays the chemist for the poor. If the sick or hungry can walk to Walton Hall, they eat with the servants. If they cannot, I send bread, milk and eggs to their home.

Ogden became both mason and keeper. I employed Tommy Barnes as his assistant along with his wife, Lucy, as a maid.

Recalling Warwick's drunken behaviour brings to mind the circumstances in which I came to have an arrangement with a Wakefield shoemaker. One fine and bright morning I met a miserably poor looking man. He had no shoes, and I took pity on him. The only coin in my pocket was a half crown, enough to buy shoes and stockings and have change to spare. In all conscience I could do no other than give it to him. His face lit up like a lantern on a frosty night.

"Thank-you, kindly, Squire. You are the kindest man who ever walked, and thanks to you I shall walk in shoes."

Imagine my disgust when, later that same day, I met him again when on my way to Wakefield, still shoe-less, and clearly inebriated, but not so much as to fail to recognise me.

"How do you do, old boy? I owe you," he slurred, "come, let me buy you a pint with what is left of your half crown."

Needless to say, I turned down his offer. The incident put my mind to working out a way of helping the barefooted poor without giving them hard cash. I carried on into Wakefield, where I visited a shoemaker and told him of my quandary.

"Perhaps, Squire, you could devise a token of some description. If a person were to show me such a thing, I would know they had come from you, and I would exchange it for a pair of shoes."

The simplicity of his idea appealed to me. I had in my pocket an old knife which I had used for many years when hedging. Its handle and blade were well worn, making it distinct from any other. I showed it to him.

"What do you say to this?" He agreed it would do the job, and so a system was set in place whereby shoes were supplied to the bearer of the knife, and the next time I was in Wakefield, I paid the shoemaker and he returned the knife to me.

It was not, however, an infallible system, and I was indebted to Ogden for saving me from another mistaken act of charity. We were just outside the park walls, repairing a tree. Warmed by our work, we had removed our jackets and laid them against the wall. As we sawed the damaged branches, I was approached by a seemingly distressed man. He did not speak but pointed to his bare feet. Without a second thought, my hand was in my pocket, feeling for the knife. Ogden beckoned me to one side, and whispered,

"I saw this vagabond take his shoes off earlier this morning as I came to meet you. He hid them in the hedge at the entrance to the lower field. I thought he might try a trick on you, and retrieved his shoes. They are in my jacket pocket."

We grinned at each other like conspiratorial schoolboys. "Ogden," I said loudly, "do you think my shoes would fit this poor fellow?"

"No, Squire, yours won't fit him, but I have a pair in my pocket that seem to be about his size." He then took the shoes from his jacket and gave then to their owner, saying, "try these on your poor feet."

The would-be fraudster recognised his own property, and looked suitably cowed. Ogden would have issued summary punishment, but I waved him back, and turned to the man as he put his shoes on.

"If I ever see you in Walton again, I shall have you in prison. Do you understand me?" He nodded vigorously, and ran off, never having uttered a single word in the entire encounter.

But to refer back to my half crown, there is no sight of civilised society more horribly disgusting than that of a human being in a state of intoxication. The good Jesuit who advised me never to allow strong liqueur to approach my lips did me a great favour. I have seen manly strength, and female beauty, and old age itself, in ruins under the vice of alcohol. The drunkard makes himself vulnerable to the criminal who will trick him in his state of inebriety.

At this time, a great change took place in our little household. My son was eleven years of age. Sick as I was with the dysentery, I determined to accompany him to Stonyhurst. We travelled by train. The journey from

Wakefield Kirkgate Station to Preston could now be accomplished in two hours. We were met by Mr Danniel, the stableman at Stonyhurst, who drove the pony and trap for the final miles.

As I left, I gave Edmund a letter.

Walton Hall,
Sept. 6th 1841

To my dear Edmund,
You are now, my dear boy, about to enter into a college conducted by professors famed far and near for their learning, for their sanctity and for their paternal care of those who are entrusted to their charge. This college will either be a paradise or a purgatory to you. If you love God above all things, if you respect your superiors, give good example to your equals and attend to your studies, you will indeed be happy. But if you neglect in your duty to God and man, you will be irritated as if scratched by brambles and thorns with every step as you go along. You will never again have such an opportunity of acquiring knowledge and virtue to ensure your superiority on this side of the grave, and your salvation on the other.
Treat the good Fathers with attention and gratitude. They sacrifice everything to lead you safely along the path of knowledge. Should any of your companions ridicule them, do not listen, for they are fools. A youth who scoffs at his superiors will not succeed when he enters the world of adults. Never give an impertinent answer to your superiors. Love them and obey them to the best of your ability and they will repay you with kindness and care. The scholar who respects his tutors will be well educated, but he who takes pleasure in avoiding his studies will become a dunce in college and a failure after he departs. Turn a deaf ear to any criticisms your fellow pupils make, whilst at the same time trying to persuade them that they would be better off to follow your example. Show them, if you can, how you are gaining, and they are losing.

Believe me, my dear boy, I would never send you to Stonyhurst were I not convinced beyond all doubt that you cannot go to a better place for education. I have the very highest opinion of it, and I hope that you will have the same. I am sorry that we are to be separated but know that it is in your best interests in the long run. In the meantime, you will find a parent at every step in the good Fathers of Stonyhurst. Never do anything that will cause them to regret taking you under their charge, and always obey the college rules.

Take St Aloysius for your model. Pray to this angelic servant of Jesus Christ with confidence. Take part in all the games, and be friendly with every boy, rather than have one particular friend. Always remember, in the words of Doctor Benjamin Franklin.

"Early to bed, and early to rise,
Makes a man healthy, wealthy and wise."

Farewell, my dearest boy. I give you my blessing, and I promise that you shall want for nothing, provided you perform your duty and follow implicitly the Holy and excellent instructions which you will receive.

I have one parting request to make of you. Say a short prayer for me, once a day, to St Francis Xavier, the glorious apostle of the Indies.

I remain, your ever-affectionate father,
Charles Waterton.

Oh, how we missed the dear boy. Walton Hall felt like a house in mourning. Eliza walked around with a face like a codfish with a headache, and Little Helen's stifled sobs flushed her face as if she had a head cold. At the time, I wondered if my parents had felt any such sadness when they sent Christopher, Thomas and me to Stonyhurst. I had never given a thought as to whether or not our parents missed us. In those days, when a boy went away to school he stayed there, the poor condition of the roads prohibiting unnecessary travel. Thanks to the railways, which have carved up pasture land with the efficiency of a sharpened knife, this was no longer the case.

During my return journey, I once again felt the rumblings of my enemy within the bowels. The jostling of the carriage from Kirkgate Railway Station to Walton Hall aggravated my discomfort. I suffered a considerable weakening of my constitution, and was too far gone to object when, a few days later, my sisters-in-law sent for Doctor Hobson. His face gave nothing away despite my weakness and he remained as calm as if he were attending a bruised eye or some such trivial condition. He made arrangements with our family surgeon, Mr Bennett (no relation to the old housekeeper), for him to attend me daily with pills and potions, which eventually put me to rights.

Meanwhile, Edmund's letters gave no sign of homesickness. He had clearly taken to life at Stonyhurst as I had hoped he would and was full of praise for the good Fathers. By the end of October, I could no longer bear the miserable faces of my sisters-in-law and their constant speculation as to what Trotts might be doing at any particular time of day.

"You could visit him, you know." They stared at me as if I had suggested they might grow wings and fly over the Pennines. "I am sure you would be made welcome." We were sitting at the fireside. The wind hurled itself at the windows as dusk fell. Mary Ann entered the room and drew the curtains.

"Mary Ann," I said, "My sisters-in-law are considering a short journey and will require your assistance."

A look of horror crossed her face. "I cannot go on the sea, Squire. I cannot, not for all the tea in China."

"There is no sea between here and Lancashire, my dear. You will be quite safe." She bobbed a curtsy and with a look of relief spreading across her pale face, left the room.

I turned back to my sisters-in-law. "I shall make the arrangements. Bear in mind I have only just this moment thought of this, but Mary Ann will accompany you."

"Oh, thank-you, Charles." Eliza leapt to her feet. We are not, generally speaking, ones for demonstrative affection, and I feared she was about to throw her arms around me, but thankfully she did not.

"You could stay at a good hôtel in Preston, and then have an early start for Stonyhurst." The transformation of their faces from grief to happiness was a joy to behold.

"But you will come with us, Charles."

"I think not on this occasion. I have much to do here."

"Can we go tomorrow, Charles?" Little Helen asked.

Eliza smiled and put her hand over that of her sister. "Charles will have to write a letter, sister dear."

"Indeed, I must, and also study the train timetables."

"Are you sure you cannot come?" Little Helen pleaded, "Trotts might be disappointed if you are not with us."

"I could not bear the shaking of the carriage, my dear."

"I thought you were recovered." Eliza's tone held accusation.

"I am much better, but dysentery is a fickle enemy. I think I had better stay close to the closet."

All was soon put in place, and a journey which could not have been contemplated for ladies in winter prior to the railways was accomplished without incident. In their absence, Walton Hall was quieter than ever, but I was happy enough with my own company.

Upon their return, Eliza and Little Helen enthused about Stonyhurst as if I had never been there, telling me of the joy within. Everything had gone splendidly. Good wishes were conveyed from the Fathers, and entreaties for me to visit as soon as my health permitted.

"He insisted we call him Edmund," Little Helen said. "He was very definite about it."

"He asked not to be called Trotts, ever again." Eliza concurred.

They looked so serious, I could not help but laugh. "My little boy is growing up!"

A sharp frost decorated the landscape with hoar. The air was clear, a low sun filtered through the trees. I was working away with my trusty hatchet on the bank of the creek, cutting back some shoots from some tree stumps, when I slipped into the water up to my middle. This placed me in a better position to continue my work on the shoots and brambles which overhung the water, and so I remained there for upwards of an hour. The water was cold, and my feet as numb as they had been on my walk from Baccano to Rome. Again, I was not aware of my injury until I saw the blood, and the tear in the side of my shoe as I walked back to the house. Had it been summer, the leeches would have had a fine supper served, but they are not ones for the cold and would have been deep in the mud. My sisters-in-law fussed dreadfully. Eliza was waiting for me as I came over the bridge.

"Why are you limping?"

"Am I late?"

"No, Charles, you are not late."

"Then why the exasperated frown? Is something amiss?" I followed her in, and took off my boots. The cut was quite deep. "I seem to have cut my foot. Send for Mr Bennett, would you?"

I changed into some dry clothes and we ate our dinner. Shortly afterwards, Mr Bennett arrived. He cleaned and bandaged the wound. Needless to say, I was generally in poor favour with Eliza, but Little Helen was all concern. I was to rest, keep my foot elevated, and apply linen cloths dipped in cold water.

The following day, being anxious to complete my work with the shoots and brambles, I waited until Eliza was busy with household matters before slipping out, undetected. I set forth in *Percy* but the hounds were soon on my trail. That is to say, Ogden and the pointers were dispatched to find me.

"Mr Bennett is at the house, Squire." Ogden stood on the little bridge over the creek, calling to me. "Miss Eliza says you must come back and have your foot attended to."

I willingly agreed. My foot throbbed, but I had completed my task and was prepared to argue my case. Mr Bennett caught the rope as I moored.

"Do not be too harsh on me, sir. As you can see, my foot has been elevated in the boat."

"Mr Waterton, that was not what I had in mind, as I am sure you are aware."

Water squelched from the hole in my shoe, and I pointed to it. "And as you can see, I have slit open the upper leather and my foot has been continually doused in cool water, as instructed by your good self."

"I implore you, sir, to have more caution. The wound will not heal if you persist in disregarding my advice."

"Have no fear, my task is complete, and I shall be a good patient from now on. I have suffered worse and survived." As I spoke Old More chimed one o'clock. "I am in good time for dinner, so should not be in too much trouble. Do you forgive me?"

"On condition that you go straight away and put on some dry clothing, and then permit me to dress your wound without delay."

I did as he asked, and we had a jolly fine dinner, but my dip in the water had further punishment in mind. My old foe, dysentery, returned the following day, and Doctor Hobson was called to arms. His ministrations, alongside my tried and tested methods, triumphed and the dysentery was put to rout.

My surviving little owls had wintered well in their cage. They were all in good health thanks to a diet of slugs, beetles and mice (the latter of which we always have in plentiful supply thanks to the cats) and to being kept in the warmth of the stables for their first Yorkshire winter. They were freed at seven o'clock on the 10th of May, after I gave them the following advice.

'The whole world is your home, little birds, but if you stay in my park, I shall be glad of your company and always be your friend and benefactor.'

They flew to an adjacent thicket, their immigration to Yorkshire a success as testified by generations of their offspring which fly about the place.

Not until the benefits of my Lenten fast were realised, and the fair weather of June upon us, was I able to climb a tree and generally resume my life as I wished to live it. My foot hindered me more than I cared to admit, but I was compensated by the company of the birds.

Imagine, if you will, my astonishment when I observed the nesting, close by the house, of a Canada goose with one of my barnacled ganders. The latter is about two thirds the size of the former. Notwithstanding this disparity, the old fool of a goose took the insignificant little fellow into connubial favour, despite there being twenty-four Canadas present from which she could have made her choice. For two years the infatuated simpletons paired, and the goose laid eggs, without chance, as I thought, of any progeny. I named them Canada Nisa, and Barnacled Mopsus. If I approached, Mopsus' cackling was incessant, and he would run at me with inconceivable ferocity whenever I went to pay his wife a visit, jumping at my knees, and biting my legs until I retreated.

Some years after this alliance, a Canada gander tried his luck with an Egyptian goose. There was much billing and cooing for three weeks, before they came to a mutual agreement that it was not a good idea, and parted.

That summer I had a request from Mr Bennett to accompany him to York on an urgent family matter. He wanted me to witness some papers. Naturally I agreed, taking the opportunity to visit the Minster. Whilst I was there a shivering fit came upon me with such severity that I thought I had fallen in with my old foe, the tertian ague, which had been so formidable in the unwholesome swamps of Guiana. It turned out to be the precipitation of a recurrence of dysentery, and for a third time Doctor Hobson proved his knowledge by counteracting its advances. In fact, not only was it arrested in its progress, but has never returned. Between us, Doctor Hobson and I had won the battle, and thus, the war. At the time I thought my travelling days were done. Nine months of dysentery had scared me fearfully and common sense told me not to run any more risk, lest by debilitating my constitution I would prove to be worse for wear in old age. I need not have worried.

A matter of greater concern came airborne from the village. Clouds of foul smoke emanating from Hodgson and Simpson's new factory chimney choked the air. I paid a visit. Hodgson was at his desk in the counting house, a large, two-storey building at the entrance to the yard.

"Squire Waterton, how good to see you."

I was I no mood for niceties. "Your foul chimney is killing my trees. What chemicals are you making here?"

He drummed his fingers on the desk. "Ah, yes, well you see Squire—"

"I see all right, and I smell it too. You gave me your word you would not make your own chemicals."

"You speak of the salt cake furnace."

"Is that what it is? It must stop, I tell you, or you will undo all that I have achieved."

"I'm sorry, Squire, truly I am, but my partner, Edward, has ambitions. He says—"

"I am not interested in what he says," I shouted, "you are in charge, are you not?"

"We are partners but I find it hard to hold him back. He lost another child last January, William Edward they called him. The poor mite only lived for six days."

"I am sorry to hear it," my tone conciliatory now, "but that stinking smoke will kill us all."

"You must speak with Edward, Squire, but you should know it is the work here that keeps him going."

"I think that would be a waste of breath, don't you?"

He turned his palms uppermost and shrugged. "Likely so."

"Then I must speak with my lawyer."

"We employ three men and two boys. You cannot stop progress, Squire. Their families need the wages. Think on it carefully. Do you want to deprive them of their livelihood?"

I wagged my finger at him. "Listen to me. Walton is a quiet rural village and not suited to industry. If you close your factory, I will employ your men. Soap can be made anywhere, but I cannot move my estate. Edward Simpson couldn't give two hoots about the poor, and you know it. This is all about filling his pockets. The man would argue black was white if he thought there was a penny to be made from it."

He shifted in his chair. "Edward says, it is about time Walton caught up with progress."

"I have already said I am not interested in what Edward says. You can tell him that if smoke is still coming from that monstrosity in one week, I shall have this place closed down entirely. My trees are dying."

And that was the beginning of it. My battle with Hodgson and Simpson is no secret to the people hereabouts, nor its conclusion. One week after my conversation with William Hodgson, I sat opposite Mr Nettleton in what was the first of many such meetings, and the first step upon a long and tortuous path. Mr Nettleton said he would write to Hodgson and Simpson, but pointed out that there was no scientific proof that the chimney was the cause of the damage to my trees. He advised that I evict Edward Thornhill Simpson from Beechfield House. Other than that, no progress was made. Anyone who has visited my home knows of my preference for open windows and well banked fires, but we were forced to keep the windows closed. The grotto, being no more than a hundred yards from my boundary wall, and the soap works three hundred yards beyond that, was seldom a place to linger. Fortunately, after the storm of 1834, the herons had removed themselves from the southern side of the lake to the northern edge of Stubbs Wood, otherwise they would all have either perished or left my parkland for more pleasant air.

Meanwhile, I set up a joinery workshop in the stable block where I made nesting boxes for owls and imitation pheasants, placing them on high branches just within my wall to fool the bargees and waste their shot.

My greatest scheme at the time was the construction of a starling tower. It stands on the island, a few feet from the water-gate. I planted a semi-circular yew hedge around it, making a true haven within. The tower is thirteen feet high and has sixty nesting places. As the building progressed, I could not resist adding some accommodation more suited to the jackdaw, and higher still, for the barn owl. The lower orifices are five inches square and each have a loose stone, cut away in one corner, fitted at the entrance. They are the domain of the starlings. The purpose of the loose stone is to enable a starling to enter with ease, but not the jackdaws or owls. They also enable me to have a peep at the young birds, and to clean out the tower once the breeding season is over. In designing the tower, I took into account the interest which would no doubt be shown by vermin and household cats. To address this, a projecting stone was built, one foot from the base, as a barrier to all would be climbers. I have set a wooden box into the water-gate wall, where a cat can laze. Tom Pussy, who was a great favourite with Eliza and Little Helen in his time, was often to be seen there.

Once the barn owls were in residence in the tower, I took apart the stone nesting box which had served them well until the more desirable accommodation took their fancy. I am delighted to say the whole tower has been a success, right from the first spring, and has been the birthplace of hundreds of birds over the years.

The following winter was a long one. Even in June almost every night was frosty. Against my own rule, I permitted the poor to use their rod and line. Pike, carp, tench, perch, roach, dace, gudgeon and eels were plentiful. I have never been much of a one for rod and line. When I fancy a bout of fishing, I favour the method of the South America Indians and take to *Percy* with bow and arrow, to take my aim at the pike.

July burst upon us as if the season of spring had been bypassed. Blossom came and went in a week, and on the days when Hodgson and Simpson were not boiling their vitriol, we were able to enjoy the grotto.

During the first week of August, I took the train to Preston and on to Stonyhurst with the purpose of accompanying Edmund back to Walton for the summer months. Oh, the joy of seeing the towers of that place. How my heart soars at the sight of the hills, and the memories of my adventures. I stayed one night, enjoying the hospitality and company of the Fathers. My boy had grown in stature, he was quite beefy. Broad of shoulder and bright of eye. He had undoubtedly benefitted from his education, having been awarded prizes for Latin and Greek composition, and was the proud owner of a silver medal.

The journey passed with a more adult conversation than I had anticipated.

"I am looking forward to seeing my aunts."

"I can assure you, Edmund, the feeling is mutual. They will be as proud as punch to hear of your achievements."

"I suppose everything is the same at Walton Hall."

"Not quite. We suffer from the emissions of a high chimney at the vitriol works." I pointed out the black smoke as the carriage took us down the avenue.

Eliza had continued to suffer from her cough, but because I saw her every day, I had failed to notice the extent of her decline. Edmund was mortified when he saw her.

"Father, (he no longer called me Papa) how could you let this happen? Aunt Eliza must have better air."

We were in the drawing room. "And what if I wish to stay here, Edmund?"

"But the air is foul, Aunt."

"Not every day. If the chimney is not smoking, or the wind takes the fumes to the north, your father takes your Aunt Helen and I out on the sailboat, or we walk to the grotto."

"Is that safe?" he asked.

"Edmund, I have sailed since my childhood, honing my skills on the rivers of South America. I—" but he cut me off.

"Pardon my interrupting, Father, but your skill at the helm is not my concern. I was referring to the quality of the air."

"If your Aunt Eliza wishes to go to the coast, or to a sunnier clime, we shall do so."

"So, what do you say, Aunt?"

"I will think about it, Edmund." A bout of coughing forced her to pause. "For the summer, I intend to remain here, under the care of Doctor Hobson."

During that summer, foul air permitting, much of my time was spent in the creation of a new garden at the stables where I knew the south facing wall would be ideal for growing vines. In order to have any chance of a harvest of grapes, I needed to prepare the soil. An appropriate diet of sunshine and food are key to the health of all living things, flora and fauna alike. I dug a trench, ten feet long and two feet wide, right against the wall, and put a layer of rough gravel in the bottom, followed by some old roots which would rot down. On top of this I shovelled leaves and rotted matter, which I trampled down to fill the gaps between the roots. Next, I added a layer of bones which I acquired from Cook after they had been boiled for stock. Fine garden soil was the icing on my layer cake. My labours have been well rewarded as the vines are as thick as they are productive. Being a teetotaller, I have no desire to ferment, but come harvest time no visitor leaves Walton Hall without a bunch of grapes.

When I was forced indoors, with the windows shut tight, I worked either on my taxidermy or on my first series of 'Essays on Natural History'.

To Edmund's relief, his aunts and I intended to spend the winter in Rome, and with this assurance he was happy to return to school early in September. The following week, Eliza's cough was worse than it had ever been, so much so that we were forced to abandon our planned trip. My weakness of the chest also made its presence known.

Eliza and Little Helen, who was also suffering from a cough, went to Hornsea on the east coast, where the air is nothing if not bracing. I accompanied them, and saw them settled in a fine hôtel with Mary Ann, before returning to Walton.

As the breeding season approached, the incongruous and persevering Canada Nisa and Barnacled Mopsus once again took up their position on the island. He stood guard day after day, often on one leg, as she sat on her five eggs. From a safe distance I would sometimes ask Nisa how she could lose her heart to such a diminutive fellow.

The whole affair seemed ridiculous, and I was quite prepared for its failure, as in the two preceding years, when, to my astonishment, out came two young ones, the remaining three eggs being addled. The exertions of the faithful couple were rewarded at last, and Nisa's unpromising choice vindicated.

The vociferous gesticulations and strutting of Mopsus when he first had sight of his longed-for progeny were beyond anything I had ever seen or heard. A proud father indeed. They had nested as far as their island home could be from the water's edge. I approached the nest in order to convey the young ones to the water, having decided to launch them close to the cherry tree. Mopsus screamed loudly as he and Nisa attacked me, but once my self-appointed task was complete, the parents jumped in after their babies and swam to the opposite shore. With hindsight, I admit I should have left them to it.

My old school friend, Edwin Jones, visited that year. I wish he could have seen the jolly goose family, but his eyesight was failing and his legs would barely hold him up. He heard the cackling of the ever protective Mopsus and Nisa, and I described their plumage to him.

"I would like to have painted them for you, Charles." He said it without sadness. At sixty-two years of age, we could still laugh together like schoolboys. We knew, without putting it into words, that this would be his last visit, and made the most of it. There would be no more tree climbing with Edwin Jones.

Mopsus and Nisa brought up their progeny with great care and success.

CHAPTER TWENTY-SIX

A Grand Tour.

Twelve months later, with Eliza much stronger, we left Hull for Antwerp on the 2nd October 1844, having spent the previous night at the Victoria Hôtel. Ireland and Mary Ann accompanied us, Eliza and Little Helen having convinced the maid of their need for her. Enough time had passed for flattery to win over her fear. Unfortunately, the passage was not a good one and we were on board for two wet and stormy nights.

I made notes along the way, and upon our return, I gave them to Little Helen as a memento. She has kindly loaned then back to me, in order that I might refer to them in the interests of accuracy. From these I see we spent a week in Bruges, where my equilibrium is always restored.

We travelled by rail to Aix-la-Chapelle in one day, and from there to Cologne, where we took the steam boat. We saw no birds on the Rhine, and the weather was bitterly cold. Adding to our general dissatisfaction, an English family from London, by the name of Sayer, did all they could to make me ashamed of my countrymen. Clearly they had more money than brain, as they studiously avoided conversation with any of the numerous passengers on board. To crown it all they actually had the bad taste and impudence to direct their three vulgar maid servants to dine with us in the first-class cabin!

"Arrangements can only get better, Charles." Eliza remarked in a stage whisper as we disembarked in Frankfurt. Happily, she was right. I heartily recommend the Hôtel d'Angleterre. A most capital hôtel, with an attentive landlord. Whilst there, I bought a very convenient travel-bag.

Less than three weeks after leaving England, we were in Bavaria. Travelling by coach, we observed the land and the people who worked it. Ireland and I sat atop, and the ladies within. Oh, happy is the October traveller, for the absence of flies and bugs. My sisters-in-law and I compared our observations each evening.

"Everything is so different to England," Little Helen said. "I particularly like the local costume with the pyramid-shaped hats, black boots, short skirts and petticoats. I think the people are rightly proud of their appearance." Eliza and I agreed, and I said I had seen no scratching of heads as evidence of nits in the hair of the hard-working, farming people.

As we travelled on, I saw the menfolk burying their crop of potatoes in long trenches close to the road, and considered it a measure of the honesty of the Bavarians. I could not help but think that such a custom in England would result in theft, and bring plenty of custom to the gaols.

I see from my notes that I was also struck by the cleanliness of the villages. The absence of obscene sentences written on walls, and of mice or rats in bedrooms.

Even the Protestant churches bore crucifixes and other sculptured ornaments which we did not expect, and which would certainly not be seen in an Anglican church. Birds were scarce throughout our journey, but at Roth we saw forty or so carrion crows. Also, in this town, we marvelled at a large representation of the death of St Francis Xaverius painted on the wall of a house. From Roth to Munich cattle and sheep enjoyed the plain, sharing the land with innumerable moles, whose little piles of soil dot the grassland like worm-casts on a sandy beach. We saw a few magpies, carrions and buntings. Little Helen pointed out two squirrels as we entered a wood of scotch fir where the hills commenced. Here, the hogs have long legs, and their curved backs have strong, upright bristles from head to tail. At that juncture, we had not seen one single head of wild game, flying or running.

There was such a silence in the streets of Munich as we drove up to our hôtel, that I fancied there was not a single woman left in that part of the town, honest or otherwise. I refrained from saying as much, not wanting to offend my sisters-in-law. We did not see one drunk person all the time we were in Bavaria or Germany, despite the propensity for growing hops! Within the city of Munich there were plenty of sparrows and domestic pigeons, the latter taking up their abode behind the statues and carved stones in the walls of the churches. They had easy pickings around the stables, gleaning the cobbles of oats and wheat. Other than this, birds were as scarce as an honest horse dealer. The cabinets of natural history in the museums of Munich are of very large scale, but as expected, the individual specimens are as deformed as those of London, Manchester and Edinburgh.

After leaving Munich, we approached Lake Tegernsee, hoping to see waterfowl, but the lake bore no duck, coot or waterhen. We dined at the inn there, but it was poor doings in the knife and fork department.

Austria came next, where the Customs Officials were exceedingly civil, showing no interest in inspecting our baggage. They wished us a happy journey, and would take no payment when returning our passport, saying they were well paid by their government.

We enjoyed delightful accommodation in this country, where the rooms were as clean as a new pin. After attending six o'clock Mass, we set forth for Innsbruck. Whilst we were there, one of the Jesuits priests of the town told us of the Holy Virgin of the Tyrol, Maria Mörl, who was blessed with stigmata, and known throughout Europe as the Ecstatica. He suggested we might visit the Convent of the Tertiary Nuns where she resided.

Sunrise quickly took the chill from the air, warming to the temperatures of an English summer. Onward then, and predictably, as we climbed the Alps, temperatures fell. There was no snow on the road, but we saw glaciers at Brenner. Our next stop was Mittewald, where our rooms were full of flies and tobacco smoke and every bit as heinous as our previous accommodation had been superb. Little Helen flapped her hands to ward off the flying insects. "I didn't expect to encounter flies in frosty weather. I would rather travel on. This place is horrid."

"I suspect they are here for the warmth of the kitchen," Eliza said, "which does nothing to enhance my appetite."

Night fell, and we drove on to Klausen by starlight and lamps, staying for one night before pushing on for Bolzen. The road followed the river on one side, and stupendous wooded mountains on the other. In a narrow pass we were slowed, and eventually stopped by a huge timber wagon with six horses. Even these strong animals could not haul the load up a particularly steep hill, and we were forced to wait for two more horses.

Caldaro (where Mother Nyren had told us the Ecstatica lived) is a full three hours' drive from Botzen. This pretty, rural village lies at the foot of the mountains, and is entirely surrounded by vineyards and fruit trees. A few carrion crowns, half a dozen finches and three wagtails were all we saw in the way of ornithology.

After a tiring day, we slept well. After celebrating Mass, we met with Father Capstrani, a monk of the Order of St Francis. Being the 1st of November, this was the festival of All Saints. When we asked to see the Ecstatica, Father Capistrani explained that he would be busy with his duties until late afternoon, but that he could meet us at the Convent in the afternoon.

We met as arranged, and Father Capstrani took us up a staircase. He opened a door softly, and we all entered, that is Eliza and Little Helen, Mary Ann, Ireland, and myself. All eyes were immediately drawn to the kneeling figure beside a plain bed. She wore a white robe, tied closely around her slender waist with a cord. The walls were hung with holy pictures, and a large crucifix at the head of the bed, above which hung a picture of the Holy Mother of God. The Ecstatica had her face turned to the crucifix and picture. She appeared quite motionless, with her eyes steadfastly fixed upon these sacred objects and her hands clasped in devotion under her chin. I stood quite close to her, but did not see even the smallest movement of her pale blue eyes. Speaking in Latin, I asked Father Capstrani if we might have more light, and he provided a candle. We now had a full and very clear view of the angel before us. Father Capstrani spoke to her, asking her to lie with her head on the pillow. Her face showed a calm resignation as she obeyed his request. I asked the Father if she took sustenance.

"She barely eats at all other than a few grapes, or an apple, or a tiny morsel of bread," he whispered, "and these, with a little water, and at long intervals from each other, I consider insufficient to support the life of an ordinary person."

"How long has she been like this?" I asked.

"Some eleven years in all. When her parents died five years ago, she accepted the invitation to live here. She needed to be cared for in peace and piety as befitted her." He then indicated that I, and my sisters-in-law, step close to her, and each in turn placed our hands on hers, feeling for ourselves the stigmata. Father Capstrani stood a little distance from us, and when I considered we had remained in the room a sufficient length of time to satisfy both our curiosity and edification, I went to him, and bowed, thanking him in Latin for his kindness to us. I then beckoned to Eliza and Little Helen that it was time for us to leave. We took our time to make our farewells to the Ecstatica, and left the room slowly, backing away, in order to have our faces towards her as she returned to her kneeling position at the bedside. Father Capstrani left first, then Eliza and Little Helen, followed by our servants. I tarried a moment longer, and in so doing missed the opportunity to thank Father Capstrani again. By the time I descended the stairs, he was away back to his duties.

As we walked back to Caldaro I thought over the extraordinary scene we had witnessed. The mild and yet imposing figure of Father Capstrani, and the complete lack of any sort of showmanship, had made a deep impression upon me. I knew I would never see the like again. I could not get the image of the Ecstatica from my mind. She floated before my eyes, haunting me for the remainder of the day, right up until the moment I fell asleep.

On leaving Caldaro, we made for Trent, and from there to Primolano, where we dined in mediocrity on soup, pigs' liver, veal and grapes in the most peculiar dining room I have ever seen, having a bed at one end, as if it had two functions. When Eliza asked a maid where the closet was situated, the servant pointed to a square piece of wooden furniture in the corner of the room. The ladies declined to go anywhere near it. Having eaten my fill, and not wishing to add extra weight to our carriage springs over a bad road, I stepped out of the dining room, and seeing the same comely little maid on the staircase, I asked her in a low tone of voice to show me where the commode was to be found.

"In the corner of the room, you have just left, sir," said she.

"But, cara mia," said I," in my own country, we never appropriate dining rooms for such purposes."

"But it is the custom here," said she positively. "However, you prefer another room, I will show you into one immediately." Thinking that I might fare worse, I thanked her for the interest she took in my comfort, and returned to the dining room, where I requested the ladies and Ireland to withdraw. I bolted the door. Thinking myself to have the required privacy, I set about my relief, only to realize I was being watched by a well-dressed woman in the house exactly opposite, across the street. She had a full view of me, and looked on with as much unconcern as though I had merely been eating a mouthful of bread and cheese.

We paid for our meal and left, thinking the worst to be behind me, but alas, I was wrong! Primolano and litter had not yet finished with me. The weather was showery, but not so wet as to remove the manure that liberally decorated the roads. I quote my notes from the time.

'Oh, you dirty people, why cannot you remove the filth before I step upon it? Oh, my shoe! There was no scraper at hand, and I was forced to go to the stable for some straw.'

Glad was I to leave that place and never return. On to Bassano, and our first sight of olive trees, assuring us of warmer times ahead. I enjoyed a good night's sleep. Poor Eliza told me at break-fast that she had not been able to sleep at all.

"Mice, Charles. My bed was infested with mice."

"Did you not ask to be moved?"

"I did, and I was given another room, but sleep still eluded me." She shuddered at the memory. "I fancied I could feel them running all over me, even when they were not."

We left early, and were in Padua by eleven, where we dined for four francs per head, which was very reasonable. The recently opened railway tempted us to make a detour to Venice, the train providing a welcome change from the jolting roads. Mist and rain made for poor sightseeing along the way and upon arrival at the hôtel, we were greeted by the sight of a large Hanoverian rat. It looked straight at us, with perfect indifference, as if to say, 'I have good pickings here, for myself and all my relatives.'

In the presence of my arch enemy, and unpleasant food, we stayed in Venice for two nights, the canals and architecture making a worthy balance. Venice is now joined to the Continent by a continuation of the railway from Padua. We saw the construction of the most astonishing series of arches that can possibly be imagined. At the time the work was rapidly advancing towards its completion. We returned to Padua by the same route.

Onward then to Bologna, via Monsilice and Pollicello. Here we stayed at the magnificent Hôtel Suisse. I can recommend it for everything except the exorbitant charges for firewood. By this time, the springs of our coach were decidedly weakened by the lumpy roads, and a stitch in time saves nine especially during the winter on Italian highways. We stayed for two nights whilst our coach was repaired.

On the morning of Saturday, the 9th of November we made for Rimini where we slept at the Post Inn. The beds were free of vermin, and I was told by Eliza, comfortable enough, but the closets were dreadful and would have made the mistress of the poorest pot house in England blush for shame. After Mass, we were soon on the road again, this time making for Ancona. The morning was wet and windy, but it cleared up about nine o'clock, and we had fine weather after. Birds were scarcer than ever this day, but Little Helen's sharp eyes spotted a tame hawk standing in an open window. At the close of day, a number of common bats were on the wing. In the fields, all along the road, there were great numbers of very fine turkeys, and poultry scratched in dunghills seeking their food. The horses were of poor sorts, but the mules and asses of good appearance. Some of the carts were drawn by three beasts abreast. Thus, we saw a horse on one side, and an ass on the other, and in the middle their stubborn half-brother the mule.

With hindsight, we would have been better to stay a night in Ancona, but were so looking forward to Rome that we pushed on for Loretto.

I sat atop with Ireland. Since arriving in Italy, we had been obliged to employ four horses and two postillions. They drove like devils, so much so our journey was almost terminated. The left rear horse fell when going at a gallop and in an instant both it and the off leader before it were literally on their backs in the ditch. How they did not drag the carriage, the other two horses and the postillions after them, I will never know. One front wheel sank in the earth which partially gave way under it. Eliza, Little Helen, and (surprisingly) Mary Ann, all behaved nobly. Although exposed to imminent peril, not so much as a sigh or a shriek escaped them. They retained their seats with astonishing composure despite the uncomfortable angle, and when they were eventually helped out, calmly awaited the resumption of our journey a little way away, standing in the pitch dark.

In the meantime, the prostrate rear horse struck out, and his foot went between the spokes of the fore wheel. I thought it inevitable that he would suffer a broken leg, or for the coach to be turned over into the ditch. However, after Herculean effort on the part of the postillions, assisted by myself and Ireland, and other passers-by, we got the leg out of jeopardy, and the horses on their feet again. The postillions then gathered up the damaged ropes and leathers, and seeing that the horses were not injured, they got into their saddles and drove off as furiously as ever.

At Terni, the inn was amongst the top ten I have ever stayed in, but to have carpets so far south is to provide shelter for fleas, and they made a hearty meal of our ankles. When I pointed this out to the landlord, he agreed with me, but justified the presence of carpets by saying they were desired by the English tourists.

We arrived in Rome in the early evening of the 11th of November, glad to put down our baggage and settle in the Hôtel d'Europe. The calming effect of the Eternal City worked its wonder and we were soon quite recovered from our journey. A day or two after our arrival we were visited by Father Glover and Father Esmonde of the Society of Jesus. We had much to talk about, past and present.

My routine became thus. I rose early, as was my usual habit, and attended Mass at the Church of the Gesù. Afterwards, I wandered the streets, sometimes detouring to the bird markets. On any day there would be a hundred robin red breasts, four hundred blackbirds and thrushes, and two hundred larks, all dead and waiting to be eaten. I found it hard to imagine that the citizens of Rome would be able to eat the vast quantities on display. I was told of seventeen thousand quail being netted on the shores of the Mediterranean during one single day, rewarded for their migration by mass murder, along with cartloads of ring doves.

"Buy a dozen delicious robins," a stallholder bawled to his would-be customers, "and you will be back tomorrow for two dozen."

I shook my head at him, "Not I." He looked at me as if I were a madman, for the Italians love their food. Every meal, no matter how humble the fare, is a theatrical performance. When I returned to the hôtel, my sisters-in-law, having been to a later Mass, would join me for break-fast, after which they went sightseeing, taking the servants with them and leaving me to work on my 'Essays on Natural History'.

To spend Christmastide in Rome is a joy to all Christians. The smiles on the faces of the priests and nuns lift the soul of all who see them. On Boxing Day we ached with smiling so much.

For our return journey we decided to sail the Mediterranean rather than cross the Alps. There had been a lot of snow, making the passes impassable.

We sailed from Rome via Civita Vecchia. Mary Ann was her usual pessimistic self when it came to travel. As she packed the ladies' trunk, I overheard her talking to herself.

"It seems to me that we risk life and limb whether we travel by sea or road. If we are not shipwrecked, we are tossed into a ditch." She went on, "If God grants us safe passage I shall never again step foot off the island at Walton Hall. All this travelling about isn't natural to my way of thinking." I could not help but chuckle. She turned quickly, and bobbed a curtsey.

"Beg pardon, Squire."

"You shall be safely home, Mary. Have no fear."

"Beg pardon again, Squire, but you don't know that. You can't know that, not for sure."

My attempts at reassurance had fallen on deaf ears. She was right, of course, but our homeward journey was without incident. We sailed past Malaga, and my thoughts inevitably turned to the plague, the earthquake, my uncles and how my brother and I had escaped with Captain Bolin.

When I told our little company of my escapade, they sat with jaws dropped. Mary Ann covered her face as if to deny such horrors, peeping between her fingers like a cat in the grass stalking a mouse. Ireland tried to remain his usual passive mode, but I saw his lips purse and drop alternately in a mixture of disbelief and astonishment.

"At the time, of course, I was a young man. With hindsight it seems more dreadful."

"I do declare," Little Helen said, "that if a cat has nine lives, then you, dear brother, have ninety-nine."

After a brief stop in Gibraltar and fair winds to push us along, we were soon sailing up the Thames. I had business in London regarding the publication of my Essays, necessitating an overnight stay before taking the train to Wakefield.

Life ticked along. My second series of Essays was published, along with a fifth publication of the first series, such was their popularity. Charles Darwin and Charles Dickens were both complimentary of my literary efforts. Three concurring Charleses!

A day or two after our return, a great sadness was conveyed to me by a letter from a sea captain. My youngest brother, Edward, had died on board ship. He had been on his way home when he fell ill, sailing off the South-east coast of Australia. I know not which disease took him. He had been bringing home two live emus, a kangaroo and a squirrel for me and the captain wanted to know what was to be done with them. Presumably, Edward had thought they would survive the journey and make interesting additions to my museum. I wrote back that the captain could keep them or release them. To have them here would have been too painful a reminder of my dear brother. Edward had gained some notoriety as a botanist in the antipodes, and was forty-seven years of age when he died. A sad loss, not only to me and my remaining brothers and sister, but also to the world of natural science.

CHAPTER TWENTY-SEVEN

Toads and Trickery.

Unlike the superstitious, I am a great admirer of the toad. It saddens me when I see one to have been trampled under the ignorant foot, in the belief that is full of venom. This innocuous little reptile, with its skin so completely adapted to its underground shelter, does no harm, but is the friend of the gardener as he gobbles up the slugs.

I now will tell the tale of the so called 'Coal Toad' and the ingenious Mr Green of Leeds. With the singular objective of duping the scientists, Mr Green killed a toad without disfiguring its skin in any way. Perhaps he poisoned it, I don't know. How he killed it is irrelevant. He then took a block of coal and split it in two. With great precision, he carved out a cavity in one half of the coal to the size of the toad, placing it inside the black coffin with its back projecting slightly, thus giving the impression that the toad had been accidently incarcerated in some bygone age when the surrounding matter was in a fluid state. Mr Green confidently asserted that this block of coal was from a colliery near Osmondthorpe, and that it had fallen from a cart in Wade Lane, Leeds, where he happened upon it.

"I was thunderstruck," he told his audiences, "to see a living toad crawl from within, and took it home. Regrettably," he continued, "on exposure to the air, "it died."

It beggars belief that reputed naturalists not only believed him but were gulled into purchasing his specimen. They were quickly disenchanted, as it became known that Mr Green told the same tale to their fellow naturalists in York, Leeds and Holbeck, saying he had found the specimen in a street of their town. Once the cat was out of the bag (or should I say, the toad was out of the coal) in Leeds, word quickly spread to Holbeck and York, but not quickly enough for the simple bird stuffer who had paid him twenty-five shillings for the abomination.

Some years earlier, I had cut back three willows which stood in a little creek. I did so as an experiment, to observe how they would react to their trim. Over the years, all three grew several stems, the largest had sprouted twelve, one of which was of spindly growth, and in high winds this weak growth creaked and moaned as if in pain. I named the tree 'The Twelve Apostles', the weak stem being Judas Iscariot. On the opposite bank, others had sprouted eight and seven stems, and I named them 'The Eight Beatitudes', and 'The Seven Deadly Sins'.

In another experiment, when I planted the oak and Scotch fir near the path to the grotto, I set one of the firs close by an English elm. I encouraged them to intertwine in close embrace. They are now fifteen feet in height, and twenty-two inches in circumference. By twisting the lead shoot of one around that of the other, the trees have become deeply embedded in each other's folds, as befits their nationalities. The English elm being the stronger of the two, I have trimmed its lateral branches, but I have named the inextricably entwined coalition 'The Church and State'.

When I first saw an old millstone laid near the stables, a young hazelnut tree, no more than a seedling, was shooting through a hole in its centre. I considered its chances of ever growing in strength and stature to the point where it might lift the stone from the ground. I thought it improbable, but after thirty years of growth, had lifted the massive stone eight inches above the ground, supported entirely by the tree. The millstone was sometimes used as a seat. The sitter's back was turned away from that which supported it and he could ignore it as he added to its burden. I named the partnership, 'John Bull and the National Debt', in reference to the eight hundred million pounds that our country's exchequer owed at the time, and ignored. The observant reader will have noted that I speak of the tree in the past tense. John Bull died two years ago. I cut away the strangled trunk sufficiently to bend a new shoot through the hole. I have named it John Bull the Second, and time will tell how he fares. I confess to a propensity for naming arboreal phenomena with a reference to politics and religion.

Further to naming a tree, I have also expressed my opinion in taxidermy with another 'John Bull and the National Debt'. I have depicted my opinion of the parlous state of the exchequer as a hairy quadruped with an almost face. The 'almost' is no accident, although it is in fact fashioned from one of my favourite creatures, the hedgehog. A tortoise's shell on his back is weighed down by purses marked 'National Debt' and a little note, bearing £8m, is guarded by four fearful creatures. A grinning dragon with spikes on its back, and horns, a winged toad, an outsized millipede, and a bloated blue lizard, open mouthed and with sharp teeth.

The position is so deeply entrenched, I cannot imagine that England will ever be solvent. The exchequer will remain as devoid of real money as the desert is of trees, *ad infinitum*.

Another taxidermy piece of sport is my 'England's Reformation, Zoologically Illustrated'. I admit to my amusement in its creation, but nonetheless it is a true representation of my contempt for those depicted. John Knox is a frog, Titus Oates a toad, Bishops Burnet and Cranmer reptiles of the lowest order. Martin Luther, Old Nick and Queen Bess at lunch, all have their place in the piece, which brings a smile to the face of all who see it.

After our trip to Europe, Eliza and Little Helen were keen to travel again, and in the November, set their sights upon Madeira. This was not an entirely frivolous notion. Winter had arrived with its icy blast and both Eliza's and Little Helen's chests were a cause of concern. Eliza had been coughing up blood, and Doctor Hobson suspected consumption. His opinion was no more than common sense insomuch as he declared the cold winter air combined with fumes from the soap works chimney were contributors. I could not risk such poison on the weak chests of my dear sisters-in-law. It is true to say they have never enjoyed the best of health, both having suffered, intermittently, from headaches and a weakness of the back and chest.

Mary Ann flatly refused to go. She stood before me with tear stained cheeks.

"Even if I am dismissed, Squire, I will not go further than Wakefield."

"My sisters-in-law have told me they do not want to lose you, Mary Ann. Dry your eyes." Her face relaxed, and she bobbed a curtsey.

"I am sure one of the other maids will go, and Mrs Hutchinson will find plenty to occupy me while you are away."

"I am sure she will. I shall ask Miss Eliza to choose another maid, although I must say I think you are wrong to turn down the opportunity. Madeira is, in every sense, a delightfully mild place."

We sailed from Portsmouth, and Madeira soon had us all in fine health. In January, Robert Edmonstone joined our little party in Funchal. Ever since their father's death, and the brothers' failure to protect Little Helen, I have had little desire to breathe the same air as the male Edmonstones, and so I returned to Walton Hall, immersing myself in the estate. The Yorkshire winter was a harsh one, and I was glad that Eliza and Little Helen were breathing warmer air. How I longed for the Demerara sun! Unfortunately, this was not to be and my travels have since been confined to Aix-la-Chapelle, Scarborough and Stonyhurst. This was not a decision, but simply the way things have turned out to be.

Matters had grown worse between myself and the soap manufacturers. Simpson denied any wrongdoing, and challenged me to scientifically prove that the fumes were causing damage. He never spoke to me directly. All was with the lawyers. His lawyer claimed that some of my more exotic trees were failing due to the harsh winters of recent years, and that his client's industry had no bearing on the matter!

At this point, it is relevant to record Eliza's purchase of Thornes Holme Dyeworks. The reason for my asking her to do so will become clear in the next chapter.

Ever since the storm of 1834, the staircase window had been a cause for concern. Whenever the wind hit it full square, the whole thing bellied inwards, flexing and straining with each gust. The putty was old and dry, and there was nothing for it but to replace it in its entirety. This was done to its original design, at a cost of fifty guineas. Other work was needed, and so during the time ladies were in Madeira, the house underwent further renovations.

By the end of February 1846, the plasterers had finished their work on the staircase. The walls were resurfaced to a high standard and changes made to the cornice and other decorations giving the whole a fine appearance.

Upon their return, Eliza and Little Helen were suitably pleased to see the plasterwork had dried, and put their energies into refurnishing the drawing room, applying themselves to the task with enthusiasm.

Messrs Isherwood did very well out of it, supplying the carpet, curtains and rugs, chairs and sofas, tables, a looking glass mirror and a chandelier of Venetian glass. My sisters-in-law had impeccable taste, and the whole gave the room a delightful air at a cost of £345:18s:10d. The summer passed in relative peace, save for the stinking chimney.

It has become my habit to travel to my old school on Boxing Day and stay there for ten days. The sight of those walls has never failed to bring joy to my bones. Edmund greeted me in the quadrangle. After our initial greetings the conversation went something like this.

"Father, you are wearing one shoe and one slipper."

I looked down, "So I am, boy, so I am."

"Do you have the others in your trunk?"

"I have no idea. I expect so."

"Did Ireland pack for you?"

"Of course."

"Then the answer is probably not. He would not pack odd shoes." Edmund was quite right, but there were other pairs in my trunk, so other than Edmund's embarrassment at his father's dishevelled appearance, there was no harm done. He was used to my lack of interest in clothes (so long as they are dry and comfortable, I have never cared a fig) but in his fellow pupils' company, I fear I did discomfit him a little. Perhaps it was my indifference that sent him the other way. Edmund is always very particular about his clothes and cuts a very stylish figure, entirely unlike his Father!

Once again, I found myself transported back to my schooldays, sitting with the prefects in the dining hall, wearing my blue swallowtail coat and taking part in the little performances on the makeshift stage. On fine days I climbed the trees and wandered the hills, wishing with all my heart that I could stay there forever. My brother, William, was suffering a shortness of breath, especially when he climbed the stairs, so I walked the hills of my childhood alone.

Several old school friends were there, including Percy Fitzgerald who drew an amusing sketch of me as I warmed my backside against the fire.

CHAPTER TWENTY-EIGHT

Soap, Solicitors and a Paddle Wheel.

Edward Thornhill Simpson employed a barrister by the name of Wilkins, and was further advised by William Middleton, both from Leeds.

Sir Thomas Pilkington, whose land was also affected by the smoke, and I joined forces and were to be represented by my brother-in-law, Robert Carr, and my family solicitor, Mr Nettleton.

We went to court like David and Goliath. Simpson gave evidence that he employed a soap boiler and eight labourers, and that these families depended upon him for their livelihood. Anyone listening to his fabrications would have thought his poisoning was an act of philanthropy. I had heard it all before of course.

Two of my tenants, Lumb and Matthewman, gave evidence of damage to their crops. They spoke of the black mud effluent from the soap works pouring down Shay Lane, poisoning the water, and the resulting sickness of their cattle when they drank from the drain beck.

At the conclusion of the hearing, Simpson was told he had no legal right to continue the nuisance, but he ignored the findings, refusing to be beaten. The whole exercise had been no more than the first battle in what became a very long and expensive war.

The next chapter in the tale was when the court appointed a referee by the name of Mr Hall. His was an impossible task, his chalice as poisoned as the drain beck. In his attempts at arbitration, he suggested that Simpson sold the works and machinery to myself and Lord Pilkington, and move elsewhere, but Simpson would have none of it. I became more determined than ever that he would not win. The immovable object had met with an irresistible force. Letters flew back and forth, and the lawyers grew fat on my misery.

The following year, we were back in court. Simpson with his barrister and I with Mr Pashley, also a barrister. Pilkington had grown weary of war and sounded retreat, leaving me as last man standing on the battle field. Simpson produced over eighty witnesses and so-called experts, all of whom were prepared to say black was white if they were paid enough for doing so.

Professor J.F.W. Johnston, who had studied chemistry and minerology at Durham University, was paid to send his written opinion that I had bribed Lumb and Matthewman to make a claim for large damages for injuries to crops and cattle, and that the claims were clearly false because no scientific proof could be offered. Other so-called experts included Dr Glover of Manchester, and Mr Leather, a leading civil engineer from Leeds. One man gave evidence, under oath, that the smoke had done no damage at all, despite the trees and hedgerows being palpable proof of its destructive power. Several said they could neither see nor smell it!

In support of my case, a Wakefield fruiterer, Mr Dudding, claimed the fruit from Mr Atha's trees had suffered greatly. Mr Atha, a former maths teacher at the Queen Elizabeth Grammar School in Wakefield, now kept a school in Walton. He lived on the opposite side of the navigation to the soap works. Mr Dudding gave evidence that in the year prior to the commencement of the salt cake furnace, Mr Atha's fruit had been worth twenty to thirty pounds, but that last year it had only been worth one pound. Wilkins signalled to his assistant at the back of the courtroom who, to my astonishment, brought in several healthy branches.

"These branches, let it be known, have been cut this morning from a tree growing close by Mr Atha's house."

Mr Pashley was on his feet in a trice. "What proof can the court be given of which tree these came branches from? I invite your honour to dismiss this so-called evidence."

Wilkins snapped back. "As the court is aware, my client is a man of honour, and he has given me his word, under oath." Mr Pashley's argument was thus dismissed, and Wilkins continued. "Fruit trees vary in their crop from year to year, whether close to industry or not, and therefore the evidence of Mr Dudding should be regarded as inadmissible."

For three weeks the arguments went in circles before falling into a downward spiral. It is true that Simpson was ordered to pay me £1,000 compensation for my trees, but the amount barely covered my legal costs. To my dismay, Simpson was not ordered to stop the furnace, only to cease the manufacture of salt cake, and so nothing was properly resolved.

On the 9th of November 1849, William Thornhill Hodgson died by his own hand. He was found hanging in one of his sheds. He was seventy-two years old. No-one seemed to know what had pushed him to this act of desperation. He had had little to do with the litigation, but it was clear enough to me that the greed and immorality of his partner had weighed heavily upon his conscience.

On the 12th of December, I effected a business deal that went some way to pay the lawyers' fees and keep me solvent. It had come to my attention that an amount of land and property in Walton was to be sold. All had once belonged to my ancestors, and so I had no compunction in taking advantage of the information that had come my way. Walton House Estate, the Cross Keys public house with its stables and barn, also many fields including the Snarey Wells and Jenny Wren, were to once again belong to the Waterton family.

The fact was I knew of a man who wanted to buy. I became the owner at eleven o'clock in the morning, and at five o'clock the same day, I signed the sale documents, all without a penny touching my hands. This was not the first time I had done such a deal. While I am no business man, I can add and subtract, which is all that is necessary.

The deal I truly desired took place five months later. I knew Simpson would not leave his premises unless it was in his best interests to do so. It therefore became my task to convince him that this was the case, and this is where Eliza's dyeworks came to the fore. Situated on the banks of the River Calder, and adjacent to other properties which were for sale, he eventually saw his future would be better served in a more industrialised area. The transport links of the River Calder and the railway were of greater advantage and convenience than the navigation at Walton. Eliza sold Thornes Holme Dyeworks to Simpson in February 1850, and three months later, for the sum of one hundred pounds, I bought the soap yard, its stabling and smithy, counting house and wooden cottages. The chimneys came down, and the soap and chemical factory closed for ever.

My spruce firs were badly affected, and several died, but the air was clean once again and we were able to picnic at the grotto whenever we wished to do so. What is more, I finally owned the triangle of land which had come to my attention as a boy whilst out riding with my father. There is a well on the land, close by the navigation wall, and I set about building a row of eight small cottages to house the poor.

In the June of 1850, the celebration of The Holy Blood of our Redeemer was to take place in Bruges. As this only happens once every fifty years, there would be no other opportunity for Eliza, Little Helen and me to see it. I had much paperwork to keep me at home in the aftermath of the court case, and so my sisters-in-law travelled ahead of me, via Hull and Rotterdam.

A few days later, with business complete, I took the night train to London, and from there another train to Dover, where I intended to board a Belgian steamer for Calais. The night was as dark as pitch, with neither moon nor stars breaking through the dense cloud as I left Dover railway station for the docks. I threw my Italian cloak over my shoulders, and with a little portmanteau in one hand and an umbrella in the other, I enquired of a porter where I might find the steamer. He had just been engaged by two gentlemen, and had a small case under each arm as well as one in each hand.

"I can carry your case for you if you wish, sir."

"You have burden enough," I replied, "but I would be obliged if you would point out my vessel."

"Do you see the blue light ahead, sir?"

"I do."

"That is the steamer. Not far ahead is a little bridge. Cross that, and you will be straight on board."

I thanked him, and we parted company. Following his instructions, I thought I was at the bridge. Oh, what a horrible mistake! I fell down fifteen feet. As I splashed about, I heard a shout.

"There is somebody in the water!" Moments later my clothes dragged me entirely below the surface. Death stared me in the face. I had no idea where I was, but found myself within the blades of the paddle wheel, quite stunned and with my head in a whirl. Clinging to the side I called for help. The water was very cold. Through the excessive chill and numbness, I could not hold on any longer, and was about to go down when I heard a voice call out.

"Courage, and I will save you." Someone seized my hand, and then, with the help of another, pulled me through the interior of the wheel and into the paddle room. Thoroughly soaked, and shivering as if suffering a severe attack of the ague, I requested that I be taken to a respectable hôtel. There could be no sailing for me that night. I knew I needed the warmth of a fire and some dry clothing if I were to have a chance of survival.

Two police officers took me to The Dover Castle, kept by a widow by the name of Mrs Dyver (a most appropriate name, given the occasion) this being the nearest suitable establishment.

"I shall call a doctor," said she, "there is one close by, he can be here in a minute or two."

"Madam," I replied, "a doctor will not be necessary. Let me have a couple of blankets. I will roll myself up in them, and lie down on the floor by the side of the fire, and I shall be better at break of day."

"You will take a drink, at least, sir."

I refused the widow's offer, much to the astonishment of those present. "I would be obliged, however, if you would dry my clothes."

Next morning, the possessions which I had thought lost forever, were brought to me by the same police officers who had played their part in my rescue. To the officers' relief, I identified them as being mine.

"There was a fear," one of them said, "that there had been a drowning. Your belongings were taken to the police station by the harbourmaster, who reported that somebody must have perished in the night. We thought to ask you, before searching for a body."

"They were not in the paddle, then? That would have made it obvious, surely?"

"No, sir. Your portmanteau and umbrella were found at the quayside, stuck in the mud, but your cloak had floated some distance, and your hat had drifted still further."

I thanked them for their trouble, and they left. Mrs Dyver put before me a break-fast fit to restore an army, and I ate heartily. There had been no ill effect upon my intestines, but a cough and a pain in my chest gave me to understand that a cold bath at midnight was more likely to do harm than good. Had it not been for the rare celebrations in Bruges, I would have returned straight away to Yorkshire. Added to this, there was a French steamer in the harbour, leaving that afternoon for Calais. Having settled my account at the hôtel and thanked Mrs Dyver for her attention to an unknown gentleman in distress, I bade her farewell, shaking her by the hand.

"I assure you, Mrs Dyver, I shall forever recommend the comforts of your establishment and excellent cheer." As we parted, she gave me a card.

Hôtel de Paris, à Calais,

tenu par Charles Ledez.

"This, sir," she said, "will be of use to you in Calais."

So indeed it proved to be, for the kind Monsieur Ledez did everything in his power to comfort me. We sat before a roaring fire until midnight, as I gave him a full account of my dip in the sea. Next morning, he arranged my train ticket to Bruges, his hôtel being close by the railway, and cleared the way for me with the passport officers, for which I was most grateful, not being in the best of health. The hospitality, cleanliness and attentions of Mrs Dyver and Monsieur Ledez convinced me of sufficient fitness to travel on without due consideration of my symptoms.

However, upon my arrival in Bruges, things were going worse for me. Heat and shivers alternated, accompanied by a cough and pains in the chest. I knew I had to take care. My sisters-in-law were duly concerned, as were the good nuns. They tried to persuade me to stay within the Hôtel du Commerce, and keep warm, but this was the eve of the great festival. I had come all the way from Yorkshire to be present at it, and was not about to give in so easily. There was only one thing for it, and that was to resort to the lancet. I withdrew twenty-four ounces of blood, and immediately became a new man. The fever, cough and headache went away as though by magic. I attended the procession for the full four hours with no sign of fever. The following morning, to ensure my continued recovery, I took a good dose of jalap and calomel, and all was rectified.

We passed a very happy month in Bruges. There were fifteen thousand tourists in the town for the spectacle of the Holy Blood being carried through the streets. To have seen it was worth my brush with death.

Edmund came home from Stonyhurst, his education completed at the age of twenty. He was as sorrowful as I had been to leave. The following morning, I took an early walk. My son approached me on the footbridge as I returned from the woodland for break-fast.

"Papa, I hope you are not too disappointed in me. I lack your interest in natural history."

"My dear boy," I rested my hand on his shoulder, "I am the proudest man alive. Come, let us go to the dining room, your aunts will be waiting." He walked ahead of me on the narrow bridge, and then fell in by my side along the cobble path.

"I think I should prefer a more religious life, Papa."

"You are telling me what I already know, Edmund."

He stopped and turned to me. "How so? I have never uttered a word to anyone about it."

I could not help but laugh. "Because I am your father, of course. Dear, dear boy, you may think me an old fool, and would not be alone if you did, but I have eyes in my head, and have known you since the day you were born." A smile cracked his serious face. "Do you not remember when we were shipwrecked? All around us were like headless chickens while you were on your knees in prayer. A father sees such things and does not forget them. Follow your heart, Edmund, as I have done."

As we break-fasted with Eliza and Little Helen, Edmund was happier than I had ever seen him. I suspect he had feared an expectation on my part, but it was plain to all who had known his mother, that it was she whom he took after. A wry smile crosses my wrinkled face when I think of it. I had been proud then, but am more so now when I think of his achievements. He received a knighthood from the exiled King of Portugal. By then he was already the deputy Lieutenant of Yorkshire, and a magistrate. He went on to be made a Knight of Malta. He received the Order of Christ from His Holiness Pope Pius IX, to whom, for two years, he was Papal Privy Chamberlain. His other interests lie in the collection of antiquities. He has a remarkable collection of papal rings. In his last letter he informed me he had been made a Fellow of the Society of Antiquaries.

Who would not be proud to make his acquaintance? How more proud his father?

Winter gripped, and the leaves had long fallen from the deciduous trees when I set about some remedial work in the orchard. Bear in mind, dear reader, that at the time I was as fit as a flea. My double-jointedness was as flexible as ever, and I was still able to touch my elbows together behind my back. If I had stuck to my usual tree climbing skills, all would have been well, but on this occasion, I set a ladder against a pear tree that had shot too high. I was about twenty feet from the ground with my pruning knife in my hand, when the ladder swerved to the left. I clung to it, and the ladder and I came to the ground with fearful force. Twisting my head at the last moment, my left side, from foot to shoulder felt as though it had been pounded in a mill. I knew straight away that this was by far the worst fall that I had ever suffered. Worse even than when, a few years earlier, I had fallen twelve feet from an elm whilst cutting away dead branches. I cannot remember the year, but I know it was during Lent because I was fasting at the time. I had the quick thinking to hold my breath as I fell, and bounced straight back up, and continued with the job. This time, however, matters were taken out of my hands, and the pain was such that I did not argue when Eliza sent for the local doctor.

"We cannot wait for Doctor Hobson to come all the way from Leeds, Charles. I shall send for Doctor Wright and Mr Bennett. You must have broken something." I lay on the sofa in their sitting room as she and Little Helen fussed about like two broody hens clucking around an injured chick.

Upon my insistence, the Doctor bled me to the tune of thirty ounces. He peered into my eyes and generally prodded me about.

"You have a mild concussion."

"I think not," said I, "I made quite sure my head did not take the fall."

Mr Bennett arrived and gave me a thorough examination, causing a great deal of pain as he bent and straightened every joint in my body and felt about for broken bones. He seemed a little disappointed when he found none.

"Rest, Mr Waterton. You must rest."

I had no choice but to obey. The following morning saw a fair bit of swelling. My elbow was a balloon, and a rainbow of bruising was beginning to colour from shoulder to fingertips. My head swam with double vision and nausea. The concussion which I had denied soon passed with no long-term effects, but as the weeks went by, I still had no use in the arm, and the pain did not lessen. The swelling and bruising varied in size and colour from day to day.

Edmund, Eliza and Little Helen were worried. I saw it in their faces. Unfinished specimens gathered dust on the dining table, and I was rendered unable to go about my business on the estate. I could walk as far as the saddle room where I sat in the warmth of the fire and fed the cats and talked to them, all to the apparent amusement of the farm workers. I would not allow anyone to smoke in there, for I am sure the cats dislike the smell as much as I. I particularly despise the habit in children.

To make matters worse, another accident befell me, this time while I was indoors. Since my fall it had been too painful for me to put on my jacket, and I had taken to wearing a Scottish plaid. My appetite was poor, and I lost all interest in desserts, leaving the table after the main course. One evening, when I stood up to adjust my plaid, my manservant thought I had finished, and quietly pulled away my chair. Flop! I fell on my backside!

Notwithstanding my letting a further thirty ounces and putting myself on a light diet with plenty of purgatives, things were going badly inside. Slowly but surely, I was reduced to such weakness that I was unable to stand. Edmund could not bear to see me in such a poor way, and went to stay with a friend.

A new year dawned, and thinking I was not long for this world, I wrote my will. Canon Browne of St Anne's Church in Leeds was sent for, and I made what I thought to be my last confession. He gave me the last rites. That I am writing this memoir is proof that such pessimism was misplaced.

The incessant pain prevented restful sleep, for when I did, I was eternally fighting wild beasts, with a club in one hand, the other being bound up to my breast. One night, I was attacked by nine bulldogs, some of which had the head of a crocodile. I had no appetite and the little I managed to eat did no good at all. I overheard Doctor Wright tell Eliza he feared 'poor Mr Waterton will have a stiff arm for life'.

After hearing the Doctor's disheartening prognosis, I walked to the stables in morose mood. Ogden was in the saddle room.

"How is the arm, Squire?"

"Badly, Ogden. Three months have passed since my fall from the tree, and no improvement whatsoever. As you can see it is useless. I am thinking of having it amputated, to rid myself of the pain."

Ogden scratched his chin in the manner of a man in thought. "Before you do such a drastic thing, Squire, if I were you, I'd go to see Mr Crowther, the bonesetter."

"I had not thought of it, although I have heard he is good at his work. He fishes here sometimes, doesn't he?"

"That's him. A big man, strong as an ox."

"My surgeon and physician both tell me there is no bone damage."

Ogden shrugged. "Up to you, Squire, but as I see it you have nothing to lose other than a few shillings."

As a last resort, I visited Mr Joseph Crowther at his home at Westgate Common. He showed me into his little consulting room and bade me remove my cloak and shirt, and sit on a small leather stool.

Let me tell you, dear reader, a bonesetter is not a quack, he does not pretend to be able to cure diseases. He does not try to sell some new medicine. His sole occupation is to set bones and put joints right, to let blood and to draw teeth. So, as you may imagine, it was only the opinions of Doctor Wright and Mr Bennett that had kept me from an earlier consultation.

"I had heard you were injured, Squire, and wondered if you might come to see me when all else failed."

"I am come for your opinion, Mr Crowther. I have been told there is no breakage or dislocation."

He walked around me a couple of times, observing the peculiar shape of my arm. He then pushed a thumb into my elbow. I yelped like a puppy.

"Ah, Squire," he said, "those fellows you have had about you have made sore work of you. You ought to have come to me months ago when I could have fixed you up without much bother. As it is, I shall have some trouble getting you to rights. Your shoulder has been driven forwards. Your elbow and shoulder are out of joint, your hand is badly injured and your whole arm has shrunk."

"Can you put it all to rights?" I asked.

"Not today, I would do more harm than good if I were to put it back in one go. I reckon it will take three weeks of manipulations before I can put your elbow back in its rightful position. The bone has begun to set in its own way, and has calloused. It will have to be undone before I can right it. Your hand and shoulder will only need about a week, but I shall need to see you every day."

Rather than travel and be jolted all the way to Westgate Common and back every afternoon, I sent the small carriage for Mr Crowther to come to Walton Hall.

I winced at every pull and push. With the manipulations being ten times more painful than the condition, I could only hope that the end would justify the means.

True to his estimation, one week later he rectified my hand, and two days after that he put my shoulder back in its rightful position.

The final repositioning of my elbow was a terrible experience. He brought a burly assistant with him. Mary Ann said she could not bear to watch and so a newly appointed maid, Lucy Barnes, brought me a glass of soda water and ginger. The bonesetter and his assistant fortified themselves with a glass of good old Yorkshire ale! Having gulped his drink, Mr Crowther directed his assistant.

"Hold him firmly in the chair, Sam." Mr Crowther rolled up his sleeves and fastened his wrist to mine with a strap, tightening it with a buckle. Lucy Barnes was instructed to loosen the strap as soon as ordered to do so. Sam held me fast with one hand on my good shoulder and his other around my neck. Mr Crowther then pulled my arm with a sharp, firm tug until it was almost straight. I heard a crack, and thought I was mended.

"I expected more pain." I sighed with relief.

"It's not quite over yet," he turned to the maid, "loosen the buckle." Before I could say 'Jack Robinson', Mr Crowther seized my arm, grasping either side of my elbow in a vice-like grip, and twisted it one way and then the other, smattering the callouses with a dreadful crunching sound. He then took my hand and bent it up to my shoulder.

"Now your arm is as good as mine."

I was not convinced, not there and then, but time has proved him to have been right. Sam released his python hold and Lucy gave me another drink of soda and ginger as my arm was bound up from fingers to shoulder. Mr Crowther continued to call daily to check the progress of his patient. All went satisfactorily, and within two weeks the bandaging was deemed unnecessary. With exercise my arm quickly regained its former strength.

Thus armed (may I say!) I was eager to return to work. Whilst incapacitated I had had several ideas regarding the nesting places of birds, and how I could make life safer and more comfortable for my feathered friends. I made scores of boxes for the owls, siting them in the upper branches of the trees. Occupancy soon followed. At times I felt as if I were being watched by prospective tenants as I climbed a tree to position their new home.

One morning, whilst on my way to the grotto, I noticed an ox eye titmouse had nested in the decaying trunk of an ash tree. The little cavity was open to the elements on one side, so I crafted a tiny hinged door for her protection. While she and her spouse flew in and out of the cosy abode from a split in the trunk, I was able to open the door and bid Mrs Titmouse 'good day' as she sat resolutely upon her eggs. She showed no fear as I stroked her back for a moment or two before shutting the door again. The happy couple returned for several years until their abode was taken over by a squirrel for the winter months. I removed all trace of the squirrel, ready for their return. Whether they came for a look, and sensed the squirrel, I do not know, but they never nested there again.

CHAPTER TWENTY-NINE

Snakes Alive!

An American man by the name of Jonathan Van Gordon brought to England thirty-four rattlesnakes from the Allegheny Mountains. He was all but destitute when he arrived in Wakefield, despite not being charged any duty at Liverpool.

"I read your book, Mr Waterton, and thought you would like to see some snakes."

The reptiles were in two wooden boxes, each had small ventilation holes and from the sounds emanating from within, the occupants were not in the best of tempers. I would have invited him to Walton Hall, but knew my sisters-in-law would be frightened to have live, poisonous snakes being in the house, so I arranged for him to stay in an hôtel. The proprietor was none too happy, but I find a little extra payment goes a long way in such circumstances. I asked Mr Van Gordon if he had had a fair sailing.

"The sea was kind enough, sir, but the ship ran short of fresh water and the captain cut the sailors' rations. It was almost the death of all of us. The sailors heard the rattling of the snakes, and thought I had bottles of water within the boxes. I caught them trying to prize off the lids."

"Have you not opened the boxes? Have you fed them at all?"

"No sir. The truth is I am as frightened of them as any man."

"I thought you had caught them."

"Not me, sir, I bought them at a fairground."

Leaving Mr Van Gordon in the hôtel, I drove back to Walton Hall to collect a more suitable glass sided case for his snakes. On my return journey I began to wonder why a man would travel all the way from America to show me some snakes. It made no sense.

A lad helped me to carry the case inside. Mr Van Gordon looked relieved to see me, but I was dismayed to see he had found enough money to buy a pint of ale.

"Tell me," I asked, "why did you bring the snakes to England? Surely not just to show them to me. I have seen plenty of snakes in their natural home, as you well know if you have read my book."

He had the decency to look ashamed. "I had a notion, Mr Waterton, that I could make money in a fairground show out of what is a commonplace thing in America, but a novelty within your shores."

"Was no-one interested?"

"Oh, yes, sir. They were interested. I paid the fairground man, but no-one would open the boxes. A Customs Officer told me that the only man in England who would willingly do so was your good self."

We carried the case to his room, and with an iron hook I had brought from Walton Hall for this purpose, we began to open one. As soon as the tops were loosened, Mr Van Gordon retreated behind a curtain, wrapping it around his body and head, so only his eyes were visible. One by one, I transferred the snakes, holding them behind the head between my forefinger and thumb. Six of them were dead. Only when the remaining twenty-eight were secured did their owner unravel himself, peering at his snakes in wary fascination.

"What shall I do with them, Mr Waterton?"

I pondered the possibilities. While I was certain they would attract the attention of the curious voyeur, there was a greater service to be performed. "I know of scientists and medical men who are interested in experimenting with venom. Perhaps something could be arranged to the benefit of science, medicine, and your pocket."

He stepped back from the case. "Then I would be mightily indebted to you, for I have lost all interest."

I bade him adieu, and set out for Leeds, and Doctor Hobson's house. Fortunately, he was at home. He was as excited as I at the prospect.

"I shall write to Daniel Evans. He experimented with puff adders and rattlesnakes quite recently. Then there is Doctor Quain, Mr Mitchell, Mr Squire and Mr Wyatt. They all took part in the observations, and have piqued the curiosity of others."

"Exactly how are these experiments conducted?"

"With small animals and birds. Observations are made, and antidotes administered. I would like to compare the results with those of wourali."

I nodded in approval.

Doctor Hobson lives in Park House, and it was here that he arranged for the experiments to take place.

Forty men of science and medicine, along with Jonathan Van Gordon, assembled in a large room with an atrium, giving the best possible light. The fact is that I do not regard myself as a scientist. I merely look at nature as I pass along. I have never yet been able to find out why a dung-hill cock claps his wings before he crows, and why a cock pheasant does the same thing after he has ceased to crow. I felt my presence to be superfluous, but it transpired that without me, no experiments could have taken place at all. In truth, no man dared to hold the rabbit or pigeon within the case to be bitten, much less dare any one venture to touch the snakes.

"Gentlemen," I said, "if you will be quite silent, and motionless, I have no doubt that I can easily accomplish all you require." Doctor Hobson raised the lid towards himself, using it as a shield. I took hold of a snake in my usual manner and removed it from his rattling neighbours. I held it high in one hand, whilst it bit a pigeon, a rabbit and a guinea pig. The victims were then returned to a compartmented case for the observations to take place. All went well, and I repeated the process several times. Then, as I was replacing a snake, another suddenly rose up and, with the speed of lightning, shot his head and half his body through the gap. Doctor Hobson quickly lowered down the lid just as I removed my hand from within, leaving the snake partly in and partly out of the case. There was no cause for alarm. All I had to do was to grasp the snake, and put him back, but the assembled men of science and medicine did not know this. Every one of them, including Doctor Hobson, who I thought should have known better, fled like the proverbial rats from a sinking ship. They ran helter-skelter down the stairs and into the street without so much as stopping for their hats. Some would not return, but to those who did I demonstrated that their fear had been quite unfounded by holding a snake before my face.

"A snake will not bite unless provoked. You were not, gentlemen, in any danger, for I soon had a safe hold on our would-be escapee. Furthermore, I had not been in danger when my bare hand was within the case. Only when within my grasp and rendered unable to bite does he feel threatened, and thereby provoked."

None of the assembly argued the point, but I am certain they were not entirely convinced either. With the experiments concluded, the snakes were returned to their wooden box and the care of Mr Van Gordon. I do not know their fate.

I returned to Walton Hall, and my ant bear was returned to his glass case.

I am of the firm opinion that the outdoor life and the observation of nature's vast panorama is beneficial to the body and mind of man. One only has to look at those who toil in the factories, breathe the foul air of industry, and wear a sickly, grey pallor. Compare this to the rosy cheeks of the milkmaid, or the ruddy complexion of the farmer.

By inviting groups of people to picnic at the grotto, I have seen the benefits of an afternoon's relaxation to those who are usually denied such a simple pleasure. I refer most directly to the inmates of the West Riding Pauper Lunatic Asylum. John Davies-Cleaton, Medical Director and Superintendent, is a much-valued friend of mine. Within the asylum he has introduced weekly dances for the patients, with music and singing. A choir has been formed and a band with seventy-two players. How they love to perform when they come to visit, to sing and dance, to kick off their shoes and feel the grass between their toes. The smiles, the laughter and the twinkling eyes are all a joy to behold. On other occasions, groups of school children come with their families, and queue for a turn on the swing, all dressed in their Sunday best. On one occasion when the Choral Society visited, they sang 'A Fine Old English Gentleman,' and 'God Save the Queen' as they left. This has since become a custom for all parties, and my visitors now wait at the far side of the footbridge for me to listen to their renderings before they depart. Parties also come from scientific, mechanical, and choral associations. All are welcome to enjoy that which

I am fortunate to call home. One year, there were more than seventeen thousand visitors, and the path to the grotto became well worn. No-one is permitted to venture to the pasture or woodland around the far end of the lake. I do not go there myself in the breeding season unless I spy a young bird fallen from its nest, when I will go quietly and carry it back to its home, and retreat.

Eliza and Little Helen send invitations and are meticulous in their scrutiny of suitably deserving persons. This may seem at odds with the list of recipients, as society generally shuns the company of the mad, the epileptic, or the cripple, but it is the poacher who makes the guarding of my borders a necessity, not the infirm of mind or body. This ever-present threat gives employment to keepers from John O'Groats to Land's End. Were it not for these thieves, I would need only one gamekeeper.

An entirely welcome visitor arrived. Charles Weld, the grandson of Thomas (who had given Stonyhurst to the Jesuits) was our guest for a whole week, along with his wife, Mary, and their retinue of servants. The young couple were most delightful, and we all revelled in the jolly atmosphere of a full house. For once, I was happy to clear the dining table of taxidermy. Thankfully, my arm was sufficiently mended for me to don my swallowtail coat.

"I believe I recognise your jacket, sir."

"As only a Stonyhurst pupil would," I smiled. Although a barrister, he was interested in my work, and asked more intelligent questions than many a supposed naturalist had posed. Being from such a strong Catholic family, we were never short of conversation.

"My grandfather," he told us one evening, "was a friend of the King, and as such did much to improve the Catholic lot."

"How so?" Eliza asked.

"He gave his personal permission for a chapel to be built in the grounds of our ancestral home, Lulworth Castle."

Little Helen's eyes grew wide at this. "A Catholic Chapel?"

"Indeed so. I believe it was the first to have proper consent."

"Your Grandfather must have been very close to the King." I said.

"Not so close as his widowed sister-in-law." At this, his wife, a dainty little thing, looked at him sharply. He spoke to her in a hushed tone, placing his hand gently over hers. "Mary, dear, our hosts will not judge us upon the behaviour of my ancestors."

"Perhaps—" I began, but he cut me right off.

"It is no secret, Charles. In 1785, the King's eldest son, who later became George the Third, secretly married my grandfather's widowed sister-in-law. All long before my time, but the matter, without doubt, placed a Catholic family closer to the throne than the politicians would have liked."

The story was one I had heard before, but nonetheless, to hear it from Charles Weld gave great amusement. Eliza and Little Helen were truly astonished.

On the departure of our guests, the house fell to a comparative silence.

As previously explained, I have never felt any obligation to dress in anything other than comfortable and practicable clothes. This was especially necessary when in the tropics. In Walton, I dress in a manner that suits my working day, that is to say, an old brown jacket, wide trousers, worsted stockings and loose-fitting shoes. Because my clothes do not give me away, I am often mistaken for a working man.

Once, when visiting a neighbour, the butler showed me into the servants' hall. On another occasion, as I was walking towards the village, I saw a fellow who appeared to be lost. He kept turning around, as if not sure whether or not to retrace his steps. When he saw me, he quickened his pace in my direction.

"Good morning, my man," he blustered, "can you direct me to the home of Squire Waterton?"

"I can indeed." I replied. "You are on the right road, and will see Walton Hall if you continue another half mile. His house lies in the valley, over yonder."

I thought that to be the end of it, but he engaged me further. "I hope to buy some wood from him, but I hear he is an odd sort. Do you know him?"

"Yes, I do." I said, seeing an opportunity for some fun. "In fact, I know him better than anyone hereabouts, I spend a lot of time with him."

He smiled at this, his bluster turning to friendliness, "Then our meeting is my good fortune. Come with me to the Cross Keys, and I will buy you a pint of beer, bread and cheese also, if you will pave the way for me with Waterton." He waved towards the public house. "It would be in both our interests."

"I thank you, sir, but I have already break-fasted. If I were you, I would keep well clear of the old chap. If you want some wood, go to the stable yard, and ask for the woodman, Morley. He is a decent fellow."

He thanked me profusely and set off. As I returned home, an hour or so later, I saw the man again. He was shaking hands with my woodman, in a manner that said, 'deal done.' They were close by the stables, Morley had his back to me as I passed by, and would not have seen me, but the man tipped me a wink by way of thanks for my advice. Morley turned and doffed his cap to me, with a short bow.

"Good day, Squire." He said. "This man has bought wood." All was then embarrassment on the man's part, confusion for Morley, and amusement for me.

"I-I ap-apologise. I thought—"

"No need, no need," I assured him. "You are not the first, and won't be the last. Take our friend to the house, Morley. See he is fed and given ale before he leaves. An odd sort you may call me, but not a mean one." I left him gaping like a cod fish as I chuckled my way towards the heronry.

On the 19th of January, 1852, I received a black-edged letter from Stonyhurst. The handwriting was not known to me, and I opened it with some apprehension. My uneasiness was not misplaced. William had not been well for some time, and so the news of his death came as a great sadness, but not as a shock. He had died two days earlier, and was to be buried there. I think it was, in some part, because there had been no possibility of my attending either Christopher or Edward's funeral, I determined to leave straight away for Stonyhurst to be present for William's interment. He had been fifty-eight years of age. I was approaching my seventieth birthday, and as fit as a flea.

Later that year, Catholic burial grounds were made legal in England, but in the remote Lancashire estate of Stonyhurst, Catholic ceremonies had been practised for centuries, unnoticed.

Two years later, I received another black-edged letter. I had been in Scarborough with Eliza and Little Helen, and returned with further additions to my egg collection, but my enthusiasm for these acquisitions was quickly dashed to the ground. The letter was from France, and could only mean one thing. My brother, Thomas, who had been so happily settled as a priest in Rouen, had died. He had suffered a partial paralysis of the limbs whilst walking in an orchard, and had died in his sleep that same night. He had been sixty-nine years of age, so had not quite made it to his three score and ten. All four of my brothers and one sister had gone ahead of me to St Peter's Gate. It remains to be seen whether I, or Isabella, will be the last of the once young and bustling Waterton brood to leave this world.

That Christopher, Thomas, Edward, Helen and William had gone to a better place was beyond doubt. My sadness was for myself, for the dead do not grieve. To counter my melancholy, I threw myself into work on the estate, where the vista is more contrived than it seems. At first sight, all appears to be perfectly natural, but as described at the beginning of this memoir, it is not. I have spent many an hour trying to imagine what my little valley would have looked like had man not stamped upon it. The lake is man-made and the water birds, whether imported by myself or here by choice, have a man-made home. When my geese are in moult, and unable to fly, I pinion the wings to keep them here. By building my wall, I created a world within a world, and a degree of management is needed to keep the status quo.

My earlier efforts to improve the quality of the water had achieved nothing. At the time I had not appreciated that in removing the weed I was depriving the coots of their food supply. They had deserted me, en masse, for a more plentiful pantry at a neighbour's lake. After much thought, I concluded the only solution was to build a deep drain controlled by a sluice which would take the water from the lowest level, enabling me to drain away the mud whenever it became necessary to do so.

I began the project with enthusiasm, but soon after work began at the lakeside, the diggers met with rock, making for slow progress. As they toiled, day to day life rumbled on.

One day, a group of soldiers arrived unannounced at the gate, where my gate-man bade them wait. The first I knew of it was when one of his children came running over the bridge with a fistful of visiting cards.

"My pa says the soldiers want to look at your museum and your paintings. They are riding big horses."

"Then run back and tell them to take their horses to the stables, and then come to the house."

I greeted six young men wearing impeccable uniforms and began to show them my specimens in the hallway, and on the staircase. They told me they had heard of my collection from a general, and ridden from the neighbouring barracks at Pontefract.

A few months earlier I had received a gift of my portrait by Charles Willson Peale in Philadelphia. Mr Peale had died, and his collection of paintings and taxidermy split up and sold. My friend, George Ord, bought my portrait and had it shipped to me. It is a fine painting by a gifted artist, and while my frame remains as supple as ever, it served to show the passing of the years. I had been forty-two years of age when Mr Peale took up his brush, and much had changed in the intervening years. Eliza and Little Helen had insisted it be hung in the entrance hall. My military visitors were polite enough about it, but imagine my disgust when one of them pointed to The Nondescript, whispering to his friends, 'That is a shrunken head from South America'. I said nothing as they proceeded up the staircase. They were ignorant of the significance of my satirical pieces, and critical of two of the paintings from Mr Berwind's collection where no criticism could be justified. In all, they were the epitome of assumed knowledge.

"Perhaps," I said, "you would like to visit Nostell Priory. It is not far from here, and the paintings there are far superior. The owner is an eccentric old fellow, but knowledgeable, and always willing to show off his paintings."

I suspect they thought themselves superior due to their uniforms and my casual apparel, but this is conjecture on my part. For whatever reason, they began to laugh.

"I think," one of them smirked, "that I can speak for my fellow officers in saying we would be delighted to view his paintings, and the man himself if what you say of him is true." His companions fell upon the idea in raptures, without the slightest suspicion that their ignorance was about to be uncovered. I directed them to Nostell Priory, but not by the most direct route.

As luck would have it, I had been preparing a disguise for a fancy-dress dinner at a neighbour's house. I quickly bundled it up and set off on foot via the northern gate.

I knew my friend Charles Winn and his family were absent from their home, and that Fenton knew me well enough to be in on the joke. My disguise consisted of a faded red wig, an old green eye patch over one eye, and a monocle put to the other. I had stuffed some rags into the back of a threadbare coat to give the impression of a hunch back, and employed a crutch to relieve a supposedly crippled leg.

By the time the soldiers arrived at the house, I was prepared to greet my guests. The lower entrance is dark within, with low ceilings giving a mysterious air. This entirely suited my game as I peered at the letter which I had written less than two hours earlier.

"That old devil, Waterton, said you had valuable paintings. I hope you do, because he doesn't have one worth the canvas it is painted on."

"I have many. Follow me," I beckoned, limping off with the aid of my crutch. I showed them several paintings, which they admired in glowing terms, whilst pretentiously gesticulating and making fabricated comments. I showed them the Etruscan vases and told them they were from China. They nodded in agreement.

"Anyone can see they are from China," said one.

The officers nodded as they muttered amongst themselves of how it was easy to spot a genuine antiquity. At this, it all became too much to bear, and I slowly removed my disguise.

"Your humble servant, Charles Waterton, can inform you that the vases are Etruscan, and were bought by the brother of the present owner. If there is anything else you wish to know about the art in this house, this old devil is happy to educate you, on the proviso that you apologise for your rudeness."

They were all over with embarrassment, and rightly so, but I bore them no malice. I had been entertained at their expense. My love of practical jokes has resulted in my not always being taken seriously, but that is of no consequence to me.

I recounted the tale to Doctor Hobson. He roared with laughter, and insisted I tell the tale over again. When I had done so he shook his head, as tears of laughter rolled down his cheeks.

"And did they apologise?" he asked.

"Oh, yes, profusely. They were shamed by their own ignorance. I told them it is better to confess ignorance than falsely profess knowledge, and that a crippled leg does not affect the mind, and a threadbare coat does not imitate the brain of its wearer."

"Quite so," said the Doctor, "quite so."

"If I thought the whole world were so blind, I would indeed despair, but when the York Naturalist Club visited, they declared the staircase at Walton Hall to contain the finest exhibition of paintings and natural history that they had ever seen and were especially complimentary regarding the latest addition of the chimpanzee."

There were occasions, I confess, when I tried Doctor Hobson cruelly. Whenever I saw him approach, I would run out to greet him and kick my slippers in the air, catching them one handedly. Once, when I saw his carriage coming down the driveway, I hid under the table in the entrance hall. It has a long cloth which trails the floor, so I was completely hidden. Upon hearing Warrener open the door and take the Doctor's greatcoat, I began to growl fiercely before springing out and biting my friend on the leg. Oh, the momentary terror! Oh, the laughter! I was helpless, rolling about on the floor. My mirth became infectious and the Doctor doubled up, forcing him to sit down.

By way of apology for his fright, I secretly told Warrener to stuff my guest's coat pockets with hazel nuts and fill his carriage box with apples, pears, eggs and cherries.

The autumn of 1855 saw the completion of the new drain, right to the lower level at the John Bull tree. Here, the water reappears beneath a seven-foot-wide archway and flows on past the keeper's hut and fish trap pond to the second sluice. From there, the water takes its course past the grotto in a deep, stone lined channel, around the eastern edge of the wood, and down to the beck which was once so polluted, and on to the River Calder at Wakefield.

All was made good on the surface, so that as soon as the hay seeds came up there was no sign of the feat of engineering that lay beneath the sod.

Being in a constructive mood, I set Ogden to the task of constructing a wall at the southern end of the kitchen garden, with fifty-six little pipes built into it, the express purpose being the creation of nesting sites for the sandmartins. The little birds approved of the cavities as I had hoped, and raised their families within for three successive summers. For some reason only known to themselves they then removed to a nearby sandbank behind the haystacks. To my delight they returned to my pipe wall last spring after an absence of six years.

To quote Alexander Pope, 'Hope springs eternal in the human breast.'

Edmund was in Rome, and Eliza and Little Helen in Bruges when I ordered the new sluice be opened. Hundreds of thousands of gallons of muddy water rushed through the tunnel. I had hoped to retain the fish in the trap pond, but the cast iron gate which should have prevented their escape gave way, such was the force of water. As soon as the disaster was discovered, I ordered the sluice be closed, and draining suspended until a new gate was put in place. The gate which had been there previously had been made of oak by my father's carpenter, but was no longer fit for the purpose. I ought to have had another made just like it, and then our stock of fish would have been wonderful.

I had thought the water fowl would abandon me when the lake was drained, but instead they assembled on the hillside, observing their abode with disdain. The valley took on a strange appearance as the stream twisted its way across the mud as if trying to find its original path.

Now you may think, dear reader, that having emptied the lake, all I needed to do was to close the sluice, and watch the water rise. Indeed, I had thought so myself, but this was not the case. The mud had accumulated to such a degree, that in places it lay ten, twelve, and even twenty feet deep.

I can say in all honesty that my two greatest achievements within the parkland have been the building of my wall and that of the drain, with the subsequent sludging of the lake. The latter construction being considerably less expensive than the former.

At the height of the work, I was sent the body of a monkey from the royal menagerie. I could ill afford the time to work on what would normally have been a fairly simple job. Furthermore, having cut my hand in three places whilst working on the mud, I was forced to work with my left hand. The specimen was an interesting one, and quite young. It is displayed on the upper staircase. About the size of a large terrier dog, and in appearance half like a baboon and half monkey, he has a dog-like face, and a long tail which is bushy at the end. His hair is grey and in long bunches around his ears.

Each morning, when I had done the necessary with the monkey, I was at the sludging work. Close by the water-gate, we uncovered an iron swivel cannon, eight feet deep in the mud, and resting on the remains of the medieval swivel bridge. I left the men hauling it onto the water-gate step, and ran to the house, calling for Warrener to fetch me the little iron cannon ball which my father had given to me. It seemed to take an age for him to return, and had I not been covered in the stinking mud, I would have fetched it myself. Imagine my delight upon finding it fitted the gun! I cleaned the cannon, and with the assistance of Ogden, placed it within the yew hedge by the starling tower, with the ball alongside, where they remain to this day.

Subsequent to this discovery, I asked the men to be more diligent when digging, and as a result several musket balls, a sword blade, a battle spear, two daggers, hammer heads, an axe, many coins, four keys of very ancient type, a silver spur and two silver plates were all found, deep in the mud, along with a good deal of broken crockery and glass. Nothing whatever had been known of these articles, but my father had often said that our silver was put underwater when Charlie Stuart's father made his appearance from abroad.

The sediment was taken to the kitchen garden and tipped down the slope where the bee hives stand, to be spread on the kitchen garden. The smell was terrible, but this short-term inconvenience has proved its worth. By autumn we had finished the work, and the sluice gate closed. As the valley began to fill, I had other fish to fry.

I took the train to London to finalise the publication of a third series of my essays. I take comfort that their popularity is the evidence which shows my observations are not entirely dismissed by fellow naturalists. In this edition I wrote of pigeons, dogs, foxes, snakes, humming birds, and a history of the monkey family. A second edition was soon underway, and translated into French.

Thus ended an eventful year.

That winter was a harsh one, with many small birds falling victim to the frosts. Wagtails were particularly affected. I saw many of their number lying in the snow, apparently starved to death. Ice built up to a miniature glacier at the far end of the lake. The thaw came with a sudden rise in temperature with all snow and ice disappearing within hours, churning the lake with melt water to reveal a murky, partially filled lake. Weeds sprang up and invited an extraordinary show of water fowl.

When the lake had filled, the quality of the water improved beyond all hope, so that it is now forever crystal clear. With the restored, sweet water, and new growth of their favourite food, I have coots in abundance. They are joined by wild ducks, pochard, tufted ducks, waterhen, widgeon, and last year's young of the golden eye, a sight not possessed by any other country house in Great Britain. Fish stocks were low, but have recovered year on year. The water in the oblong fish-trap pond is as fresh and sweet as the lake, and puts on a fine show of waterlilies. From start to finish the project had taken three years, including the filling of the lake, which took twelve months.

CHAPTER THIRTY

A Summer Storm.

One summer's evening, as I rode home from a visit to Doctor Hobson, I heard the distant rumble of thunder. It had been a fine, sunny day. The hay crop was in and all was well in the farming world, but a storm was brewing. As I crossed the bridge over the navigation, large raindrops began to fall. By the time I reached the stables, I was soaked to the skin. Three omnibuses were there, waiting to take the picnickers home after a day at the grotto. One hundred and twenty good folk had been enjoying the gardens, which were in full bloom and the best I had ever seen them. I recall having congratulated the gardener the previous day. Tables and chairs had been set out in the lower temple and the singing and dancing was in full flow. I instructed the omnibus drivers to collect their passengers right away and bring them to the stables. The thunder rumbled ever closer. A fisherman stood under the Lombardy poplar, and I shouted to him to get himself off home, fearing the tree may be struck. The sky was as black as a starless night, and I could see that candles had been lit in the house. With the sky now flashed with lightning, I advised the picnickers to delay their journey.

"Those of you on the upper deck will be soaked if the storm catches you. There is plenty of shelter here."

Some went back to the grotto and some took cover in the stables as day became night. As I hurried towards the footbridge, the ground shook violently beneath my feet and I turned to see that the Lombardy poplar had indeed been struck with such a force that it had almost split in two. I quickened my pace, not wanting to be caught on the iron footbridge.

Hailstones as large as pullet's eggs came with force enough to bruise a man, bouncing back up from the cobble path a foot high. Eliza, Little Helen and I watched from the dining room windows as the lake was whipped into waves, crashing over the old water-gate. The wind came from the south, and its warm hand blasted the house furiously on its backside so that the sycamores which usually shielded the house gave no protection at all. Constant lightning forked with brilliance, reflecting in the clouds with red and yellow hues.

The hail eventually gave way to rain and I sent for Ogden and Totty. None of the window frames were in good repair other than the new staircase window at the back of the house. Had it not been replaced it would have shattered all over my museum. Ogden, in turn, sent for two more men to bring wood, a saw and nails. How they managed to cross the bridge without being blown off their feet, I shall never know. Little Helen was terrified.

"All will be well," I shouted above the roaring of the wind and the rattling rain. Then the wind turned around to the east and the first window blew in. "I suggest you go to your rooms and draw the curtains."

"Come, sister," Eliza said, "we must do as Charles says."

"Why must we draw the curtains?" Little Helen asked as they went upstairs." I want to watch the storm." Another window blew in, and glass flew around like leaves in autumn.

"For your safety. That is why." I shouted. Between us, Ogden, Totty and I fixed lengths of timber across the casements, leaning on them with all our strength between the gusts.

I stayed up all night, sitting by the fire with Warrener, listening to the sound of breaking glass and splintering wood as casements and panes succumbed to the blast. Curtains flapped about, footloose and fancy-free like a sail that had lost its rigging. Dawn broke and the wind still blew, but with less ferocity. Shards of glass littered the floor from front to back. I put on my coat and went outside. Eighty-one panes had been blown in, but thankfully, the roof and chimney pots were unaffected. I walked over to the stable yard where I was greeted by Ogden.

"The picnickers, Ogden. Have they left?"

"Aye, Squire. They went last night."

"Was that wise?" I asked.

"I'd say not, but the omnibus drivers said they needed to get back. I saw one man felled to the ground by a hailstone right here in the yard."

"No-one was seriously hurt, I trust."

"A woman's parasol was struck, and her arm went quite numb, right up to her elbow. She was upset all right, but not injured."

"Any damage here?" I looked around, pleased to see the buildings appeared to be intact.

"A cherry tree has been struck, the hothouse glass is almost all broken."

"I shall need the services of a glazier for the house, so will ask him to attend the gardener's cottage and speak with him."

Break-fast was being served when I returned. Eliza and Little Helen were sitting at the dining table wearing their winter bonnets and capes. Two housemaids were sweeping glass from the carpet as another served at the table. Despite a roaring fire, the room was as cold as charity. My sisters-in-law looked at me expectantly.

"What shall we do, Charles?" Little Helen's eyes pleaded. "There is broken glass everywhere, and the new curtains are in tatters."

"Don't look so worried. I shall have a man board everything up until the windows can be replaced, and I would be obliged if you dear ladies would go to the drapers and choose some fabric for more curtains."

My thoughts turned to the fisherman. I was in no doubt that had he remained under the Lombardy, he would have been killed. As it was, he would have had a thorough soaking but live to return and fish another day. With this in mind, I resolved to build a refuge for the fishermen.

"The surprising thing is, Squire," Mr Clarke (of Clarke and Heaps, Glaziers) took off his cap and scratched his head, "is that there are any panes left at all. This glass is no thicker than I would use in a glass house and the casements are rotten." He ran a putty knife along the groove of the casement, releasing woodlice as prolific as those of Tudhoe. "My advice," Mr Clarke's voice brought my wandering mind back to the present, "if you care to take it, would be to replace all these windows for some nice big sashes. You'd be surprised how much more light they let in."

During the following winter, we had reason enough to be glad of our new windows. The frosts were keen and the weather colder than it had been for many a year.

The water hens were so moribund they sat under the drawing room window, waiting for a crumb, while other water fowl congregated on the lake. I counted almost fifteen hundred. They seemed subdued, barely moving, making my counting of them a simple task. In the depths of such a winter it is difficult to imagine a warm summer's day.

During the building works at the stables, a millstone engraved 'T K W 1679' (these being the initials of my ancestors, Thomas and Katherine Waterton) had been uncovered. Like the one raised by the tree, (I refer to John Bull and the National Debt) it must have lain there since the time my ancestors had ceased to mill their own flour. I decided to use it as the roof for the fishermen's shelter. Raising it up proved to be quite a feat of engineering. Ogden and I constructed a wooden frame with ropes and pulleys. The millstone is supported by three stone pillars, and I have placed an old armchair within, which is there for anyone to enjoy. A yew hedge, with a gap to the southern side so the occupant can view the lake, further protects from the elements.

The Lombardy survived, scarred with its history burnt into the bark. I tied it together with stout ropes to prevent further splitting.

I have never returned to Canada, and to my regret have not had the opportunity to visit the town and lakes which have borne my name since 1858, when Lieutenant Thomas Blakiston, in his role as a surveyor for a proposed railway, sought a route through the mountains of Alberta. I can only assume that he read my little book. Blakiston, I am told, was so struck by the natural beauty and abundance of wildlife and that he named the little town 'Waterton.' I can think of no greater compliment.

Recent years have passed with ease, with old habits forming a routine of sorts. Late summer usually finds us in Aix-la-Chapelle, and my Christmases are spent at Stonyhurst. Edmund joins me when he can and we have such a jolly time. The number of pupils increases each year, such is the popularity of the school. One year I succumbed to a cough so dreadful as to be a cause for concern to the good Fathers. For my part, I was not so worried, but agreed that Doctor Hobson could attend. Word was duly sent to Leeds, but by the time Doctor Hobson arrived, I had responded to my usual methods, and was as fit as a flea.

As evidence of my recovery, let me say I can still scratch the back of my head with my big toe, and the strength in my leg muscles enables me to rise from being cross legged, sitting on grass, to standing without the aid of either hand. I can run for a hundred yards and jump over a fence, much to the amusement of Doctor Hobson. On his last visit I think I scared the daylights out of him by hopping on one leg on the upper wall of the grotto.

"Fear not," I shouted as I hopped along, whirled around, and landed on my other foot, facing the opposite direction. "*Non de ponte cadit, qui cum sapienta vadit.* He falls not from the bridge who walks with prudence."

"Prudence?" my friend retorted, "has never been your habit."

"How so, my friend? I know what risks I run in exposing myself to dangers. I settle all my accounts every week, and if I were to die today, my executors would not have five minutes' trouble. My continued presence upon earth is proof that no lasting damage besets me, other than my chest. I think if my lungs were as strong as my legs, I should live forever."

We sat for a while in my favourite spot in the upper temple, facing south over the precipice.

Doctor Hobson always showed the greatest interest in my provision for nesting sites. He could barely believe his eyes when I took him to see an old tree trunk in the far reaches of the woodland. The decaying trunk stood about seven feet high, and with the assistance of my mason, I had put a roof on it.

"And who," he laughed, "has taken up residence?"

"This," I pointed to lowest of the three holes I had drilled, "is the front door shared by Mr and Mrs Barn Owl, and Mr and Mrs Jack Daw."

"Do they use the other holes?"

"Not they, no. The middle one is not used at all, but the top hole is the entrance for a pair of redstarts."

The doctor stared incredulously. "And have they bred?"

"Oh, yes." I replied, "the owls have three young, and the jackdaws have five eggs. Look inside if you don't believe me."

"I believe you, Charles. Why would I not?"

As a measure of our friendship, he was amused, and not at all offended, when I named a deformed duck after him. The story is worth telling. A fellow doctor had given him a duckling which had no webs to its feet. Doctor Hobson gave it to me, and I set it free at the lakeside. To my astonishment, it survived. In honour of his former owner, I named the little gander, 'Doctor Hobson'. He could fly as well as any wild duck, and his swimming was good enough for him to find food in the shallows. My friend took the naming in good part.

One day, when I was in the stables, a farm worker approached me. "Squire, I have bad news. Doctor Hobson is dead." For a moment I thought he spoke of my physician. "I saw him, all spread out at Nostell, by the lake dam."

I repaired to Nostell immediately and recovered the body. I brought the little duck back to Walton Hall where I preserved him and then gave the human Doctor Hobson his little namesake, which I believe he still has in his possession.

Some years ago, I made the estate over to Edmund, reserving the right to raise £10,000 upon it, should I need to do so. Edmund, I admit, is useless with money, which is why I have made provisions for Eliza and Little Helen in my will. Whilst Edmund is the first to admit he has no interest in natural history, he is very complimentary about my museum, especially when showing a visitor around. Three years ago, he pointed out a water hen's nest with thirteen eggs in it, which even he knew to be unusual. I told him I thought two hens must have laid in it because I had never seen one with more than seven eggs, at which point he lost interest.

Edmund is a good, kind, generous, pious man. He can describe any one of his papal rings as I can describe any one of my collection of eggs. I am convinced the value of his collection is beyond anything at Walton Hall.

I have two criticisms of my son, and he is well aware of them. Firstly, he is a smoker. I have already alluded to my detestation of this foul habit. The smell of his pipes and cigars permeates every room, the carpets and the curtains. We have argued about it, but to no avail. Secondly, while he has faultless taste, he is extravagant in the extreme. Testament to this is the jewellery he buys without thought to cost.

Conversely, I am aware of his annoyance at my indifference to dress. In fact, I think it fair to say our tastes in all things are entirely diverse.

Anyone who is in any doubt as to the pride I hold for my son need only lay their eyes upon the full-length portrait of him in the vestments of Cameriere Segreto which hangs above the fireplace in the drawing room. His aunts prefer the one of him in highland dress which hangs in their sitting room on the first floor, but I suspect that is more to do with their Scottish ancestry than the skill of the artist.

Edmund stands six feet and three inches tall. He wed Margaret Alicia Josephine Ennis in the Convent des Anglais in Bruges, the very place where I wed his dear mother. We had all been in Bruges, and Eliza, Little Helen and I had travelled on to Aix-la-Chapelle when the marriage took place, much to our annoyance.

The new Mr and Mrs Waterton live in her family's home of Ballinahown Manor, County Westmeath, and have a son and a daughter.

Charles Edmund Maria Joseph Aloysius Pius (known as Charlie) was born on the 10th of June, 1863, and Mary Paula Pia on the 5th December 1864.

When I heard of Charlie's birth, I sent the little cannon ball, with a written account of its history. It is my hope that Edmund will pass it on to his son in due course.

Of my visitors, Charles Darwin is the most famous.

William Thackeray visited during Lent and expressed astonishment at my diet of bread and weak tea.

If a visitor convinces me by his questions and manner that he warrants my time, I invite him to an accompanied walk in my park. To my amusement, all have been foiled by my decoy pheasants. Sir George Head was one such. Our conversation went thus.

"The pheasants are tame, Mr Waterton. They sit in the trees as if they know there are no guns here."

"Look more closely, my friend, and consider also the time of day." I replied.

He peered into the branches for a minute or two. "His tail is drooping, as if asleep, but at this hour he should be on the ground, foraging for food." He walked around the tree and looked up again before turning to me and smiling. "I do declare, Mr Waterton, your pheasant is made of wood, but why, when your parkland is so prolific, do you have need for a wooden bird?"

"Not one, Sir George. I have constructed two hundred and forty of them and they have succeeded admirably in their role. They frustrate the poachers who cannot tell the difference between a wooden bird silhouetted against the moonlight and a real one. My woodwork has had considerable effect as they do not like to waste their shot."

"Admirable," he chuckled.

I liked the man. I showed him the little watchtower situated in the rookery. On my instruction, John Ogden has built six of these and, like the wooden pheasants, they serve their purpose with great effect. Sir George went inside. "'Tis well built, Mr Waterton, like a circular sentry box, but what is its purpose in such a remote part of your parkland?"

"I had not thought of them in such military terms," I said, "but you are right. My keepers are my soldiers in the war against the poachers. They have fought a few battles, and the watchtowers provide shelter as well as providing a good point of resistance during attack."

We walked on through the woodland towards the far end of the lake where we diverted from the path, down towards the waterside where, a few yards from the shoreline, stands my hollow oak. We sat side by side on the bench within. Had Sir George not impressed me with his true interest, I would not have shown him the little sanctuary.

"I sit here in peace, unseen by the birds as they go about their business."

"Extraordinary, quite extraordinary."

"I think, Sir George, it is more extraordinary than you think, for the tree did not grow here."

His eyes widened, and then he frowned. "Explain to me, Mr Waterton, if you will. Ivy grows all around, and has made a roof, and yet you tell me—it is an oak, is it not? This tree must have been a magnificent specimen—I am puzzled, entirely puzzled."

"You are right, it was once a magnificent specimen, seen and no doubt admired by my grandfather, and his father too, but when I returned from my last visit to South America, I found it to be quite dead and hollow at its base. Being situated on a hillside, with the aperture facing away from the lake, its position did not suit my purpose, so I told my woodman to fell it at the lowest possible point. It came down with a mighty crash. I then instructed the woodman to saw through eight feet from the base. Two horses were needed to pull it on a timber-tug to its present position, where I had it placed upright. I then planted ivy all around it.

"No-one who came across it would guess it did not have its roots beneath."

"That was my intention."

I found Sir George to be an easy-going man. He was on a tour of the northern industrial towns, so his visit must have been a welcome respite. He wrote of it in his book, 'A Home Tour Through the Manufacturing Districts of England'.

My reputation as a naturalist brings invitations to this or that exhibition, and requests to visit my parkland come from some of the most unlikely people. The strangest of all was the French tight-rope walker, Jean-Francois Gravelet, known world-wide as Blondin. He had crossed Niagara Falls, and asked if he might stretch a rope over my lake. The request came just three years ago. I considered it, of course, but feared the crowds which this feat would have inevitably attracted would not have been to my liking. Blondin is a money-making showman, a circus act. Had he suggested any profits be given to the poor, I might have been tempted to permit it. I asked myself at the time, 'where would such a precedent take me?' Would each and every decision thereafter be governed by its fiscal value? The very thought ran at such odds to my principles, that I could not risk the opening of such flood-gates. For the rest of my life, and hopefully beyond my grave, my parkland will forever be a place of refuge for the birds, and worthy of the appreciation of all true naturalists. That, I hope, will be my legacy.

Severe attacks of dysentery and ague have made no inroad into my constitution, for although life's index points at eighty-two, I am a stranger to all octogenarian disabilities, and can mount to the top of a tree with ease in the sure knowledge that I owe this vigorous state of frame to a total abstinence from all strong liqueurs.

I have never celebrated my birthday, but when I turned eighty-two, I took Eliza and Little Helen for a sail in *Percy*. I showed them the stone cross which I have had erected at the far end of the lake. It stands at the water's edge between two great oak trees.

"I have not seen this before," Eliza said. "Who is interred here? The cross looks new."

"Indeed, it is new." I replied. "The vault is unoccupied."

"Then who..." her voice trailed off with the realisation that it was I who would be buried there.

"I have a little plaque in my room which is to be fixed to the base of the plinth. I am pleased to say it cannot yet be completed. It reads ORATE PRO ANIMA CAROLI WATERTON CUJUS FESSA JUXTA HANC CRUSEM SEPELIUNTUR OSSA. NATUS 1782 OBIT

"What does that mean?" Little Helen whispered.

"It translates, my dear, as 'Pray for the soul of Charles Waterton, whose weary bones lie close to this cross. Born 1782 died...'

"The inscription will not be finished for some time, I hope." She flung her arms around me. "I cannot bear to think if it," she sobbed.

"Come, my dear. Do not be sad, for when my bones lie here, my soul will be with that of Anne."

Eliza sat straight as a ramrod, staring at the cross. "Is it not too close to the water?"

"I think not. As you can see, the vault is behind the cross, not at the shoreline, and it is brick lined. My feet will be dry enough." I pushed the oar into the mud and set the sail to carry us back to the house. Little Helen was soon distracted from her melancholy by the sight of the nesting birds. As I recall it, Eliza said not one word until she was back on the island.

And so, my friend and reader, I say goodbye to you. I think I may call you my friend if you have read thus far. In truth, this is not the end. For I am writing it, I must leave the last chapter for another hand. I leave you with a list of my feathered friends, all of whom have enjoyed my protection, as I have enjoyed their company. My grandchildren, Charlie and Mary, are here at present, along with their mother. Edmund is in Rome in attendance to Pope Pius IX. Yesterday, my young friend, Norman Moore, arrived, so we have a house-full. I am happy to say this young man has become a regular visitor. We climbed a tall oak together to look at a nest.

I have recently been presented with the corpse of a gorilla and last night Norman and I began the process of dissecting it. After supper, when my sisters-in-law had retired to their sitting room, we brought the huge beast into the dining room in a wooden trough. The colour of the hair is mostly grize, whitest on the back and some four inches long in parts. The head is immense, but I am sorry to say that, due to delay in transit, the specimen is a complete wreck. The epidermis (and with it the hair) is peeling off all over, especially on the ears and feet. Altogether it is a sad case. The smell is as bad as a vulture's dinner, but not so bad as a salt cake furnace!

Norman and I are taking the sail boat on the lake after break-fast. His opinions entirely concur with my own in all matters of nature. His enthusiasm buoys me up into thinking there is a future for my knowledge, and that one day all species will be appreciated for their contribution to the natural world. We shall take my carpenter with us, as some repairs are needed to the bridge over the creek. Once I have set him to work, Norman and I will take a walk. He does not know it, but I intend to show him the spot I have chosen as my final resting place. I shall soon be eighty-three years of age, so it cannot be long before I lie between the two oak trees, forever at the water's edge.

Birds I have observed in my parkland.

Birds I have observed in my parkland.

Osprey.	Green woodpecker.	Blackcap.
Peregrine.	Spotted	Willow wren.
Kestrel.	woodpecker.	Gold crested wren.
Sparrow-hawk.	Lesser woodpecker.	Common wren.
Hobby.	Creeper.	Wheatear.
Merlin.	Crossbill.	Whinchat.
Wood Owl.	Grosbill.	Stonechat.
Barn Owl.	Bullfinch.	Oxeye titmouse.
Long-eared owl.	Goldfinch.	Blue titmouse.
Little earless owl.	Yellowhammer.	Cole titmouse.
Woodcock owl.	Common bunting.	Long tailed
Raven.	Black-headed	titmouse.
Carrion crow.	bunting.	Bearded titmouse.
Hooded crow.	House sparrow.	Nuthatch.
Rook.	Mountain sparrow.	Yellow wagtail.
Jackdaw.	Hedge sparrow.	Pied wagtail.
Magpie.	Reed sparrow.	Grey wagtail.
Jay.	Chaffinch.	Chimney swallow.
Mistle thrush.	Brambling.	Sandmartin.
Song thrush.	Siskin.	House martin.
Fieldfare.	Brown linnet.	Swift.
Redwing.	Green linnet.	Kingfisher.
Blackbird.	Lesser redpole.	Nightjar.
Skylark.	Pied flycatcher.	Ringdove.
Titlark.	Nightingale.	Stockdove.
Starling.	Robin.	Turtledove.
Cuckoo.	Redstart.	Pheasant.

Partridge.
Snipe.
Quail.
Land-rail.
Water-rail.
Lesser-rail.
Little land-rail.
Thick-kneed plover.
Lapwing.
Golden plover.
Wild swan.
Common swan.
Wild duck.
Shoveler.

Widgeon.
Teal.
Tufted duck.
Pochard.
Golden eye.
Chestnut duck.
Common scoter.
Dabchick.
Dusty grebe.
Eared grebe.
Canada Goose.
Egyptian goose.
Barnacle goose.
Cape goose.

Goosander.
Smew.
Garganey.
Cormorant.
Coot.
Water-hen.
Heron.
Common sandpiper.
Four of the gull
tribe.
Common tern.
Black tern.

Well I know thy penetration
Many a stain and blot will see
In this languid long narration
Of my sylvan errantry.

Post script.

Norman Moore wrote of the following days.

'I happened just then to be reading for an examination, and Waterton asked me, whenever I was up at twelve, to go and chat to him for a few minutes after he came back from his midnight visit to the chapel. I went accordingly on May 24th, 1865, and found the dear old wanderer sitting asleep by his fire, wrapped up in his Italian cloak. His head rested upon his wooden pillow, which was placed on a table, and his thick, silvery hair formed a beautiful contrast with the dark colour of the oak. He soon woke up, and we talked together for three quarters of an hour about the brown owl, the night jar, and other birds. The next morning he was unusually cheerful and said to me, "That was a very pleasant little confab we had last night. I do not suppose there was another going on in England at the same time."

'After break-fast we went in the sail boat with a carpenter to repair a bridge. The work was completed, and as the Squire crossed the bridge, a bramble caught his foot, and he fell heavily. He was greatly shaken, and said he thought he was dying. He walked a little way and was then compelled to lie down. He would not permit his sufferings to distract his mind, and he pointed out to the carpenter some trees which were to be felled. He presently continued his route and managed to reach the spot where the boat was moored. Hitherto he had refused all assistance, but he could not step from the bank into the boat, and he said, "I am afraid I must ask you to help me in." He walked from the landing place to the house, changed his clothes, and came and sat in the large room below.

(Norman Moore rode to Wakefield for Mr Horsfall, the surgeon)

'When the surgeon arrived and applied leeches, Charles joked, 'now let's do things neatly.'

'The pain increasing, he rose from his seat, and though he was bent double with anguish, he persisted in walking upstairs without help, and would have gone to his own room in the top-story, if, for the sake of saving the trouble to others, he had not been induced to stop half way in the Misses Edmonstones' sitting room. Here he lay down upon the sofa and was attended by his sisters-in-law. The pain abated, and the next day he seemed better. In the afternoon he talked to me a good deal, chiefly about natural history. But he was well aware of his perilous condition, for he remarked to me, "This is a bad business," and later on he felt his pulse often, and said, "It is a bad case." He was more than self-possessed. A benignant cheerfulness beamed from his mind, and in the fits of pain he frequently looked up with a gentle smile, and made some little joke.

'Towards midnight he grew worse. The priest, the Reverend R. Browne, was summoned and Waterton got ready to die. He pulled himself upright without help, sat in the middle of the sofa, and gave his blessing in turn to his grandson, Charlie, and to his grand-daughter, Mary, to each of his sisters-in-law, and to myself, and left a message for his son, who was hastening back from Rome. He then received the last sacraments, repeated all the responses, Saint Bernard's hymn in English, and the first two verses of the *Dies Ira*. The end was now at hand, and he died at twenty-seven minutes past two in the morning of May 27th, 1865. The window was open. The sky was beginning to grow grey, a few rooks had cawed, the swallows were twittering, the land rail was craking and a favourite cock, which he had used to call his morning gun, leaped out from some hollies and gave his accustomed crow. The ear of his master was deaf to the call. He had obeyed a sublime summons and woken to the glories of the eternal world.'

Author's Notes.

Edmund came home to organise the funeral which took place on the 3rd of June, 1865, the date of the Squire's eighty-third birthday and exactly one year since he had taken his sisters-in-law to see his chosen burial place. The funeral commenced at 9.00. a.m. with Mass being celebrated in the chapel of St Catherine of Alexandria. Hundreds of villagers congregated at the gates of Walton Hall, and, in accordance with the Squire's will, eighty-three of them (one for each year of his life) were invited within to attend his funeral, and were given sixpence and a loaf of bread.

According to Moore, there were four funeral boats. The first carried the Bishop of Beverley and fourteen priests. Next came Charon's ferry, which bore the coffin, followed by the third boat carrying the mourners, Edmund, Norman Moore, Doctor Wright, and Mr Horsfall. The final boat was *Percy*, fittingly empty and towed along, draped in black.

The ladies remained upon the island.

At the time of his death, Charles Waterton had twenty-three pounds in cash and £585.18.2d in the bank. Edmund had already mortgaged the house and was in debt. He quarrelled with his aunts, having borrowed money from both of them. Eliza was a strong-minded woman who was very annoyed when Edmund insisted his wife was to sit at the head of the dining table, a position which Eliza had held for thirty-five years. The sisters left Walton Hall to live on the east coast. Charles had left his personal effects to his sisters-in-law and the estate to Edmund, but by 1870 Edmund was bankrupt. On May 30th 1870, the furniture was on view for sale by auction.

Edmund leased the house to a fellow antiquarian on a twenty-year agreement. When sold by auction, the estate was bought by none other than Edward Simpson. Charles must have turned in his grave, although a wry smile may have crossed his face, for Simpson bought at an inflated price as it was thought there was a rich coal seam beneath the parkland. This turned out to be poor quality coal and not worth extracting. Furthermore, due to the lease, Simpson was unable to move into the house for almost twenty years, until a few months before the lease expired, when the leaseholder died.

Edmund was not a bad man, he was known for his kindness and generosity and his many colourful waistcoats, but he was clearly hopeless with money. He had four more children with his first wife who died in 1879. He then married Helen Mercer, with whom he had two daughters.

The following letter to Mother Superior of the Convent of the Good Shepherd, Dalbeith, demonstrates both Charles Waterton's generosity and his desire to remain anonymous in such matters. It is dated November 30th, 1853.

Dear Madam,

In your letter of petition, in support of your excellent institution, you have asked for the crumbs which fall from my table. If a joke may be alluded on so serious a subject I would say in answer that all the crumbs which fall from my table are mortgaged to a huge Chochin-China fowl which receives them in payment for awakening me by his crowing every morning at three o'clock. But as he does not feed on my cheese, I find that I can spare a mite from it.

Pray accept it, and if you enter the trifling donation in your book, please put it down as coming from a friend.

I always make this stipulation on similar occasions.

I remain, dear Madam, your humble and obedient servant,
Charles Waterton.

In a further demonstration, I quote,

'It came to my attention that John Loudon, a naturalist of my own mind, had died leaving his widow badly off. My first Essays had proved popular, and as a fitting tribute to Loudon I made arrangements for all profits from the second series to be paid to his widow.'

Waterton's Taxidermy belongs to Stonyhurst. The exhibition at Wakefield Museum, which includes the cayman, the Nondescript and John Bull and the National Debt, was opened by Sir David Attenborough,

I believe he also gave anonymously and generously to the construction of St Austin's Church in Wakefield. I dare say he was heavily criticised at the time for failing to give to this cause.

Anyone who has had a general anaesthetic owes a debt of gratitude to Charles Waterton. Wourali is now known as curare. It stills all muscles, with the exception of the heart, enabling the surgeon to carry out his work without the jiggling about of internal organs. It has largely been replaced by safer neuromuscular blocking drugs.

The fabled Lake Parima is now accepted to be a flood plain.

Walton Hall is now Waterton Park Hôtel, which says it all regarding the current use of the house. The beautiful setting makes it a very popular wedding venue, although I think naming the bar 'Charlie's Bar' would not have pleased the teetotal Squire.

His grave stands on private land. The stone cross was stolen many years ago and has been replaced with one made of concrete. The area is neglected and the lake has silted up so much that he is no longer at the water's edge. Having said that, it is a very peaceful place and but for the Yorkshire climate, it has the feeling of a jungle about it.

The saintly ancestors of Charles Waterton.
Saint Matilda, Queen of Germany
Saint Margaret of Scotland
Saint Humbart of Savoy
Saint Louis of France
Saint Ferdinand of Castille
Saint Vladimir the Great of Russia
Saint Anne of Russia

To close, I can do no better that to quote William Makepeace Thackeray, who, after Charles' death and in response to those who would dismiss his friend as an eccentric, wrote:

"It was eccentric to dine on a crust, live as chastely as a hermit, and give his all to the poor. It was eccentric to come into a large estate as a young man, and to have lived to extreme old age without having wasted an hour or a shilling. It was eccentric to give bountifully and never allow his name to appear on a subscription list. It was eccentric to be saturated with a love of nature. It might be eccentric never to give dinner parties, preferring to keep an always open house for his friends, but it was a very agreeable kind of eccentricity, and the world would be a much better place if such eccentricity were more common."

Acknowledgements.

Burke's Peerage

Dr David Knight, Stonyhurst

The nuns of the Convent des Anglais, Bruges.

Wakefield Museum and Local History Archives, with special thanks to John Whittaker.

Kevin Grundy and Ian Illingworth WHAS

Charles Waterton, his home, habits and Handiwork. Richard Hobson. M.D.

Essays on Natural History, including Some Account of the writer, by himself. Charles Waterton.

Wanderings in South America, Charles Waterton.

St. Omer's to Stonyhurst, Hubert Chadwick.

The Squire of Walton Hall, Philip Gosse.

Natural History Essays by Charles Waterton, edited, with a life of the author, by Norman Moore.

Printed in Great Britain
by Amazon